Multicultural Students with Special Language Needs

Practical Strategies for Assessment and Intervention

✦ Fifth Edition

Celeste Roseberry-McKibbin, Ph.D., C.C.C.-SLP
Department of Communication Sciences and Disorders
California State University, Sacramento

Academic
Communication
Associates, Inc.

P. O. Box 4279
Oceanside, CA 92052-4279

D1127449

This book is dedicated to Mike for always being there!

About the Author

Dr. Celeste Roseberry-McKibbin is currently a Professor of Communication Sciences and Disorders at California State University, Sacramento. In addition to teaching at the university level, she continues to work on a part-time basis as a speech-language pathologist in the public schools.

Dr. Roseberry-McKibbin lived in the Philippines for much of her childhood and came to live in the United States permanently at 17 years of age. She has lectured and given workshops nationally and internationally on issues relating to multicultural assessment and intervention. Her previous publications include textbooks, assessment instruments, and professional journal articles. She is a Fellow of the American Speech-Language-Hearing Association (ASHA) and recently received the presidential Daily Point of Light Award for service to children in poverty. She is also a recipient of ASHA's Certificate of Recognition for Special Contributions in Multicultural Affairs.

Information about Dr. Roseberry-McKibbin's literacy outreach to children is available at lovetalkread.com.

Multicultural Students with Special Language Needs - Fifth Edition
Copyright © 2018 by Academic Communication Associates, Inc.

Academic Communication Associates, Inc.

P. O. Box 4279
Oceanside, CA 92052-4279

WEB: **www.acawebsite.com**
Telephone Order Line: (888) 758-9558
Fax: (760) 722-1625
Printed in the United States of America
International Standard Book Number: 978-1-57503-157-6

Table of Contents

Preface to the Fifth Edition

When students from culturally and linguistically diverse backgrounds fail to perform successfully in the classroom, the cause of their poor performance is often difficult to identify. Educational professionals who serve students with communication disorders and other special needs are being challenged to think creatively and strategically about best practices for assessing and teaching these students. Meeting the needs of the ever-increasing English language learner (ELL) population is especially challenging for educational professionals who speak only English. How does one determine if a child's learning problems can be attributed to limited proficiency in English or to a "disorder" that is affecting his or her ability to acquire language skills? Should instruction be provided in the home language, English, or in both languages? Can the language learning needs of the student be met within the general education curriculum or are the services of a speech-language pathologist needed?

Designing appropriate programs for the diverse population of multicultural students in our schools is a complicated puzzle that has many pieces. Close collaboration among classroom teachers, bilingual specialists, speech-language pathologists, and other professionals is necessary to put the pieces of the puzzle together in a way that will maximize learning of the language skills that are necessary for academic success and for effective communication in social contexts.

 Students who speak a language or dialect other than Standard American English can be easily misidentified as having language impairment if standardized tests are used as the sole basis for educational decisions. The language needs of students with "differences" resulting from limited exposure to the language of instruction should be met within the general education curriculum. Enrollment in speech and language therapy programs is appropriate only for students who have an impairment that affects their ability to acquire language skills.

Educators need to evaluate their instructional programs to determine how these programs can be adapted to best serve the interests of students from diverse cultural and linguistic backgrounds. Speech-language pathologists especially need practical assessment strategies and resources to help them differentiate language difference from language impairment in ELLs.

The previous edition of this book included a comprehensive review of strategies for assessing and teaching culturally and linguistically diverse students with special language needs. The current edition includes updated research information and evidence-based practices for identifying and teaching culturally and linguistically diverse students who have special language needs. Recent research on second language acquisition is reported that has direct relevance to the identification of communication disorders in ELL populations. This book addresses many of the challenges faced by educational professionals who work with culturally and linguistically diverse students:

1. *Increasing linguistic diversity within individual classrooms.* Many schools throughout the United States have experienced dramatic increases in the number of languages spoken by students within individual classrooms. A single classroom may have students who speak Spanish, Vietnamese, Arabic, and other languages. By the middle of the 21st century, approximately half of school-age children will come from linguistically and culturally diverse backgrounds.

2. *Impact of poverty on school performance.* Many more children are impacted by poverty today than in past years. Refugees who enter the United States often have limited resources. Poor living conditions, limited access to medical care, and a variety of other problems can affect children's development and learning. School professionals often need to provide parents with sources of support to help them deal with problems that can affect their children's development and learning.

3. *Pressure to target specific curriculum standards.* Federal legislation continues to have a major impact on the educational services provided to students with special learning needs. The Common Core State Standards, for example, are designed to provide students with the sophisticated knowledge and thinking abilities necessary for careers in a globally competitive market. Learning these skills is often a challenge for ELL students who have been identified as having language impairment. Although it is important for students to develop language skills relevant to success within the classroom, it is also important for them to acquire the skills necessary to satisfy basic needs, communicate with family members, and interact in everyday social contexts.

This book was written to provide speech-language pathologists and special education specialists with information about cultural differences and with practical strategies for assessing and identifying culturally and linguistically diverse students with speech and language impairments. Among the topics included in this book are the following:

1. Research-based "best practices" are described for distinguishing language differences from problems that result from language impairment.

2. Issues are reviewed relating to the impact of poverty on school performance. Recent world events have increased the number of refugee and immigrant students in the U.S., and many of these students and their families experience poverty.

3. Guidelines are presented for using nonstandarized methods of assessment. Research-based, reproducible tools are included that can be used to assess ELLs. These forms can be used with speakers of any language and can be helpful in identifying students with language impairment.

4. Strategies are described to help students develop language and literacy skills that are critical for success in mastering classroom curriculum standards (e.g., Common Core State Standards).

5. Suggestions are included for use of the iPad and other technological innovations with ELL students. Specific iPad apps are recommended that have been used successfully with ELLs from a wide range of language backgrounds and cultures.

6. Suggestions are included for developing collaborative approaches to instruction and for implementing Response to Intervention (RtI).

7. Study questions are included at the end of each chapter. Some of the questions are based on "case studies" and require students to think about what they have learned in the chapter. These questions should facilitate learning of the "multicultural" competencies that are critical for the Certificate of Clinical Competence in Speech-Language Pathology.

8. Information relating to second language learning and bilingual language instruction has been updated to reflect new research.

9. Information is included about the Every Student Succeeds Act (ESSA) signed by President Obama in December, 2010. At the time of this writing, with the current administration in Washington, the future of the ESSA is in question. Time will tell whether or not it continues to guide policy in the U.S.

10. New "Immigrant Insights" have been added to the current edition of this book to help readers understand real-world experiences of individuals from diverse cultural backgrounds.

11. Quick Response Codes (QRCs) and website links provide readers with easy access to information and videos that are relevant to topics covered in this book. iPads, iPhones, and other devices can be used to scan these codes while reading this book.

12. New Quick Response Codes and website links provide access to YouTube videos that show the use of specific assessment and intervention techniques with children. Viewers have reported that these videos are extremely helpful learning tools. The videos are all available free of charge from my YouTube channel: *Celeste Roseberry Love Talk Read.* These videos will help readers to better understand information presented in this book.

13. In designing the current edition of this book, format changes were made to improve readability. Many long paragraphs have been replaced by a "bullet point" format to accommodate the learning style of today's students. Rather than dealing with long paragraphs, New Generation Z learners (individuals born between 1996 and 2012) tend to prefer that information be presented in short bits or chunks (Stillman & Stillman, 2017).

It is impossible to offer easy answers to many of the challenges that speech-language pathologists, special education teachers, and other specialists encounter in their efforts to identify and provide appropriate services for culturally and linguistically diverse students with communication disorders and other special learning needs. It is my hope that readers will be able to use information from this book to provide culturally and linguistically appropriate intervention programs for the diverse student populations that they serve.

Finally, I feel it is important to mention a few of the people who provided valuable help and guidance during the writing of this book. I want to offer my sincere thanks to Larry Mattes and Patty Schuchardt for their detailed editorial work, helpful suggestions, and continued support over the years. This book would not exist without them. I am also thankful for the support of my Dean, Dr. Fred Baldini, and my department Chair, Dr. Robert Pieretti.

Some of the "immigrant insights" in this book were provided by my students. I am so grateful to these students for generously letting me share their experiences with readers of this book.

My husband Mike and my son Mark continue to be my greatest supporters and cheerleaders, shoving food under the study door and encouraging me to continually pursue my dreams of doing whatever I can to promote justice and equal opportunities for all children. Most of all, I thank God for His gifts of life and health and strength; with Him, all things are possible.

Part 1

Cultural and Linguistic Variables Affecting Service Delivery

Chapter 1

Learning About Cultural Diversity

When learning about other cultures, it is important to understand that not all members of a culture have the same beliefs, values, or customs. Much heterogeneity exists within cultural groups. Although cultural norms tend to influence behavior, each individual and each family has unique experiences that influence beliefs, attitudes, and actions.

Outline
- **Understanding Cultural Diversity**
- **Cultural Competence**
- **Cultural Variables Influencing Behavior**
- **Working with Immigrants and Refugees**
- **General Background Information**
- **General Characteristics of Immigrants and Refugees**
- **Acculturation**
- **Difficulties Commonly Experienced by Immigrants/Refugees**
- **Possible Family Concerns**
- **Public Perceptions About Immigrants/Refugees**
- **Implications for Professionals**
- **Conclusion**

Children's cultural experiences can have a profound effect on performance within the classroom learning environment. To meet the learning needs of a student population that is becoming increasingly more diverse, educational professionals must develop an understanding of cultural differences and how these differences affect behavior in the classroom and in social situations. An awareness of cultural differences is essential to ensure that students from culturally and linguistically diverse backgrounds are provided with appropriate educational options and programs. It is also important for professionals to be aware of the impact that immigrant/refugee status can have on students and their families.

Students from ethnic and racial minority groups often have limited proficiency in English or speak a dialect of English different from that used by the classroom teacher. Implementing effective instructional programs for culturally diverse students who have limited knowledge of English is often a challenge. Children from homes where a language other than English is spoken have often been referred to as "ESL (English as a Second Language) students." Because of the heterogeneity of this population, acronyms such as *EAL* (English as an Additional Language), *EDL* (English as a Dual Language), *ENL* (English as a New Language), *ELL* (English Language Learner), and *EL* (English Learner) have become popular when referring to students with limited proficiency in English. Many children with limited proficiency in English come from homes where English and one or more other languages are learned simultaneously. Children of parents that speak only Spanish, for example, may learn English from older siblings that speak English most of the time.

In this book, the term **English Language Learner** (ELL) is used to refer to individuals with English language learning needs who come from homes where a language other than English is used. Many ELLs are exposed to two or more languages at home. In addition to having limited proficiency in English, these children are not necessarily "fluent" speakers of their primary home language.

As our population increases, special educators will be providing services for an increasing number of students who speak languages other than English. The number of foreign-born persons in the U.S. has more than quadrupled since 1965 and is expected to reach 78 million by 2065. By 2055, less than half of the population in the United States will be from a single racial or ethnic group (Pew Research Center, 2017b).

A continuing concern for professionals is the educational disparities experienced by many ELLs in our schools (Muñoz, 2017). Between the years 2014 and 2015, approximately 665,000 ELL students were identified as individuals with disabilities. ELL students with disabilities represented 13.8% of the total ELL population enrolled in public elementary and secondary schools in the U.S. (National Center for Education Statistics, 2017).

Because of the rapidly-increasing diversity within the school population and the number of ELLs identified with disabilities, special education professionals must have an understanding of cultural characteristics and the impact that these characteristics have on students' performance in

---

Tech Tie-In

Visit http://www.asha.org/practice/multicultural/ELL for a collection of resources from the American Speech-Language-Hearing Association (ASHA) that address issues related to working with ELL students.

the classroom learning environment (Moore & Montgomery, 2018). This book includes information about a variety of cultural groups to show the diversity that exists in our schools and to help professionals understand general trends within various cultural groups. Learning about other cultures facilitates development of a better understanding of student behaviors observed in the school setting. By becoming culturally competent, professionals will be able to appropriately adapt their instructional programs to accommodate and meet the needs of students from culturally and linguistically diverse backgrounds.

UNDERSTANDING CULTURAL DIVERSITY

Culture can be viewed as a framework through which actions are filtered as individuals go about the business of daily living. Values are at the heart of culture; thus, when we study other cultures, it is important to examine their basic values.

One of the dangers inherent in the study of any cultural group and its values is that stereotyping may occur. A **stereotype** is an oversimplified, fixed image that we have of members of a group. A stereotype is an ending point. No effort is made to find out whether the individual in question fits the statement (e.g., "Hispanics have large families."). Stereotypes can be viewed as a means of categorizing others based on perceptions that are incomplete.

When learning about other cultures, it is important to understand that not all members of a culture have the same beliefs, values, or customs. Much heterogeneity exists within cultural groups. Although cultural norms tend to influence behavior, each individual and each family has unique experiences that influence beliefs, attitudes, and actions.

It is my profound hope that readers will not be led to form stereotypes of other cultures as they read about "cultural tendencies" in this book. The values, behaviors, and customs described for a specific culture serve as a framework for understanding individuals and gearing assessment and intervention toward their specific needs.

It is also hoped that readers will gain a sense of cultural relativism, not ethnocentrism. **Ethnocentrism** is the view that members of one's own culture do things the right way. All other ways of doing something tend to be viewed as unnatural, inferior, or maybe even barbaric. Proponents of **cultural relativism** hold the attitude that other ways of doing things are different yet equally valid; the goal is to understand other people's behavior in its cultural context. This is the goal of the culturally competent professional.

CULTURAL COMPETENCE

Cultural competence is the ability of professionals to respect, recognize, value, and honor the beliefs and values of the individuals and families they serve, as well as engage in continual self-assessment regarding cultural differences between themselves and their clients.

Cultural competence includes valuing diversity, being conscious of the dynamics inherent in communication when cultures interact, and adapting to diversity and the cultural contexts of communities served (ASHA, 2011).

On our journey towards cultural competence, we need to be willing to accept that there is often no single right way to do things. Our cultural background influences how we expect others to act in specific situations.

The American Speech-Language-Hearing Association has emphasized the importance of "cultural humility" which involves the recognition of limits, critical self-assessment, and ongoing acquisition of knowledge (ASHA, 2011). Professionals who possess cultural humility will become students of their clients, remaining open to learning new information about how to most capably serve those particular clients.

Though cultural humility is an important component of cultural competence, it is not enough. The professional must possess knowledge about the client's culture and language (Crowley, Guest, & Sudler, 2015). Helpful strategies for gaining this knowledge are listed in Table 1.1.

KEY TERMS

- **Culture** (defined in more detail later) is the shared beliefs, traditions, and values of a group of people that are used to define their social identity.

- **Race** is a classification that distinguishes groups of people from one another based on physical characteristics such as skin color. It is a statement about a person's biological attributes.

- **Ethnicity** is the social definition of groups of people based on shared ancestry and culture. Ethnicity includes race and also factors such as customs, nationality, language, and heritage.

CULTURAL VARIABLES INFLUENCING BEHAVIOR

Many variables influence the behavior of individuals within a culture. The manner in which services are provided may be influenced by general cultural practices in combination with variables unique to the individual. Thus, culturally competent professionals must understand not only general characteristics of various cultural groups, but also the variables that interact to make each student and family unique within that cultural group. An understanding of these variables can be enhanced by interacting with family members and asking questions. Many families appreciate the opportunity to share their stories and appreciate being viewed as unique. The following variables are important to consider when services are being provided to students and families:

❏ Educational background of family members

❏ Languages spoken

❏ Length of residence in an area

❏ Country of birth (immigrant vs. native born)

❏ Reasons for immigration to the United States

❏ Urban vs. rural background

❏ Individual choice within the intrapersonal realm (e.g., idiosyncratic behavior)

❏ Socioeconomic status/upward class mobility in the United States

❏ Socioeconomic status/upward mobility in the country of origin

❏ Age and gender

❏ Religious beliefs and their impact on daily life activities

❏ Neighborhood of residence and peer group

Table 1.1

Suggestions for Increasing Cultural Competence

1. **Team up with persons from the local cultural community who can act as mediators.** Utilizing the knowledge and skills of these individuals is generally the best way to obtain the information necessary to serve multicultural students and their families.

2. **Read as much as possible about the family's culture and language.** Such information may be gathered from local community libraries, university libraries, and individuals in the community who are from that cultural group.

3. **Visit students' homes.** Ascertain first that the family is willing to be visited, and choose times that are convenient for these visits.

4. **Evaluate your own assumptions and values.** Consider how your own assumptions and values influence your way of communicating information about students' achievements, instructional needs, and goals for school success.

5. **Consider the student's needs in the larger context of the family and community.** If you want the student to receive additional services above and beyond those available in the regular classroom, examine the student's needs within the context of the family as a whole. Be sure to include family members in the decision-making process.

6. **Consider the value system of the family when setting goals.** For example, educational professionals often stress the importance of helping physically disabled students become as independent as possible. However, in a particular child's culture, independence may not be emphasized or considered important; instead, family members may be expected to care for all of the student's needs. Intervention plans will not likely succeed unless the family's values and style of living are taken into account.

7. **Be aware that both verbal and nonverbal communication can affect a family's attitudes toward the school and the professionals working with the student.** Professionals need to show that they are truly interested in helping the family.

8. **Talk with individuals from a variety of cultural backgrounds.** Participate in social interactions with people whose cultural, ethnic, and linguistic origins are different from yours. This can be accomplished by attending holiday celebrations, community functions, etc.

9. **Ask students to share important aspects of their culture with you and other students.** Some students may not be comfortable talking about their cultural/language background. However, when students are willing to share, everyone benefits from this exchange.

10. **Learn some basic communication skills (e.g., vocabulary, simple phrases) in the student's language.** Many American professionals are monolingual English speakers. When these professionals begin learning a second language, their empathy for ELL students may increase greatly! In addition, multicultural families appreciate professionals' efforts to relate to them, even if they speak only a few simple phrases of the family's home language.

11. **Be aware that students from different cultural backgrounds may begin school with different cultural assumptions about human relations and about the world.** These assumptions may cause conflict for the student initially. Professionals need to be sensitive to this possibility, especially for students who enter the country as immigrants or refugees.

12. **Learn to pronounce and use students' actual names rather than just "Americanized" versions of these names.** Show an interest in learning how to pronounce the student's name correctly.

❑ Degree of acculturation into mainstream American life

❑ Generational membership (first, second, third generation)

❑ Beliefs about health care and disabilities

❑ Possible presence of post-traumatic stress disorder (PTSD)

If a family has immigrated to the United States, reasons for this immigration should be considered. It is also important to find out about generational patterns of immigration. To what extent are other relatives living in close proximity? To what extent are members of a cultural group marrying those from different ethnic backgrounds? These questions and all of the above factors need to be considered when professionals provide services to students and families from diverse cultural backgrounds.

Immigrant Insight   Natalya, university senior, speaker of Ukrainian, daughter of immigrants from Ukraine

Many Christians have fled from Ukraine to the U.S. due to religious persecution. We in the Slavic community tend to marry within the community to preserve our culture. We are very close knit, and prefer to receive services from other members of the Slavic community rather than mainstream American professionals. Schools in the U.S. are much less formal than in Ukraine, where teachers are very strict and we fear them. Disability is a touchy subject; parents may try to cover up a child's disability because they don't want to look bad. It might be hard to obtain accurate information from them. Remember that we have large families—children are very highly valued, and must respect elders. Young children in our community don't go to day care or preschool—they are cared for by relatives. Sometimes older children will be taken out of school to care for younger ones. Marrying young is common—marrying at 17, 18, or 19 is not at all unusual. We frown upon premarital sex, and no one lives together without being married. There is no divorce. Church is a huge part of our lives; we don't participate in extracurricular activities because we devote all our spare time to church. At school, we hang out with church friends. Many of us don't mingle much with mainstream American students. We are generally quite conservative, and it's important to us to preserve our identity.

WORKING WITH IMMIGRANTS AND REFUGEES

Many professionals in the schools work with large numbers of students who are from immigrant and refugee families. For example, the school district where I serve part-time as an itinerant speech-language pathologist is the third largest recipient of immigrant and refugee students in the U.S. The majority of these students are from the Middle East (e.g., Afghanistan and Syria) and the fastest-growing languages in my district are Farsi and Arabic.

The term **immigrant** is used to describe an individual who enters a country with the intention of becoming a permanent resident. The term **refugee** is used to describe an individual who flees to another country because of fear of persecution, war, or imminent danger. Religion, nationality, race, political opinion, or an affiliation with a particular social group may account for the individual's departure from the homeland. Political refugees who are fleeing arrest, torture, or other forms of oppression receive asylum in the U.S.

A critical component of cultural competence is the awareness of the effects that immigrant/refugee status have on students, their families, and the delivery of instructional services. For the purposes of efficiency in this section, immigrants and refugees are often referred to as "immigrants/ refugees." It is important to remember that not all immigrants are refugees, and not all refugees are immigrants. Professionals should keep the above definitions and distinctions in mind when reading this section.

GENERAL BACKGROUND INFORMATION

❑ Nearly 59 million immigrants have arrived in the U.S. in the past 50 years, mostly from Latin America and Asia. Today, a near-record 14% of the country's population is foreign born compared with just 5% in 1965. Over the next five decades, the majority of U.S. population growth is projected to be linked to new Asian and Hispanic immigration (Pew Research Center, 2017b).

❑ From 2010-2015, the Asian American and Pacific Islander communities in the U.S. grew by 17%, compared with 11% growth of the Latino community (Center for American Progress, 2017). In the U.S., by 2025, one in every four school-aged children will be an ELL (Pew Research Center, 2017b).

❑ There is enormous diversity among immigrants/refugees. They represent every echelon of society from wealth, privilege, and education to poverty and illiteracy; they speak varying degrees of English.

Profile

Thuy, a 12-year-old Vietnamese boy, was referred for a speech-language evaluation. He was making poor academic progress in comparison to other Vietnamese students, and an underlying language impairment was suspected. Thuy was the youngest of eight children and had spent the great majority of his life in Southeast Asian refugee camps. Apparently he had been placed in school at one point, but the family moved so frequently that he received a very fragmented education. He had minimal literacy in Vietnamese. The speech-language pathologist's challenge was to determine the extent to which Thuy's limited formal education was contributing to his lack of academic progress. Did Thuy truly have a language impairment, or was he struggling because of lack of educational opportunities in his home country?

GENERAL CHARACTERISTICS OF IMMIGRANTS AND REFUGEES

Due to the diversity of the immigrant/refugee population, it is impossible to construct a paradigm into which they will all neatly fit. The following characteristics are true of *SOME*, but not all immigrants/refugees. Students and families must be evaluated and served based on an understanding of their unique characteristics, backgrounds, and needs. They should not be stereotyped.

❑ Persons who wish to immigrate legally to the United States must meet the requirements of United States immigration laws. Medical screenings, for example, are required of all immigrants.

❑ Many immigrants/refugees are educated, financially successful individuals who come to the United States because of a desire for greater freedom and increased economic opportunity.

❑ Some immigrant/refugee students come to the United States with strong literacy skills in their native languages; others are nonliterate and have had minimal education.

❏ Students from homes in which immigrant parents have a strong focus on education tend to perform better in school than those from homes in which education is not a focus.

❏ Many refugees have spent time in camps in "countries of second asylum," during a period of transition while preparing for resettlement. Some refugees have even lived in countries of third asylum. For example, refugees from Vietnam might have lived in Cambodia and then in the Philippines before finally coming to the United States to settle permanently. Some families from Syria may have spent time in Greece before coming to live in the United States. Consequently, children may have had little or no formal education before coming to the United States.

❏ Historically, immigrants/refugees were encouraged to adopt American values and to speak English rather than their native language. However, the importance of respecting and celebrating linguistic and cultural differences is now recognized.

❏ Immigrants have higher birth rates than native-born Americans. It is estimated that if current trends continue, by 2050, 37% of the U.S. population will be immigrants or children of immigrants. As much as 93% of the growth of the working-age population between 2013 and 2050 will be accounted for by immigrants or their U.S.-born children (Pew Research Center, 2013).

❏ There are some common ways in which refugees/immigrants adapt to United States culture. Locke (1998) proposed a model of acculturation that is based on attitude as well as involvement with one's culture of origin and the society in which one is currently living. Locke delineated four levels of acculturation that professionals should be aware of as they work with refugee/immigrant families:

1. **Traditional**: Individuals do not adapt to the new culture and continue to adhere solely to the practices and values of their culture of origin.

2. **Marginal**: Individuals adapt minimally to the new culture.

3. **Acculturated**: Individuals adapt to the new culture but lose some parameters of their culture of origin.

4. **Bicultural**: Individuals retain strong ties with their culture of origin while successfully adapting to the new culture.

Profile

I held a parent conference with the mother of José F., a Filipino kindergartner. José had never been to preschool and was cared for at home by his grandparents while his parents worked. During his preschool years, at home with his grandparents, he had been allowed to watch approximately 10 hours of TV a day. Mrs. F. spoke Tagalog; her husband spoke Visayan; the grandparents spoke Pampango. José came to kindergarten at 4 years, 9 months of age speaking no English.

José was referred by his teacher for a speech-language screening because he was struggling in class and she thought he might have a language impairment. The teacher said that José could not pay attention, follow instructions, or complete his work in a timely fashion. The Filipino interpreter told me that José spoke so little of any of his Filipino languages that she could not validly assess him in any of the languages spoken. At the parent conference, Mrs. F. (a bright woman with excellent English) ruefully shared that she and her husband had virtually no time to spend with José. The mother had read a lot to José's older sister, who was doing well in school, but she was just too tired at night to do the same with José. I empathized with her situation and asked if she and/or her husband could read for just five minutes in the evening. She said that this might be possible. We did not place José into any type of special education program because we wanted to give him time to develop and adjust to the routine of school. José was provided with a peer "buddy" to help him with class routines and work. The teacher was given specific suggestions to promote greater success in the classroom.

ACCULTURATION

The term **acculturation** refers to the merging of two cultures as a result of prolonged contact. As a result of the interaction between cultures, individuals are able to identify with the primary community in which they have been initially socialized as well as with the broader majority community. It is important for professionals to determine the degree of acculturation experienced by students and their families. Generally, immigrants/refugees who experience a high level of acculturation tend to have smoother transitions and experience greater success in the mainstream society. Factors that may result in a higher level of acculturation include the following:

- ❑ a relatively high level of formal education

- ❑ middle to high socioeconomic status

- ❑ being born into a family that has lived in the United States for at least a few years

- ❑ immigration to the United States at an early age

- ❑ limited migration back and forth to the country of origin

- ❑ previous residence in an urban environment

- ❑ extensive contact with people outside the family and/or ethnic network

Ideally, when immigrants/refugees acculturate to the U.S. way of life, they do not weaken connections with their families, communities, or cultural traditions. Children born to immigrants in the U.S. tend to become acculturated and lead prosperous lives. For example, compared with all Americans, U.S.-born children of immigrants are more likely to go to college, less likely to live in poverty, and equally likely to be homeowners. On average, children of immigrants meet or exceed the educational attainment of third-plus generation natives (Center for American Progress, 2017).

Immigrant Insight   Kahoku, male speaker of Laotian, Laos

I came to the U.S. when I was 11 years old. We came to the U.S. because of the war. My parents' breaking point was when the government told them that I had to become a soldier at the age of 9. My dad got everyone together in the church and told the other families with sons ages 10 and over that their boys were too young to die. He knew the way to the refugee camp in Thailand, and he asked who wanted to go with him. We left that night with 15 families. I remember hiding in the forest with no food or water for two days. Our parents covered our mouths so the soldiers wouldn't hear us if we talked or cried, and we made it. In Laos, soldiers often arrested people and claimed that they broke a law, even if no law was broken. When I lived in Laos, the soldiers would arrest anyone who made enough money to feed their family.

In Laos, if you are disabled, they will chase you out of the city. It is believed that you are a demon or monster there to eat the children. If they think you are only there to scare them and that you won't eat them, you may live on the city outskirts, but you cannot talk to or look at anyone. I remember my dad chasing disabled people out of the city because he thought they were vampires killing our people in the night.

School in the U.S. was hard. I never learned how to read or write English. I was big for my grade, and the other kids would laugh at me because I didn't understand the language.

DIFFICULTIES COMMONLY EXPERIENCED BY IMMIGRANTS/REFUGEES

❏ Today, of the 20 million refugees worldwide, 51% are under the age of 18 (United Nations Refugee Agency, 2017).

❏ Refugees leave their homeland for a variety of reasons. There are two types of refugee movements: **acute** and **anticipatory**.

1. Refugees who anticipate leaving their country sense danger and leave early; they resemble voluntary migrants.

2. Refugees in an acute movement situation have not planned to leave their country and are not prepared for it. For example, in recent times, thousands of Syrians fled from the city of Aleppo into countries of second or third asylum.

❏ Today, many refugees are displaced people. In the context of emergencies, displaced people are those who have had to leave their homes as the result of a deliberate, natural, or technological event (World Health Organization, 2017). For example, they may leave because of a tsunami, earthquake, civil war, or religious persecution.

❏ Today, there are 65.3 million forcibly displaced people around the world. On average, 42,500 people a day flee their homes to seek protection in their own country or within the borders of other countries. More than 11 million Syrians, or 45% of the Syrian population, are currently displaced (United Nations Refugee Agency, 2017).

❏ Many displaced people have witnessed and/or endured oppressive and traumatic experiences such as disease, persecution, death, atrocities, forced labor, separation from family members, starvation, and forced dislocation. Such experiences can result in post-traumatic stress disorders, health problems, and many other negative consequences.

❏ Political turbulence in many areas of the world has increased the number of displaced people who are fleeing from complex disasters and emergencies. They often end up living in large camps where health resources are insufficient (World Health Organization, 2017). Persons with disabilities are especially vulnerable (Battle, 2015).

❏ In addition to a scarcity of health services, there is also a scarcity of educational resources in these camps. Many refugee children have spent years in camps and have had little to no school experience. For example, in my school district, we have enrolled 9-year-old Afghan and Syrian children who have never attended school.

Immigrant Insight   Noma A., speaker of Nepali and Bhutanese,
                           daughter of immigrants from Nepal and Bhutan

My father helped establish a camp for refugees in Bhutan. He stayed in the camp for 18 years, helping other refugees. Since the camp was overpopulated, there was no sanitary system in place. My sister almost died due to food scarcity and diarrhea. We fled to Nepal since people were threatening to kill my dad. When we fled to Nepal in 2007, I was in sixth grade. A group of rebels came to our home; they had masks on, and started destroying our home with shovels, knives, and iron rods. Our neighbor heard the commotion and helped us escape. I still remember that scary night like it was yesterday. I didn't attend school for almost a year. We came to the U.S. in 2008 and became naturalized citizens in 2014. It finally felt like we were home! I learned English after we arrived in the U.S. We were extremely poor; I will never forget the fried garlic cloves that we ate for months. I slept on the floor in our crowded home. I started working at a very young age. My brother is now an RN, and I am finishing my Bachelor's degree in speech-language pathology. I had heard about SLPs because of a cousin diagnosed with autism spectrum disorder, but most Bhutanese have a complete lack of awareness of speech-language pathology (SLP). Most older Bhutanese never attended school. However, if you explain SLP services to Bhutanese refugees, they will be very interested. Remember that parents may not be able to carry out speech-language or academic homework with their children because they work long hours and are not educated themselves. Be sure not to call older persons by their first names—no one does that!

❏ Many refugees/immigrants have been separated from their families due, in part, to situations in which some family members come to the United States while others remain in their homeland. It may be years before family members are reunited.

❏ Undocumented immigrants/refugees may be quite fearful of forced repatriation. If they must return to the homeland, consequences can be quite severe. For example, some Chinese repatriated refugees have been sentenced to forced labor camps.

❏ Students may experience problems adjusting to schools in the United States with rules and expectations different from those in the homeland.

❏ Some immigrants/refugees from rural areas have experienced difficulty adjusting to the technological emphasis in the United States urban work environment.

❏ Many immigrants/refugees experience substantial poverty in the United States, even if they are from middle-upper class socioeconomic backgrounds.

❏ Older immigrants who have moderate or heavy accents in English may encounter vocational and social barriers because of their accents.

❏ Many highly-trained immigrants (e.g., doctors, dentists, architects) are not allowed to practice their professions in the U.S. because educational credentials from their homeland are not accepted. Sometimes these professionals end up working as truck drivers, dishwashers, etc. after arriving in the U.S.

❏ Despite the fact that many immigrants experience poverty in the U.S., working-class, immigrant-headed households with incomes less than 200% below the federal poverty line rely less on public benefits and social services than comparable U.S.-born households.

Immigrants are becoming homeowners at a faster rate than the U.S.-born population, and more than half the foreign-born population are homeowners. The incarceration rate for immigrants between 18 and 54 years of age—both authorized and unauthorized—is substantially lower than that of the U.S.-born population (Center for American Progress, 2017).

❏ Of the many health issues faced by immigrants, the most challenging are those related to insurance and access to health care. Families' lack of access to health care is related to several key variables, including lack of knowledge of available resources, language barriers, and cultural barriers. Low-income immigrants are twice as likely to be uninsured as low-income U.S. citizens.

❏ The United States has experienced a macro-economic shift from a manufacturing- and agricultural-based economy to an information-based economy. This shift has made circumstances more challenging for immigrants who are not educated and do not speak English; these immigrants are especially vulnerable to poverty.

❏ For many immigrants, the language barrier is a formidable one in terms of obtaining gainful employment and health-related services. In an unpublished study of 376 immigrants from 82 different countries around the world, Roseberry-McKibbin (2013) found that 51% of the immigrants stated that learning and communicating in English was their greatest challenge in coming to the U.S.

Immigrant Insight   Kedar, male speaker of Hindi, India

In India, my parents were doctors and had many years of medical practice under their belts. By Day 2 in the U.S., they were working in a kitchen washing dishes at a local college. They were not able to go through the many years of medical school required by the U.S. system. They continued working in jobs at places like McDonald's, Shop-Rite, and WalMart until they eventually retired. My parents have a drive that I don't often witness in Americans.

❏ Other problems cited by these subjects included loneliness, missing friends back home, the busy and fast-paced American lifestyle, poverty, transportation problems, and discrimination. Many respondents talked about how hard it was for them living in a country where it is necessary to drive everywhere you need to go. In their countries of origin, many interviewees walked or used public transportation (Roseberry-McKibbin, 2013).

❏ The interviewees were also asked about their perceptions of speech-language pathologists (SLPs) and services provided for individuals with communication disorders. Over half (56.6%) indicated that in their home countries, there was a lack of awareness about disabilities; in many cases, disabilities were viewed as a source of stigma or disgrace. Eighty five percent of interviewees said that in their countries, there was a lack of awareness about SLPs and their services. Of the 15% of interviewees who demonstrated awareness of the profession of speech-language pathology, the majority were from Canada and Europe.

Immigrant Insight   Selva, Indian, male speaker of Afrikaans, Zulu, Tamil, and English

In South Africa, I felt like a walking time bomb, not knowing when I was going to be robbed or attacked. On three occasions, my business staff and I were held at gun point and robbed of cash. I always had to be looking over my shoulder to make sure my family and I were safe. In the U.S., I can confidently take walks during the evening with my family and not be afraid of being mugged or robbed. I drive with ease because I am not afraid of being hijacked. In South Africa, if you even stopped at a stop sign, especially at night, you were afraid of either being gunned down or having your car hijacked. We became prisoners in our own homes. In the U.S., we enjoy a beautiful, secure, and safe life.

POSSIBLE FAMILY CONCERNS

Many researchers have documented the existence of intergenerational tensions in families as they immigrate to the United States and experience changes in almost every area of life (Coelho, 2012; Sue & Sue, 2016). Some of the sources of tension are as follows:

❑ Family members may often be separated from one another for long periods of time. In one study of a subset of foreign-born children with at least one parent in the U.S., 21% were separated from their mothers and 34% were separated from their fathers by one year or more (Enchautegui, 2013).

❑ Young people often want to become Americanized, but they are expected by their elders to maintain traditional customs. For example, in many Hmong families, parents have strict curfews and expect girls to marry early and spend their lives bearing and raising children (Vang, 2005). This can produce conflicts when girls want to obtain a higher level of education.

❑ Children often learn English more quickly than their elders and thus become spokespersons for their families. Children have to adopt adult roles, caring for their siblings, and serving as negotiators and interpreters for their parents. For example, many of my diverse university students have shared that they served as interpreters for their parents at doctors' visits, parent-teacher conferences, etc. Because these children have greater responsibilities than their U.S.-born peers, they may demand greater rights. This can produce conflicts in the home, including usurping the elders' traditional role as authority figures.

❑ Some family members (e.g., parents) must work long hours in order to survive financially and may not be available to their children for much of the day and night. Sometimes these children engage in delinquent activities because they are unsupervised after school hours. Some of these "latchkey kids" join gangs.

Tech Tie-In   In a moving YouTube video, Hawa Bashir, a Kenyan Muslim refugee, describes moving to the U.S. at the age of 10 with her family and helping her non-English-speaking parents adjust to American life. She also describes the challenges of being Muslim.
https://www.youtube.com/watch?v=-YNj1ad8vDM

❑ Children may want to marry Americans instead of persons from their home culture; elders may greatly disapprove of this practice. The acceptance of interracial marriage varies greatly from family to family.

❑ The harmonious nature of marital relationships may be disrupted in certain circumstances. For example, women who have previously worked inside the home with no salary and obeyed their husbands may have to begin working outside the home to earn income for the family. This can cause a shift in the balance of power between family members.

❑ Many families have traditionally been interdependent; the American social emphasis on in- dependence may cause upheaval in families with members who traditionally relied on one another. For example, in some countries, the elderly live with their adult children and grand- children. If these elderly family members are not able to live with their families in the U.S., they may feel very distressed and abandoned.

❑ As mentioned, immigrants who received specialized training in their home country often en- counter occupational barriers in the United States because their professional training is viewed as inadequate. They may need to "jump through the hoops" by completing additional school- ing, obtaining additional credentials, etc. For example, an individual who was a heart surgeon in his homeland may end up working as a dishwasher in this country. Thus, families from mid- dle-upper class socioeconomic backgrounds in their home country may experience new-found poverty in the United States.

❑ Families who were of middle- and upper-class status in their home countries may be ac- customed to having servants to care for their children. They are often shocked to learn that in the United States, they are expected to do things such as transporting their children to therapy or helping them complete homework assignments.

❑ Many immigrants/refugees have suffered from great trauma in their home countries; often, their children suffer from mental health consequences through the intergenerational trans- mission of trauma. Parent-child bonding and attachment may be negatively affected.

❑ Today, trauma-informed organizations recognize the prevalence and impact of trauma among immigrants/refugees, and respond in a trauma-sensitive manner. These organizations strive to address and mitigate the effects of trauma on children, youth, and adults (American Institutes for Research, 2017).

❑ Statistically, children in immigrant families may be at somewhat greater risk for abuse than children from non-immigrant families. The stresses described above may lead parents to abuse their children; in addition to the above-described stresses, many immigrant parents find themselves isolated and missing the help that was provided previously in their home countries by their extended families and servants.

❑ Some immigrant parents may discipline their children in public for behavior that they con- sider to be disrespectful or disobedient. This action can bring the parents to the attention of protection and advocacy services.

❑ Some cultures engage in disciplinary practices that would be considered abusive by U.S. standards. For example, in some Central American cultures, children may be given potions containing mercury to ward off "mal ojo" (evil eye). When children in Jamaica misbehave, parents may flog them. Many parents from Singapore believe that caning their children on the buttocks and limbs is the best method of punishment to prevent further misbehavior.

❑ Many immigrant parents believe that in the U.S., their children have too much freedom and too many choices and consequently are disrespectful, "wild," disobedient, and difficult to control.

❑ In a study of Chinese immigrant families, it was found that parent-child acculturation discrepancy is a risk factor in children's development (Kim, Chen, Wang, Shen, & Orozco-Lapray, 2013). In this study, children of parents who used unsupportive parenting practices showed depressive symptoms and lower academic performance in early adolescence.

Immigrant Insight   Saminder, daughter of Sikh immigrants from India

I was born in California. My grandparents were very strict and believed that girls should not play sports—so I didn't. Growing up, I got a lot of comments like, "Does your dad own a gas station?" Among my people, sons are favored over daughters. Most Indians in my community want their kids to marry other Indians—even dating Whites is unacceptable. My parents will never allow me to marry a White guy. My aunt did, and the whole family disowned her.

PUBLIC PERCEPTIONS ABOUT IMMIGRANTS/REFUGEES

As the number of immigrants/refugees to the United States increases, it is important to look not only at the facts and numbers, but also at the attitudes of Americans toward immigrants/refugees. Beliefs about immigrants/refugees help determine public policy, including educational and financial provisions and services. These provisions and services affect the availability of school resources that serve immigrant students. The attitudes of professionals toward immigrants/refugees also impact service delivery to these students and their families.

The United States is a nation of immigrants and descendants of immigrants. Some came voluntarily, others involuntarily. Immigrants/refugees bring many positive qualities to the United States. Many immigrants/refugees are diverse, young, and dynamic persons who have great potential to contribute positively to American society.

Despite this, many people living in the United States have negative feelings about individuals who immigrate to this country. These perceptions are reflected in increased legislation to stem the flow of immigrants into the United States. Many believe that these immigrants cause social and economic problems. Professionals who work directly with immigrants/refugees must make certain that they personally do not hold biases that could negatively impact the effectiveness of service delivery.

IMPLICATIONS FOR PROFESSIONALS

❑ The degree of acculturation and education of immigrant/refugee students and their families may affect how they view the general education curriculum and special education services. A highly-educated immigrant/refugee family might be more responsive to special education, for example, than a family with limited educational experiences.

❑ Students from undocumented immigrant/refugee families may suddenly "disappear" from school, possibly because of forced repatriation.

❑ Emotional problems that affect school performance may be experienced by students who have encountered great trauma. Help may need to be provided for these problems.

❑ Professionals can help students express feelings through art and writing. For example, there are art therapy classes that allow students to express their grief over loss of family members. Speech-language pathologists may need to refer students and their family members to mental health professionals.

❑ When professionals collect case histories from members of immigrant/refugee families, they should remember that revisiting past experiences may be painful for some families. Recently, one of my university students from a refugee family became tearful in class when I asked her a question about her past experiences in her home country. She stated that she was not able to talk about this topic.

❑ Professionals can facilitate mutual enrichment experiences for both immigrant/refugee students and their mainstream peers by asking these students to share information about their home languages, cultures, and experiences. However, professionals must be sensitive in cases in which this sharing brings emotional pain to the student involved.

❑ Professionals can also encourage parents to share their culture at their children's schools. Both immigrant students and their mainstream peers in schools are enriched when immigrant parents share their culture and life experiences with others.

❑ One of the best ways to assist immigrant/refugee families is to connect them with local support networks, especially those consisting of persons from their own culture who can provide needed information and resources. In Sacramento, California, for example, Russian immigrants have been assisted by Russian churches in a variety of ways. Muslim temples have provided many services for Middle Eastern refugees.

❑ Pregnant female refugees who are malnourished may deliver babies with health problems or specific disabilities. Some refugee mothers receive no prenatal care, seeing a doctor only on the day that the baby is born. In addition, many refugee children in our schools have poor health and/or medical conditions that may affect their ability to learn.

❑ Some families do not know the exact birth dates of their children; for example, refugees who are fleeing for their lives may not attach great importance to birth certificates and other records.

❑ Professionals should stress that their concern is to help the family. Some families suffer the daily torment of never knowing when and how they may be discovered and subjected to deportation.

❑ Some families have difficulty planning for the future because they have put so much effort into trying to survive from one day to the next. Thus it may be hard for them to understand or appreciate the concept of long-term goals that is often emphasized in special education programs.

❑ Lum (2004) found that many of his clients who felt despair or anger because of hardship masked their feelings with a flat emotional affect. However, as they began to feel comfortable with and respected by professionals, they were able to relax. Professionals, therefore, should not take it personally if clients seem angry, unresponsive, or "hard" initially.

❑ In the aforementioned study of immigrants from around the world, Roseberry-McKibbin (2013) found that American professionals were often viewed as "cold" because they jumped quickly into business discussions with no friendly preamble. Professionals should make an effort to show personal warmth and a small amount of friendly, personal "chitchat" before delving into the business at hand. I have personally found that even a few minutes of this type of interaction pays great dividends in terms of increased cooperation and enhanced communication.

❑ Many immigrant/refugee students need to acquire the practical, functional skills necessary to read bus schedules, use cell phones to obtain information, etc.

❑ In the United States, school is compulsory for all immigrant students, even those who arrive in their teens. However, in some cultures, adolescents are not required to attend school. A conflict between American law and family traditions often occurs if the parents feel that their child needs to work. In one dramatic instance in California, the mother of a teen-age Vietnamese boy wanted her son to drop out of school so that he could help run her beauty parlor. After dropping out against his wishes, the boy ended up participating in criminal activities with his peers.

❑ For some families, the informality found in American schools is quite a culture shock. Many immigrant students come from countries where teachers have strict rules and allow students little freedom. In addition, in many countries, there are no extracurricular activities. Professionals may need to point out the learning benefits of extracurricular activities (e.g., joining a theater group to increase expressive language skills and opportunities to interact with other students).

Immigrant Insight   Chanmi, speaker of Korean, daughter of
                                   immigrants from Korea

In Korea, physical punishment is common in schools. It's all about studying, not extracurriculars. There are no sports. Starting in junior high, we attend school from 7:00 A.M. till 10:00 P.M. When we moved to the U.S., I couldn't get over how big and spread out everything was. My parents are business owners. In third grade, I became involved in the family business through serving as a translator for my parents. My father makes all family decisions, and we must obey them. I wanted to be a music therapist, but my dad became extremely upset and told me that this profession was too flaky.

❑ Because some immigrants/refugees have had family servants in their native country, the children may be unaccustomed to caring for themselves and functioning independently and may therefore be viewed as "too dependent" by teachers and other school professionals. Professionals can gently encourage the families of such children to help these children become more independent so they can fit in well in mainstream U.S. settings.

❑ As previously stated, some parents may feel uncomfortable participating in their children's activities because servants assumed this responsibility in their countries of origin. Professionals can sensitively share with the families that in U.S. culture, parents are often encouraged to read to their children, to provide language stimulation activities, and to assist with homework.

❑ To increase employment opportunities, professionals should encourage immigrant families to participate in programs designed to build English language skills.

❑ Speech-language pathologists may need to help families understand the profession of speech-language pathology and audiology and the services offered by speech-language pathologists. As mentioned previously, disabilities are stigmatized in many cultures and immigrants are often unaware that help is available. (Mahendra, 2012; Parette, Chuang, & Huer, 2004; Roseberry-McKibbin et al., 2013)

❑ Professionals must constructively deal with parents who punish and discipline their children in ways that are considered unacceptable and illegal in the United States. Professionals need to ensure that parents understand U.S. laws relating to child abuse. Parents also need to understand that children may be removed from their custody for behaviors that are considered to constitute child abuse.

❑ Professionals should recommend alternatives to physical discipline (e.g., use of "time-out"). Explain to parents that their children are more likely to perform well and become successful in life if forms of discipline are used that do not cause physical pain.

❑ In some countries, schools emphasize a specific set of morals or religious beliefs that may not be taught in U.S. classrooms. Cultural mediators may be able to provide information about places in the community (e.g., local churches) where this moral or religious training is available.

Profile

José is a 13-year-old, monolingual Spanish-speaking student from Mexico. He experienced a head injury after being struck by a car and received language and cognitive rehabilitation at the local facility. José's family was very supportive of the services offered by the speech-language pathologist and often expressed gratitude for the services that were being provided.

After 34 weeks of treatment, José suddenly stopped coming to therapy. A somewhat incomprehensible phone message was left on the facility's answering machine. Numerous phone calls were made and it was learned that José's family returned to Mexico after being identified as "illegal aliens." The family left the country without any written documentation about the intervention program that had been provided.

CONCLUSION

American society has been enriched by immigration. Providing services to students and families from immigrant/refugee backgrounds can be both challenging and rewarding. As professionals work with culturally and linguistically diverse student groups, they expand their knowledge and cultural competence, become more flexible, and expand their expertise in service delivery.

Learning about cultural differences helps educational professionals to better understand how their students view the world around them and how they interpret experiences. Behaviors commonly observed among specific cultural groups should be viewed as "cultural tendencies." We should never assume that all individuals from a particular cultural background have the same beliefs, customs, or values.

STUDY QUESTIONS

1. Professionals are likely to encounter families who discipline their children in ways that are considered abusive in the U.S. How can professionals help these families to understand and accept U.S cultural expectations regarding discipline?

2. Describe three ways in which professionals can increase their cultural competence.

3. Describe four specific ways in which professionals can help immigrant/refugee students and their families deal with problems commonly encountered after entering the U.S.

MULTIPLE CHOICE

4. Which one of these factors does not tend to impact a family's acculturation into U.S. life?

   A. Urban vs. rural background
   B. Educational level
   C. Neighborhood of residence and peer group
   D. Length of residence in an area
   E. Number of times church is attended each week

5. You are working with the Fa family from Beijing, China. They immigrated to the U.S. two years ago, and their sixth-grade daughter, Meuy, is experiencing difficulties in the classroom. The classroom teacher tells you he thinks that Meuy feels as though she is "losing" some aspects of her Chinese culture as her parents work hard to adapt and fit into U.S. culture. Which level of acculturation are Meuy and her family experiencing?

   A. Acculturated
   B. Traditional
   C. Marginal
   D. Bicultural
   E. Compensatory

6. Difficulties commonly experienced by immigrants and refugees include the following:

   A. Forced repatriation is feared.
   B. Students who have had servants in their native countries are often considered "immature" and "dependent" by American teachers.
   C. Separation from family members may make it difficult for them to function in society.
   D. Choices B and C
   E. Choices A, B, and C

7. When working with immigrant/refugee students and families, it is helpful for professionals to do which of the following?

    A. Ask immigrant/refugee students to provide information about their home language, culture, and experiences living in various countries and situations.
    B. Help families connect with local support networks consisting of persons from their own culture who can provide needed information and resources.
    C. Assure families that even though professionals may report their illegal status to the INS, services will still be continued if the families remain in the U.S.
    D. Encourage use of English in all social situations.
    E. Choices A and B

8. You are working in a high school where many students are children of immigrants. One of the young ladies on your caseload, Senbo, is the daughter of immigrants from India. Her parents are loving and hardworking people, but they are also very strict. They speak only Punjabi. Senbo is the oldest of five children. Recently Senbo has shown signs of depression and has been unwilling to complete speech-language homework. You refer her to the school counselor and continue to see her for speech-language therapy. Based on your knowledge of the issues experienced by some immigrant families, which of the following do you think Senbo might be experiencing?

    A. Senbo may want to date a friend of hers who is "white" even though she knows that her parents will disapprove.
    B. Senbo may be spending little time studying because she is serving as a translator and conducting business for her parents.
    C. Senbo may be staying home too much and "being safe," although her parents want her to "get out more" and have typical teenage American experiences.
    D. Senbo's parents may think that school is too stressful for Senbo, and they want her to relax more and not work so hard on her academics.
    E. Senbo may be spending a considerable amount of time helping her younger siblings with their homework because her parents don't speak English.

9. Which one of the following is FALSE?

    A. In the year 2025, one out of every four children in our schools will be an ELL.
    B. Ethnocentrism is the view that members of one's own culture do things the "right" way.
    C. Today, there are more Hispanic immigrants to the U.S. than there are Asian and Pacific Islander immigrants.
    D. The incarceration rate for immigrants between 18 and 54 years of age—both authorized and unauthorized—is substantially lower than that of the U.S.-born population.
    E. In the context of emergencies, displaced people are those who have had to leave their homes as the result of a deliberate, natural, or technological event.

10. In your job as a public school speech-language pathologist (SLP), you are serving a number of students of immigrant parents. You notice that many of the parents do not attend IEP meetings, and that they seem "unsupportive" of your efforts to improve their children's communication skills. You know that these parents work hard and care deeply about their children's education. Based upon current research, what might be some possible explanations for the parents' behavior?

    A. They have never heard of SLPs and are not familiar with assessment and treatment for persons with communication disorders.

B. Persons with disabilities tend to be stigmatized within their culture, so the placement of children in special education might be considered a disgrace by people in their community.
C. They believe that schools do not prioritize education for English Language Learners.
D. A, B
E. A, B, C

ANSWERS TO STUDY QUESTIONS

    4. E
    5. A
    6. E
    7. E
    8. A, B, E
    9. C
  10. D

Chapter 2

The Impact of Religious Differences

Outline
- Islam
- Buddhism
- Implications for Professionals
- Conclusion

It is important for professionals to understand and respect the religious beliefs of the culturally diverse families that they serve. These beliefs influence behavior in social contexts and attitudes relating to the education of individuals with disabilities.

Two major religions, Islam and Buddhism, are described briefly in this chapter to illustrate how religious differences influence behavior and attitudes. The purpose of this section is to give the professional a general overview of each religion's basic tenets. These ideas and tendencies are described as generalities, not absolutes. Each religion has great variety within it and, therefore, each family and student must be considered individually. The information presented should help professionals to better understand how various beliefs impact attitudes relating to disabilities. Moreover, the information should help professionals to become more sensitive to family dynamics that might be influenced by religious beliefs and values.

This chapter includes recent statistical data and factual information that was compiled primarily from the following sources: Pew Research Center: Religion and Public Life, 2017; Pew Research Center Fact Tank, 2017; Southern Poverty Law Center, 2017; Sue & Sue, 2016.

ISLAM

KEY TERMS

- **Islam** is a monotheistic (one god) faith. Islam means surrender or obedience to the will of God. Islam, not Muslim, is the name of the religion.

- A **Muslim**, also spelled Moslem, is a follower of Islam. Allah is the term used for "God."

- **Muhammed**, also spelled Mohammed, is the prophet and founder of Islam. He was born in 570 A.D. in Mecca, and began to spread his teachings around 612 A.D.

- The **Quran** (also spelled Koran) is the sacred book of Islam. It has 30 parts, contained in 114 chapters. A central message in this sacred book is that submission to one god results in peace. The primary act of faith is to perform/obey the will of Allah in both public and private life.

- **Mecca** is the principal holy city for Muslims. Most Muslims try, at least once in their lives, to complete the *Hajj,* or pilgrimage to Mecca.

❏ Islam has existed for over 13 centuries. Today it is practiced in at least 180 countries, with more than 1.57 billion followers worldwide. It is the second largest religion in the world (after Christianity) (Pew Research Center: Religion and Public Life, 2017).

❏ Muslims are not a homogeneous group; they represent a variety of ethnic and cultural backgrounds. Two major Muslim sects are the Sunnis (Majority) and the Shi'ites (Minority). Approximately 90% of Muslims worldwide are Sunnis. Shi'ites comprise the remaining 10% and can be found primarily in Iran and Iraq.

❏ Muslims are the fastest-growing religious group in the world. It is projected that between the years 2010-2050, there will be a 35% increase in the overall global population. The Muslim population will grow by 73%, while the population of Christians will grow by 35%.

❏ It is projected that in the U.S., by the year 2050, Muslims will outnumber Jews. If current demographic trends continue, it is expected that by the end of the 21st century, the number of Muslims will exceed the number of Christians (Pew Research Center Fact Tank, 2017).

❏ Islam is a comprehensive way of life. Unlike mainstream Americans, who separate church and state, Muslims believe that religion cannot be separated from political and social life. Many passages in the Koran support a strong relationship between Islam, the society, and the state (Pew Research Center: Religion and Public Life, 2017).

❏ In Islam, there are five basic *pillars*, or principles, that are commonly accepted by all Muslims:

1. Belief in one god and the belief that the prophet Muhammed was his last and final prophet.

2. Prayer (*salat*). Muslims pray at five specific times during the day, turning toward Mecca and reciting a prescribed prayer.

3. *Zakat*, or the alms tax. Most Muslims donate a percentage of their wages to help and support the poor and needy.

4. Fasting (*sawm*), which is completed during the month of Ramadan (no food or drink from sunrise to sundown); Ramadan is the ninth month of the lunar calendar.

5. *Hajj*, or pilgrimage to Mecca. This pilgrimage occurs once in a Muslim's lifetime. When Muslims arrive in Mecca, located in southwestern Saudi Arabia, pilgrims are required to perform a complex set of rituals to commemorate the lessons learned by Abraham. Muslims believe that in Mecca, Abraham and his son Ishmael built the first house of worship on earth.

❏ Muslims are not supposed to drink alcohol or use drugs. Drug and alcohol use can result in severe punishment; the Koran prescribes 80 lashes, and local authorities may impose additional penalties.

❏ Muslims do not eat pork. Many Muslims eat only hallal foods, or those foods that come from an animal slaughtered in the name of God. The purpose of the slaughter is for all the blood to be drained, thus making the food cleaner and healthier.

❏ In many Muslim countries, people never show the bottom of their feet because feet are in contact with the ground, and the ground is dirty. To show the bottom of your foot to someone is to imply that they are "as low as dirt."

❏ In some areas, patriarchal hierarchies allow the father/senior male of the household almost complete authority over the rest of the family. In more traditional families, members may believe that women should obey their husbands in all matters (Sue & Sue, 2016).

❏ There is often a traditional division of labor in the household; the woman takes care of the house, cooking, and children (even if she has a paying job outside the home). The man is the provider and makes the important decisions. He usually has the final word when decisions are made.

❑ Muslim marriages are often arranged; the bride and groom may not meet one another until the day of their wedding. Muslim parents often prefer that their children marry other Muslims. I have personally spoken with young Muslim women in California who believe that arranged marriages are very beneficial. One 21-year-old Pakistani said to me, "My parents are older, and they love me. They know what is best for me and will make a much better choice for me than I would for myself. Why wouldn't I trust them?"

❑ Among Muslim Arabs, especially in nomadic and rural communities, families prefer that first and second cousins marry each other. This within-family marriage helps ensure that people marry a "known quantity" and also that money and possessions remain in the family.

❑ In some Muslim societies and Muslim-American communities, polygamy is a religiously sanctioned practice. According to the Koran, a man may marry up to four women if he is able to treat them equally in all aspects (Word Press, 2013).

❑ The Koran originally sanctioned polygamy in response to times of war, where widows and orphans were left without husbands and fathers. These widows and orphans were allowed to be integrated into previously-existing families for protection and safety.

❑ Women are valued as mothers and guardians of the family, and modest dress for women is regarded as symbolic of this value. Theoretically, dressing modestly preserves women's respect, dignity, and virginity and protects them from abuse and harassment by men. Women are not to dress in a manner that will entice men (Harris, Mukati, & Ghandchi, 2012). Modesty requirements may range from a simple *hijab* (scarf) to a full body and face covering (*burqa*).

❑ The wearing of coverings may be determined by individual preferences and cultural norms for each country, not just religious dictates.

❑ Among some Muslim groups, sexual activity outside of marriage is considered to be so wrong that for a woman, it is punishable by flagellation, imprisonment, or even death. Forms of punishment, however, vary greatly from area to area.

❑ Islam encourages mothers to breast feed their babies; breast feeding may continue until the child is 2 to 3 years old. Generally, Muslim women do not breast feed in public and only do so discreetly in front of family members.

❑ Muslims in the United States have been increasingly singled out for racial profiling and persecution. In an effort to reduce terrorism, President Donald Trump made a campaign pledge to bar immigration to the U.S. from specific Muslim countries. Simultaneously, in the year 2016, the number of anti-Muslim hate groups in the U.S. nearly tripled, going from 34 in 2015 to 101 in 2016. This growth has been accompanied by an increase in hate crimes such as burning mosques and physically attacking Muslims nationwide (Southern Poverty Law Center, 2016).

Immigrant Insight   Wyme, female Filipino American stationed in the Air Force in Bahrain

When I was serving in Bahrain, women did not have the same rights as men...especially regarding independence. One time I left our military base and drove a military truck to a local store to get something. While I was getting back into the truck, I noticed a group of men sitting under the shade of the mosque where I was parked. They were very mad and were shouting at me in very angry voices. I felt so threatened and drove away as fast as I could. When I returned to the base, I was told that women were not allowed to drive, especially alone. So the men were quite mad that I did not follow these rules even though I was clearly in a U.S. military uniform driving a military vehicle. After that encounter, I never left the base alone without being accompanied by a man.

I also learned that I should never be alone when I left my hotel room, even to go to the lobby. One time I went to the lobby to call home. There was a man who stared at me the whole time—he was very unhappy that I was alone and that my ankles were exposed.

At work, even though I was the lead jet mechanic, I was not allowed to openly give my advice or opinions. Instead, I had a male co-worker relay the information so that the others would never know that a female was calling the shots.

Profile

Shahirah M., a 17-year-old Muslim high-school girl on a female speech-language pathologist's caseload, came to therapy one day feeling unhappy. She related that she wanted to go to college to become a physician. Her father, however, didn't want her to attend college. He told her that she should get married and start a family after finishing high school.

A husband had already been selected for her. Shahirah explained that she wanted some independence and freedom. She wanted a career so that she would be able to support herself if necessary. The speech-language pathologist discussed this matter with several Muslim friends. Upon their recommendation, the speech-language pathologist approached a male Muslim teacher, Mr. Mojibi, at the high school and asked for his assistance and support.

Mr. Mojibi contacted Shahirah's father and an Imam (religious leader) from a local mosque. The three men had a conference. Mr. Mojibi and the Imam communicated to Shahirah's father in a sensitive and kind way that in Shahirah's family's country of origin, early marriage and motherhood were indeed very appropriate. They stressed, however, that in the U.S. women are encouraged to be independent and to prepare for careers. This preparation would allow her to achieve financial independence and would make it possible for her to support her parents when they are elderly and need assistance. The Imam told Shahirah's father about several Muslim mothers, members of his mosque, who worked part-time outside the home and successfully balanced the demands of career and family. After some discussion, Shahirah's father agreed to allow her to consider pursuing her dream of attending medical school.

BUDDHISM

KEY TERMS

- The title **Buddha** means "Enlightened One," literally, a supremely enlightened person. The Buddha himself was Siddhartha Gautama, a former Indian prince, who lived from approximately 584-563 B.C. Buddha is not considered to be a god; he made no claims to divinity. Rather, he is considered a great man and teacher, a guide for those seeking enlightenment.

- **Karma** means that a person's fate or destiny in this life is determined by what happened in a previous life. Karma also embodies the principle that those who do good receive good and those who do evil receive evil.

- **Reincarnation** is the repeated cycle of being born into the world as we know it, until enlightenment is achieved.

- **Nirvana** is a divine state that liberates one from the cycle of reincarnation. It represents separation from pain and escape from misery and trouble. It is the highest state of spiritual bliss that one can achieve.

Various forms of Buddhism are practiced throughout the world. The two primary types are *Theravada Buddhism* (found predominantly in Sri Lanka, Burma, Laos, Thailand, and Cambodia) and *Mahayana Buddhism*, commonly practiced in Vietnam, China, Korea, Japan, Mongolia, and Tibet. It is estimated that 7% of residents of the U.S. are Buddhist. The state with the highest percentage of Buddhists is Hawaii (Pew Research Center, Religion and Public Life, 2017).

Four principles are emphasized in Buddhism:

1. All of life is suffering and is inevitably sorrowful.

2. People suffer because they experience craving, are attached to the world, and are not content with what they have.

3. One must eliminate desire to extinguish suffering and attachment.

4. One can eliminate desire by living a virtuous life of carefully disciplined and moral conduct. This involves the eight-fold path of enlightenment, which stresses the correct view, intent, speech, conduct, means of livelihood, endeavor, mindfulness, and meditation.

Buddhists believe that one's chance of a better life in the next rebirth is determined largely by the number of good deeds accomplished in the present lifetime. Buddhists are encouraged to avoid evil and to achieve merit. Buddhism emphasizes supreme human effort.

Immigrant Insight   Chelsea S., university senior, daughter of immigrants from Sri Lanka

My family is Buddhist. Buddhism is more of a philosophy than a religion to us. We believe that if you have a good life now, you did things right in a past life. If bad things happen to you in this life, it's because of actions in a previous life. We also believe that Nirvana is a state of non-being where the ultimate goal is to not feel anything. Life is about suffering, and we suffer because we desire things. There are several branches of Buddhism, and we belong to the Theraveda branch. My Buddhist family members back in Sri Lanka say things to me like "What are you doing becoming a speech-language pathologist (SLP) to help people with rehabilitation? People are just born that way." For American SLPs who are bubbly and animated, it's important to remember that older, more conservative Buddhist clients may show little emotion, even if you share good news with them such as treatment progress, etc. These clients are living on what we call the "middle path," where they are more reserved and strive to accept life as it comes.

Tech Tie-In

Visit www.buddhanet.net for succinct explanations of beliefs and practices in Buddhism.

❏ Most Buddhists believe that meaningful life events such as marriage, birth circumstances, or serious illnesses can be affected by unknown past actions.

❏ Some Buddhists regard illness as a personal failure; there may be an assumption that if we are living truly spiritual lives, we will not be subject to illness.

❏ If a Buddhist family is informed that a child has a communication disorder, the family may think that the problem is the fault of family members. Communication disorders are believed to occur because family members acted in ways that were not truly spiritual.

Immigrant Insight   Hao, female immigrant from Vietnam, speaker of Vietnamese

Buddhists traditionally believe that a child's disability is the parents' karma and many people feel shame. Men will blame the wife for the child's disability, and sometimes parents hide their child. People will also sometimes hang the child up like a pig and beat him or her to try to get the "monster" out.

❏ In Buddhism, there is an emphasis on accepting things as they are. Most Buddhists believe that suffering comes from our mind and heart. How we interpret and respond to what we encounter in life is responsible for our experience of suffering.

❏ To live a virtuous life requires the avoidance of lying, theft, immoral sexual conduct, excessive alcohol consumption, and various "frivolous" activities such as dancing.

❏ For Buddhists, the Middle Way is a way of life that avoids both extreme forms of self denial and uncontrolled satisfaction of human desires.

❏ Buddha believed that it is important to live in the present moment and to be mindful, or aware, of the present. Ultimately, Buddha emphasized that when we live in the present moment, it is possible to know true happiness.

❏ Quiet reflection is an important practice among Buddhists. They may chant, or quietly repeat specific mantras or prayers many times. Meditation is a central practice for many Buddhists.

❏ The individual's responsibility for actions taken is an important value among many practitioners of Buddhism.

❏ Buddhists may visit a Buddhist temple when ill in order to facilitate the healing process.

❏ Many Buddhists are vegetarians. Many practice acupuncture and believe in herbal therapy.

Profile

Phuong was an incarcerated 18-year-old Laotian Buddhist with limited oral and written language skills. He was placed in San Quentin Prison after killing eight people. He did not think that the speech-language pathologist could help him because he had a "bad spirit." Efforts to improve his language skills were unsuccessful at first.

The speech-language pathologist talked to some Buddhist members of the community and, based on their recommendations, implemented a novel strategy to help Phuong. She tied a new white string around Phuong's left wrist. Many Buddhists believe that a white string represents "salvation." After wearing this string for a period of time, Phuong told the speech-language pathologist that the bad spirit had left him and that a good spirit had entered him. Phuong suddenly began to make progress in developing oral and written language skills.

Immigrant Insight   Bhupinder, female from India, speaker of Hindi and Punjabi

In India, I was brought up with a school of girls. I didn't know how to interact with boys when we arrived here in the U.S. In my religion, we do not cut our hair. I was not allowed to cut my hair, pluck my eyebrows, or shave my legs. I faced a lot of hurdles in junior high. Girls made fun of me because of the black hair on my legs, and they would call me a man. I asked my dad if I could start shaving my legs; he said "no" because he didn't want me to start changing and forget about our culture. I was the laughingstock of my school for two years. The other students spit on me and threw rocks at me. My brother used to wear a mini turban to school. He got jumped multiple times just for wearing it. People made fun of us daily; it really took a toll on our self esteem. Another challenge here in the U.S. was the early sex education in school. In India, these things are not discussed openly. I remember in science class—the teacher was talking about condoms, and I raised my hand to ask what those were because the term was unfamiliar. The whole class started laughing at me. Every day after that was worse—I was not only the girl who didn't shave her legs, but I also didn't know what a condom was.

IMPLICATIONS FOR PROFESSIONALS

When professionals are aware of a family's religious background and basic beliefs, they can relate to the family in ways that are sensitive and culturally appropriate. Some of the following implications may apply in various situations when working with families from diverse religious backgrounds:

❏ In some families (especially those from Muslim backgrounds), a specific family member such as the father may be the spokesperson. It is considered inappropriate for professionals to address questions to the wrong family member during meetings relating to the needs of a student.

❏ If the family believes in seniority and authority based on age, the grandparents might have the final say in any decisions that are made relating to assessment and intervention.

❏ If there is a possibility of miscommunication between a professional and a Muslim family, it can be helpful to consult with an Imam, or Muslim religious leader. An Imam can help the professional understand legitimate religious variables that may be impacting a family's receptiveness to services. An Imam can also inform the professional if the family's negative reaction to services is outside the expected norm.

❏ It might be considered inappropriate for a female professional to make any kind of physical contact with a male in the family. Muslims generally do not shake hands with or embrace members of the opposite gender. When a Muslim university student invited me to her home to celebrate her graduation, she warned me that I shouldn't try to shake hands with her father. She told me that he would never shake hands with a woman.

❏ Buddhist and Muslim families often do not want their children to work with professionals who are of the opposite sex.

❏ When interacting with Muslim families, take care not to sit in a way that reveals the bottom of the feet.

❏ Muslims may have negative views of female professionals who wear "immodest" clothing. Thus, female professionals should consider dressing conservatively when interacting with traditional Muslim families. For example, short skirts and low-cut blouses might not be acceptable.

❏ Families of Muslim children may not want home-based services because they view the home as a private place (Davis & Banks, 2012).

❏ Many Muslim immigrants get frequent support from other members of their mosque. Support groups for families who are struggling to meet the needs of a child with a disability might be found in a mosque, and families may feel comfortable attending those groups.

❏ Students from Muslim backgrounds, after age 8 or 9, might not be allowed to eat during the day in the month of Ramadan. Professionals should try to avoid serving snacks during this period or offering food or drink to family members during meetings.

❏ Professionals should be careful about serving snacks to Muslim students. Some chocolate contains alcohol, and some candies have enzymes that are not acceptable to ingest.

❏ Some Muslims discourage anthropomorphism. Thus, stories with talking animals will be viewed as inappropriate if used in the instructional curriculum (Davis & Banks, 2012).

❏ Many Muslims are discouraged from revealing information about familial or personal affairs to individuals who are not members of the family. Self-disclosure and focus on the self (not the group) may be discouraged. Because of this, professionals may need to build trust before asking questions about personal matters.

❏ Muslims have often been the targets of hatred and discrimination in our country. It is important for professionals to show that they are supportive and understanding.

❏ Most American professionals highly value direct, honest communication. However, among Muslims, who strive to maintain group harmony, this directness may be viewed as selfish and insensitive.

❏ If Muslims are led to engage in the behaviors of direct communication and confrontation, they may be considered selfish and insulting to their community. Muslims may be especially open to ecological, holistic interventions that incorporate family members and members of the broader community.

❏ Families from various religious backgrounds may believe that disabilities are caused by the actions of God, fate, or a person's behavior in a previous life. A child's disability is sometimes viewed as part of a divine plan that was not meant to be altered. Intervention, therefore, may be viewed as inappropriate or undesirable.

❏ Some Buddhist parents believe that their actions in a previous lifetime caused their child's disability. Thus families may be willing to accept their "karmic fate" and may not support intervention.

❏ A child with a disability may be viewed as a gift from God that was sent to test the goodness of their character and their ability to provide excellent care for this special child.

❏ The family may believe that God wants family members to care for the child's need throughout life. An individualized education plan developed by school professionals to promote independent functioning may be viewed as inappropriate.

❏ Parents may feel personally responsible for a child's disabling condition. In some religious belief systems, the actions of the parents are viewed as the cause of the child's disabilities. Professionals must be especially sensitive to emotional issues surrounding the student's disability and must work in a supportive manner with families who hold these beliefs.

❏ Some families will resist intervention efforts that are in conflict with their belief systems about life and death. Some Buddhist families, for example, believe that children with disabilities will be reincarnated into a more whole form. If the parents view the disability as part of the suffering that is supposed to occur in this life, intervention to alleviate the suffering will not be supported.

❏ The family may balk at medical practices suggested by professionals (e.g., pressure equalizing tubes to drain middle ear fluid, braces, surgery to correct a physical defect) if the treatment procedures differ from those used within the culture.

❏ Most Buddhist families believe that suffering is part of life and is to be accepted calmly. Thus they may not be willing to use medication in treatment. For example, family members may choose not to use medication to treat a child who has been identified as having attention deficit hyperactivity disorder (ADHD).

Profile

Nadia, a 10-year-old child I served in the schools, was from a religiously conservative Eastern European family with 13 children. She was absent from school frequently and experienced repeated academic failure. Her poor school attendance was an important factor to consider in determining her need for special education services.

Nadia's parents believed that a girl's role in life is to grow up, marry, and raise children. Nadia and the other girls in her family were expected to take care of their younger siblings. If her younger siblings were ill, Nadia was expected to stay home and care for them. The family believed that education was unimportant for Nadia because she would not need a formal education for her future role as a wife and mother.

❏ In some religions and cultures, girls are expected to marry at a young age (e.g., beginning at 15 years old). Their primary duties after marriage are to raise children and to be faithful wives. Education for girls may be viewed as less important than education for boys.

❏ Professionals should try to avoid scheduling major events on religious holidays if these events are viewed as inappropriate. For example, planning a school party on the last day of Ramadan will be viewed as insensitive by some Muslims.

❑ Students may come from religious backgrounds that do not permit the celebration of holidays commonly commemorated in U.S. schools. For example, the majority of Muslims do not celebrate Halloween.

❑ Parents may pull their children out of school in order to celebrate or observe religious holidays or activities.

❑ Many public schools offer family life (sex education) activities for students. Some religious groups may object to this type of education.

❑ Some Muslim immigrants to the U.S. do not approve of specific aspects of American life such as premarital sex, abortion, and the display of violence on television. They may try to segregate their children from American peers to prevent bad influences.

❑ Some students who are fasting for religious reasons may not be able to participate in school activities relating to meals or food consumption (e.g., snacks given during therapy, bake sales, etc.) (Davis & Banks, 2012).

Profile

D.S., a southeast Asian (Mien) girl from a Buddhist family, was referred to me for speech-language assessment. She was being considered for a self-contained special day class placement. I found out that D.S. had a unique medical history. As refugees, the family had spent time in Laos and Thailand. When the family arrived in the U.S. and settled in Washington, it was discovered that D.S. had profound difficulties with her kidneys and needed a transplant. The family did not want to follow the Washington doctors' recommendations for the transplant or any type of "surgery." They believed that if they allowed her to pass away, she would be reincarnated into a more whole form and would not experience the pain and suffering that might occur following a kidney transplant. Finally, the Washington doctors prevailed in convincing the family to support the operation.

D.S. missed many days of school and fell far behind the other southeast Asian students academically. The team decided to place D.S. into a special classroom under the category of "Other Health Impaired." She worked with a primary language interpreter, and made excellent progress in all areas.

CONCLUSION

It is critical for professionals working with culturally diverse students to be sensitive to the religious beliefs of their families. Not every family will fit neatly into a religious category. Many people practice a combination of religions. When religious beliefs impact service delivery, professionals must be sensitive to the concerns of the family.

Often a professional can achieve the best results by working with an interpreter or religious leader from the family's culture who understands both the family's religious viewpoint and the value of intervention. If this cultural mediator can build trust and rapport with the family, chances of providing appropriate treatment to students will be greatly increased.

STUDY QUESTIONS

1. Describe the major tenets of Buddhism.

2. List six values that are important to Muslims.

3. How might some Buddhist families regard suggestions for intervention? What might their attitude be when a professional recommends placement in a special education program?

MULTIPLE CHOICE

4. The philosophy underlying the belief that a person's fate or destiny in this life is determined by what happened in a previous life is called:

   A. Nirvana
   B. Ramadan
   C. Karma
   D. Hajj
   E. Asceticism

5. Professionals who work with Muslim families and students must remember that a major cause of stress in our world today is:

   A. Poverty
   B. Pressure for arranged marriages
   C. Divorce
   D. Racial profiling, bullying, and hate crimes
   E. A high incidence of autism among Muslim children

6. When working with Muslim families, it is important to remember the following:

   A. Women dress modestly because, theoretically, this modest dress symbolizes their role as mothers and guardians of the family.
   B. Most Muslims are eager for home-based services because they appreciate the convenience of having a professional come to them.
   C. Family ties are extremely important, and extended families are common.
   D. Female teachers are likely to be trusted more than male teachers.
   E. Most parents are thankful for any opportunities that their children have to interact with American peers and to become mainstreamed into U.S. culture.

7. Which one of the following is NOT a general principle that professionals should remember when serving students from various religious groups?

    A. Girls are generally encouraged to get an education, have good school attendance, and participate in intervention if special learning needs are identified.
    B. Family members may believe that disabilities are caused by the actions of the child's parents.
    C. Female professionals may not be allowed to work with male clients and vice versa.
    D. Celebration of traditional U.S. holidays may be viewed as offensive.
    E. Parents may pull their children out of school to celebrate religious holidays.

8. Yousef, a Muslim 12-year-old male, has been diagnosed as having a language impairment by a female speech-language pathologist. Which of the following may NOT be viewed as appropriate during her meeting with the student's parents?

    A. Speak primarily with his father during the meeting.
    B. Shake the father's hand warmly upon meeting him.
    C. Assume that Yousef's family will view intervention as the will of Allah.
    D. Tell the family that you will be providing therapy to Yousef in a one-to-one situation.
    E. Show the family a short story with talking animal characters that can be used at home to build language skills.

9. Which one of the following is NOT likely to be viewed as "true" by Buddhist families?

    A. All of life is suffering, and thus suffering due to a communication disorder must be borne with courage.
    B. Medications such as those used to treat ADHD are welcome because they help the child concentrate better when meditating.
    C. Some Buddhists regard illness as a personal failure; there may be an assumption that if we are living truly spiritual lives, we will not be subject to illness.
    D. If a Buddhist family is informed that a child has a communication disorder, the family may think that the problem is the fault of family members; if they were truly spiritual, the communication disorder would not have occurred.
    E. Buddhists may visit a Buddhist temple when ill in order to facilitate the healing process.

10. Dae-Hyun, a 3-year-old child of Buddhist parents that recently came to the U.S from Korea, has been referred to your early intervention clinic. He has an unrepaired cleft palate. The family believes that the cleft palate is "karma" for sins that family members have committed. They have come to the U.S. to obtain information about surgery and the availability of speech-language services for Dae-Hyun. Their extended family in Korea, however, is not supportive of any kind of surgery or treatment. Which of the following would be helpful in interacting with this family?

    A. Remember that the parents may be suffering from a great deal of personal guilt relating to Dae-Hyun's cleft palate.
    B. Compliment the parents for taking responsibility in seeking out services for Dae-Hyun, as personal responsibility is an important value in Buddhism.
    C. Connect Dae-Hyun's parents with a local Buddhist temple so that they will have the emotional and spiritual support necessary to deal with his proposed surgery and speech-language therapy.
    D. Discuss the importance of accepting the surgical placement of pressure-equalizing tubes for treating ear infections that may be associated with the cleft palate.

   E. Don't ever offer snacks containing alcohol or pork products when interacting with this family, as Buddhists do not ingest these items.

ANSWERS TO STUDY QUESTIONS

    4. C
    5. D
    6. A, C
    7. A
    8. B, C, D, E
    9. B
  10. A, B, C, D

Chapter 3

Families from Anglo European Backgrounds

Outline
- General Background Information
- Anglo European American Family Life
- Education and Literacy
- Cultural Customs, Courtesies, and Beliefs
- Assumptions About Americans
- Health Care and Disabling Conditions
- Anglo European American Communication Styles
- Anglo European American Language Considerations
- Implications for Professionals

Although the diversity in the U.S. population has increased dramatically, the dominant cultural group continues to be Anglo European English-speaking Americans. The cultural values of White Americans of Anglo European descent have had a major impact on policies and practices used in the education of students. Many of the assessment and intervention practices used with special needs populations are grounded in the practices and beliefs of the middle-class, White population. Unfortunately, students from culturally and linguistically diverse backgrounds have often been misidentified as having disabilities based on culturally inappropriate assessment practices.

Mainstream Anglo European Americans often have little awareness of the influence that their cultural background has on their attitudes, behavior, and social interactions. As our nation becomes increasingly diverse, speech-language pathologists (SLPs) and other professionals must increase their cultural competence through examining and understanding how their own values and attitudes impact practice with diverse populations. It is important to learn how the American way of life is perceived by individuals from other parts of the world.

The "melting pot" theory heavily influenced how the dominant culture expected immigrants to interact and behave during the early waves of immigration. Persons from "other" cultural backgrounds were encouraged to disavow their cultural and linguistic roots so that they could take on American customs and values. However, this paradigm has been increasingly viewed as unacceptable.

Thus, the purpose of this chapter is to help professionals from mainstream Anglo European American backgrounds develop a heightened awareness of unconsciously-held assumptions and values that influence their interactions with others. This knowledge will help professionals become more sensitive to cultural differences and how they might affect service delivery to students and families from various cultural groups. Most people tend to be less judgmental and more open-minded when they realize what assumptions they themselves hold (Riquelme & Rosas, 2014).

In this discussion, it is important to be aware of the concepts of *ethnocentrism* and *cultural relativism*. As mentioned previously, **Ethnocentrism** is the view that members of one's own culture do things the *right way*. All other ways of engaging in a specific behavior are viewed as unnatural or inferior. Proponents of **cultural relativism** view behavior within the cultural context in which it occurs; other ways of doing things are viewed as *different* yet equally valid. It is hoped that this chapter will help the reader to adopt an attitude of cultural relativism. Cultural relativism was summed up by anthropologist Wade Davis (2003) when he said, "the world in which you were born is just one model of reality. Other cultures are not failed attempts at being you: they are unique manifestations of the human spirit."

Statistical information presented in this chapter shows that the racial and ethnic composition of the U.S population is changing rapidly. Unless otherwise indicated, statistical data and information about social trends was compiled from the following sources: Centers for Disease Control and Prevention, 2017; Colby & Ortman, 2015; Medical News Today, 2017; Pew Social Trends, 2015; Pew Hispanic Research Center, 2017; Pew Research Center, 2016, 2017; Sue & Sue, 2016; Teaching Tolerance, 2017; U.S. Census Bureau, 2017.

GENERAL BACKGROUND INFORMATION

❑ The United States is the third largest country in the world (following China and India), with a population exceeding 319 million. The U.S. population is projected to reach 400 million in 2051 (U.S. Census Bureau, 2017).

❏ The United States is slightly over 200 years old, making it one of the youngest countries in the world.

❏ The original inhabitants were indigenous peoples, primarily Native American Indians, who were displaced by European settlers beginning in the 17th century. The Europeans slaughtered Native Americans, spread diseases among them, and attempted to annihilate them in order to take over their land.

❏ Since that time, the United States, which has been composed primarily of people of Anglo European descent, has been rapidly changing in ethnic composition.

❏ In 2013, for the first time, the majority of newborn babies in the U.S. were from racial or ethnic minorities. By 2055, less than half of the U.S. population will be from a single racial or ethnic group. In the past 50 years, nearly 59 million immigrants arrived in the U.S., mostly from Asia and Latin America (Pew Research Center, 2016).

❏ By 2030, one in five Americans is projected to be 65 and over (U.S. Census Bureau, 2017).

❏ There are currently more Millennials (individuals born between 1982 and 2002) than Baby Boomers (individuals born between 1946 and 1964) in the U.S. Forty three percent of the 75.4 million Millennials are non-white, and they are the most educated generation to date. Thirty-nine percent of White Americans are Millennials or younger (Pew Research Center, 2017).

❏ The number of U.S. adults living in middle-income households fell to 50% in 2015, after four decades in which those households served as the nation's economic majority. Financial gaps between rich Americans and middle-and lower-class Americans have widened (Pew Hispanic Research Center, 2017).

❏ Nearly one fourth of the U.S. adult population self-identifies as atheist, agnostic, or "no religion at all," up from 16% of the population in 2007 (Teaching Tolerance, 2017).

❏ Many White Americans are unaware of experiencing "white privilege," a transparent preference for whiteness that saturates American society. It is associated with unearned privilege—advantages conferred on White Americans but not on persons of color. For example, when a White American receives benefits or promotions, people do not assume that these come as a result of affirmative action programs. White Americans are rarely pulled over by police because of their race. When White Americans shop in stores, they are not followed by store security (Sue & Sue, 2016).

Profile

Hannah M., a biracial White-African American student of mine, shared that her mother is White and her father is African American. Her father is pulled over by police much more than the rest of the family when he is driving. When the family shops in stores, her father is followed by store security on a regular basis; the rest of the family does not experience this.

ANGLO EUROPEAN AMERICAN FAMILY LIFE

Although the American family has been considered the basic unit of society, it has undergone substantial changes in the past few decades.

❏ The number of Americans who have never been married is at an historic high. Anecdotally, many unmarried Americans pride themselves on "having no PPK" (pets, plants, kids).

❏ American homes have traditionally been comprised of "nuclear families" that included the father, mother, and children. There has been a shift toward other family structures. Today, 40% of children are born into homes where the mother is single or living with a non-marital partner. The number of children living in a household with two parents is at the lowest point in more than half a century (Pew Social Trends, 2015).

❏ Families are becoming more mobile; many family members no longer live in close proximity to one another. The use of e-mail, cell phones, social media, and other electronic means of communication are on the rise, but the amount of family face-to-face interaction has decreased.

❏ American adults often feel uncomfortable living under the same roof as their parents. Elderly parents often desire their own dwellings, preferring not to live with their children and grandchildren.

Immigrant Insight   Mohammed, male from Iraq, speaker of Arabic

I do not understand why Americans have their children move out at the age of 18. I feel that choice of action on the family's part is wrong because it is not safe. Young adults can be taken advantage of because they do not have life experience or the family to look out for them. In Iraq, people stay within the family and are home by 9:00 at night and are not allowed to leave after that.

❏ Women are having fewer children, and the number of mothers in early forties who only have one child has doubled in the last 30 years. In 1970, the average new mother was 21 years old. Today, the average age is 26 years old (Pew Social Trends, 2015).

❏ American infants and young children may spend many hours a week in day care or preschool settings. Because many parents work outside the home, placing young children in child care settings is viewed as normal; it is a common practice in the U.S.

❏ There has been a dramatic decline in the number of women who work full time inside the home caring for their families. In the 1960s, almost 50% of American mothers were full-time at-home moms. Today, 29% of mothers work inside the home full time (Pew Social Trends, 2015).

Immigrant Insight   Steve, White male, retired, monolingual speaker of English

I've worked hard all my life, and really hoped to enjoy my retirement and my grandkids. I want to travel with my wife (also retired). But my mom and dad, who are in their mid-80s, live around the corner from us now. They want me to be over there all the time, especially my mom, who is often sick and doesn't get out much. She tells the same stories over and over, and is always negative. I love her, but it is pretty hard to spend hours over there every week. It is definitely not what I expected to be doing in my retirement years.

It is common for Anglo European Americans to hold these beliefs about family members:

1. Children should be encouraged to be independent as soon as possible. Families have high expectations for children to develop self-help and self-reliance skills. For example, approximately one third of American mothers breast-feed children who have reached six months of age; at that age, most American children are expected to drink from a cup. However, in many countries, children are routinely nursed until they are between 3 and 4 years old.

2. Many mainstream American parents and professionals consider it inappropriate for children to sleep in the same bed as their parents. However, many cultures view the practice of having infants and young children sleep alone in their own beds and rooms as neglectful and even abusive.

3. It is natural for families to be mobile and to move from place to place. Adult children do not necessarily feel obligated to live near their parents.

4. After marriage, the husband and wife should no longer live with other family members. They should seek a home of their own.

5. There are specific places and personnel outside of the home to care for children and the elderly (e.g., day care centers, skilled nursing facilities).

Immigrant Insight   Paayal, female from Fiji, speaker of Fijian

It has been hard to adjust to the importance of time here in the U.S. I don't believe time should have so much value. To me, it is more important to have good relationships. I had a hard time adjusting to the lack of community when I came here. In the U.S., people only care about themselves. In the U.S., money is first and the family is second. That is very different from Fiji, where family is the most important thing. We always help each other. In the U.S., people are very greedy. I have seen lots of families fight over money. It is very sad.

EDUCATION AND LITERACY

❏ Education in the United States is compulsory for students from 5 to 16 years of age.

❏ Americans view education as a major determinant of professional and social opportunity.

❏ Literacy is a strong focus in American schools. Most states have adopted the Common Core State Standards (Common Core State Standards Initiative, 2017).

❏ A majority of Americans believe that preschool and daycare are positive settings for children because participation in these settings can build social and pre-academic skills. However, parents from other cultures may believe that it is not ideal for young children to be away from their families in the care of "strangers."

❏ In American schools, the freedom allowed to students is greater than that allowed in many other countries. Parents educated in other countries may be shocked when they learn about the degree of freedom and informality available to American students. For example, in Hong

Kong, it would be unthinkable for students not to rise and bow when a teacher enters the classroom.

❏ Many American children are expected to attend college, regardless of their innate capacity to succeed in the academic curriculum. Parents, especially those from middle- and upper-socioeconomic backgrounds, generally expect that their children will complete college with at least a Bachelor's degree.

❏ Parents of White students from privileged neighborhoods tend to have higher educational and occupational expectations for their children than most of their culturally and linguistically diverse (CLD) counterparts, especially if those CLD counterparts are from low-income homes.

❏ Parent participation is expected and highly valued in most educational systems. In contrast to other countries, where parents respectfully "leave education to the experts," mainstream American parents expect and are encouraged to have a voice and meaningful participation in their children's education.

Profile

My husband and I currently are hosting a 16-year-old Ukrainian young lady who is part of an international youth exchange program. Solomiya speaks four languages and wants to eventually obtain her Ph.D. in astrophysics. She is very happy to be spending a year here, and is enjoying her time greatly. She has shared her views of our country, and it has been fascinating to hear her perspective. In Ukrainian high schools, there are no electives. Everyone studies rigorous subjects such as physics, chemistry, and statistics. Organized after-school sports don't exist. Solomiya is shocked by how highly Americans value football. Parents are not generally involved in their children's education and are not expected to participate. Solomiya shared that much of the time, "my parents don't even know what's going on—and I want it that way!" Parents expect the schools to teach their children; the parents' job is to provide a good home life and opportunities for success.

CULTURAL CUSTOMS, COURTESIES, AND BELIEFS

Beliefs commonly held by Anglo European Americans have been reported widely in the literature and media and are summarized below (see Table 3.1 for a summary of mainstream Anglo European American beliefs as contrasted with those of persons from other cultural backgrounds):

❏ Success is the highest value. The "American Dream" is to be successful, although success can take many forms. Usually success is related to material prosperity. Financial independence and material prosperity are hallmarks of success and of "making it" in life.

❏ Independence is extremely important; each individual's goal is to be as independent as possible.

❏ Many Americans believe in the motto "just do it." They do not like authority structures in which people are expected to review matters with others before action. Action is more valuable than planning and getting group consensus.

Table 3.1
Anglo European Beliefs and Values: Contrasting Practices

Anglo European "Mainstream"	Other Cultures
Materialism; more money and possessions equal success ("She who dies with the most toys wins.")	Detachment from money and possessions; spirituality
"Dress for success" ideal; wide range of accepted dress	Dress is a sign of prestige, wealth, position; often signifies religious beliefs
Eating is a necessity; often done as quickly as possible; "fast food"	Eating is a social experience; no rush to finish eating
Focus on nuclear family; child-oriented; youth respected and valued; status diminishes with old age	Focus on extended family; loyalty and responsibility to family; age revered; children may have much responsibility for well-being of entire family
Individualism; privacy; "looking out for number one"	Group orientation
Competition	Cooperation
Personal control over circumstances; self-help; internal locus of control: "God helps those who help themselves."	Fate; will of God or other higher Being; external locus of control
Work/goal/action orientation; rewards based on individual achievement; work has intrinsic value	"Being" orientation; enjoying life; emphasis on relationships; rewards based on relationships, seniority; work is a necessity of life
Efficiency, speed, punctuality; clock dominates ("the early bird gets the worm")	Relationships with other people dominate; time is secondary; quality of life important
Change highly valued ("That's so 5 minutes ago.")	Tradition; living in the past
Future orientation	Past orientation
Directness, honesty, openness; words carry bulk of meaning; conflict dealt with by confrontation	"Saving face;" indirectness; emphasis placed on context, or meaning surrounding words
Informality	Formality; use of titles important, especially for older and/or highly educated people
Human equality ("All men are created equal."); status and power ideally dependent on one's personal qualities (not gender, age, family)	Hierarchy, rank, status; importance of family; status based on variables such as gender, occupation, family heritage

❑ Individualism and autonomy are to be encouraged (as opposed to conformity). Many Americans believe in the importance of "looking out for number one." Group effort is not as important as individual effort and performance.

❑ Hard work is a virtue. The harder people work, the more industrious and valuable they are to their employers and to society in general. The desirable pace of life is driving, busy, and fast. Sitting quietly and doing nothing is considered a waste of time.

❑ People are defined by their work. When Americans first meet each other, a common question is "What do you do?" Work is a central part of a person's identity.

❑ Time is of utmost importance. Promptness and punctuality are necessary in social and work settings.

❑ Privacy for individuals is highly valued. Many Americans enjoy spending time alone.

❑ Youth and beauty are highly desirable. Growing old is often viewed negatively because physical attractiveness, strength, and ability supposedly diminish with age.

❑ It is each individual's right to challenge authority when injustice is experienced.

❑ Individuals tend to believe that they have control over their own destinies. It is believed that "God helps those who help themselves."

❑ It is appropriate for members of the opposite sex to show physical affection in public.

❑ If someone does a good job on a task, offering praise through public accolades is one of the most effective ways of rewarding them.

❑ All people are created equal and have the same rights. Women are equal to men; people from various ethnic groups are equal to each other. State and federal laws mandate equality of treatment for workers regardless of gender, ethnic background, age, and lifestyle orientation.

❑ Ideally, women should be allowed to have the same work opportunities as men and should be given equal pay for their work. However, this idea is not practiced in many work settings. American women tend to earn less than American men who hold similar jobs.

❑ Speed and efficiency are extremely important when completing any task. The rapid completion of tasks is valued. "Time is money."

❑ People must plan for the future. Progress and change are high priorities. The present must take second place to the needs of the future. The past is not as important.

❑ Change is equated with progress. Holding onto traditions may seem outdated and old-fashioned.

❑ Competition is a way of life, and it is healthy for children to learn to compete at an early age.

❑ Cleanliness is of utmost importance; natural odors should be covered by using perfume or deodorant.

❑ It is important to have fun. Many Americans believe that one should "work hard, play hard." Having fun is a major preoccupation for Americans when they are not working.

Profile

Meghan K. was a 16-year-old girl from an Anglo English-speaking home. Her father was a high school physical education instructor, and her mother had full-time employment inside the home caring for Meghan and her younger brother. The family came from a middle-class neighborhood. Meghan was born with the umbilical cord wrapped tightly around her neck, resulting in fetal anoxia. Meghan was slow in reaching developmental milestones, and she had been in special education settings since kindergarten. I was asked to carry out a comprehensive speech and language assessment so that Meghan could be placed in the most appropriate setting. The results indicated that Meghan was functioning approximately seven years below her chronological age. Assessment data obtained by the school psychologist indicated that she had a full-scale IQ of 70, a score that is considerably below normal.

The assessment team and I recommended that Meghan continue in special education and that she participate in a vocational training program designed specifically for students with special learning needs. Meghan's parents were incensed, and the meeting lasted for three hours. The parents felt outraged that a "vocational track" was recommended for their daughter. They shared that she was going to go to college, and they were determined to see that she attended the best college available. The parents were not interested in special education services for their child in her high school years.

ASSUMPTIONS ABOUT AMERICANS

Commonly held beliefs about Americans have been described by various sources (Global Mapping International, 2013; Hanson, 2011b; Sue & Sue, 2016). I also encountered many of these beliefs while growing up in the Philippines. In addition, I have been privileged to travel to and visit Guam, Taiwan, Japan, Hong Kong, Mexico, Canada, Greece, New Zealand, England, Austria, Germany, Switzerland, France, Luxembourg, Italy, Fiji, China, Okinawa, China, and Australia. I have spoken with individuals in some of these countries about their perceptions of Americans. Commonly held beliefs about Americans include the following:

❑ Americans have the freedom to do whatever they want to do.

❑ Americans are talkative and friendly.

❑ Americans are honest and frank.

❑ Americans are generous with those in need, especially when natural disasters (e.g., tsunamis) strike other countries.

❑ Americans are loud and shout a lot.

❑ Americans are materialistic and think only about money. A Chinese man recently told me that "The Chinese invent everything, the Japanese copy everything, and the Americans buy everything."

❑ Americans are rich.

❑ Americans do not have the ability to enjoy the present; they are always rushing toward the future.

❑ Americans do not frown upon premarital sex and are highly immoral.

❏ Americans are rude. They always rush into business without engaging in any preliminary social amenities.

❏ Americans have superficial relationships.

❏ Americans do not value their families. They are more concerned about success and "getting ahead" than about the happiness of family members.

❏ Americans are much too permissive with their children and do not demand that they respect and obey their elders.

❏ When Americans travel to other countries, they drink a lot of alcohol.

❏ Americans eat hot dogs and wear cowboy boots.

❏ Americans are very aggressive.

❏ Americans want to control the world.

❏ Americans experience so many family problems (e.g., high divorce rates, runaway children) because they are too individualistic.

❏ All Americans own guns, and the U.S. is a dangerous place because we are not able to protect our school children from being shot.

❏ Football is extremely important in the U.S., and sports are more important for students than academics.

❏ Americans are ethnocentric and ignorant about the rest of the world.

Some readers may find these assumptions and stereotypes offensive because no one wants to be "categorized" and "stereotyped" without consideration of individual differences. Most Americans would not want to be described in this way. Yet some people from other cultures hold these stereotypes about Americans as a group.

Whenever members of a cultural group hold stereotypes about members of other cultural groups, the potential for misunderstanding and conflict is great. By realizing how Americans are stereotyped by members of other cultures, one can better understand how members of other cultural groups feel when they are stereotyped. It is important to look inward at one's own cultural beliefs and assumptions. Professionals must be honest with themselves if they are to develop the sensitivity necessary to serve others without bias. As previously stated, a major part of cultural competence is contained in the statement "know thyself."

Profile

When my family and I visited China last year, our tour guide Jimmy told us that his teenaged daughter wanted to come to the U.S. to go to high school for a year or two. He shared that he was afraid to send her here because our gun use is out of control. He was afraid she would get shot if she came to the U.S. to attend an American high school. "I'm afraid to send her to the U.S. because of all your shootings," Jimmy explained. Other tourists on our trip were from Europe, Scandinavia, and the South Pacific. They questioned us about gun use, and told my 18-year-old son that they assumed he owned a gun—after all, he lived in the U.S. Didn't all Americans own guns? These tourists said things like, "The U.S. is so dangerous. Your guns are out of control. Why can't you Americans keep your children safe?"

HEALTH CARE AND DISABLING CONDITIONS

❑ Nearly 75% of deaths in the U.S. are attributed to 10 causes: (1) heart disease, (2) cancer, (3) chronic lower respiratory disease, (4) accidents, (5) stroke, (6) Alzheimer's disease, (7) diabetes, (8) influenza and pneumonia, (9) kidney disease, and (10) suicide (Medical News Today, 2017).

❑ Many of these chronic disabilities are caused by bad food choices, obesity, smoking, physical inactivity, and alcohol abuse. However, there has been a significant drop in disability and death from HIV/AIDS.

❑ Today, an estimated 5.4 million Americans have Alzheimer's disease, including approximately 200,000 persons younger than 65 who have early-onset Alzheimer's (Medical News Today, 2017). In 2015, the cost of treating persons in the U.S. with Alzheimer's was $226 billion. It is estimated that in 2050, treatment for persons with Alzheimer's will cost $1.2 trillion (Centers for Disease Control and Prevention, 2017).

❑ Approximately one in six children in the U.S. has some type of developmental disability (ranging from mild to severe problems). Approximately one in 68 American children has been identified as having Autism Spectrum Disorder (ASD). In the U.S., total costs per year for children with ASD are estimated to be between $11.5 and 60.9 billion (Centers for Disease Control and Prevention, 2017).

❑ Traditional American healthcare has focused on cures for illness rather than prevention, although this focus may be changing in some areas. Many insurance companies cover few, if any, costs for preventative care.

❑ Increasing numbers of Americans have allergies to foods, and there are more products on the market labeled as "gluten free," "peanut free," etc.

❑ Health and fitness are popular trends, especially on the West Coast. Many people try to exercise regularly. Hundreds of products are labeled "low cholesterol" and "low fat." Gluten-free foods have become increasingly popular.

❑ American medical practitioners tend to separate illnesses of the body and mind, in contrast to practitioners in other cultures who often view the body and mind as being inseparable.

❑ American medicine relies greatly on technology. American medical technology has made it possible for many with disabilities to maintain "life" that relies almost exclusively on expensive, highly technological mechanical support.

❑ In recent decades, the American legal system has mandated that persons with disabilities be given equal access to education and jobs.

❑ Americans generally view disabilities as being caused by variables such as genetics, trauma, disease, and teratogens (e.g., toxins).

❑ Americans tend to believe in mastery over nature and feel that they can fight and overcome various illnesses and disabilities.

Immigrant Insight   Tariq, male from Lebanon, speaker of Arabic

My culture sees disabilities as a weakness. If you are a disabled person in Lebanon, you are "sick" and you never have a chance at anything close to a normal life. Often the disabled never leave the house because there is no handicapped access and no special services. Speech-language pathologists are not important in my country; as long as a person can function normally and there is food on the table, there isn't much to worry about.

Profile

A Hmong child was hospitalized after undergoing surgery for a cleft palate. The American speech-language pathologist smelled smoke one afternoon when walking past the child's room. After calling for fire extinguishers, she entered the room to discover that the family had made a small fire under the child's hospital bed. The family believed that the smoke from the fire would drive out the evil spirits that had caused the cleft palate. The speech-language pathologist made an appointment with the hospital's Hmong interpreter to discuss how they might best approach the family to discuss their perspective regarding communication disorders, medical issues, and their treatment.

ANGLO EUROPEAN AMERICAN COMMUNICATION STYLES

❑ The main form of communication is in a low-context format, where information is primarily conveyed through the verbal code. Communication is straightforward, precise, and explicit. This differs from other cultures where communication is high-context—meaningful information is conveyed subtly, nonverbally, and through shaded meanings.

❑ It is generally considered impolite to ask personal questions of others. For instance, asking people to reveal information about their salary is considered inappropriate in most contexts. It is also considered rude to ask people to reveal their age.

❑ Americans tend to be friendly and to make informality a goal in interactions. For example, many Americans will call others by their first names only, not using titles even if the other person is older and/or more highly educated. This may seem discourteous and "uncultured" to people from other cultural groups.

❑ When two Americans converse, they generally stand about two feet apart.

❑ Americans tend to be outspoken and frank; they appreciate these same qualities in others. Cultural value is attached to the person who is forthright, does not beat around the bush, and is not "two-faced."

❑ In professional situations such as meetings, most Americans get to the point immediately with little preamble or small talk.

❑ Most Americans rely more on verbal than nonverbal messages; again, this can be termed "low-context" communication.

❑ When talking to others, Americans generally consider it important to make direct eye contact and to maintain an open yet assertive physical stance.

❑ Americans believe that directness and assertiveness are critical in interactions with other people. For example, if one is angry at another person, this feeling may be expressed directly. Candidness is valued.

❑ In the United States, people believe that good listeners make eye contact, ask questions, indicate when they do not understand something, nod occasionally, and make facial expressions to show empathy and understanding.

❑ American children from mainstream homes are generally encouraged to express their opinions, thoughts, needs, and wishes freely. In most mainstream American school classrooms, highly verbal students are rewarded in various ways.

❑ Electronic/digital communication is very common in the U.S. The vast majority of Americans own smart phones, and check these phones frequently. Millions of Americans also use social media, and may spend more time communicating using social media than engaging in face-to-face interactions.

ANGLO EUROPEAN AMERICAN LANGUAGE CONSIDERATIONS

❑ Many citizens of the United States speak Mainstream American English (MAE), also referred to as Standard American English or General American English. The historical, financial, legal, scientific, and educational foundations of the United States are recorded in Mainstream American English.

❑ Americans from different areas of the United States speak different dialects but are still able to understand one another. There are at least 10 regional dialects in the United States. These include Eastern New England, New York City, Western Pennsylvania, Middle Atlantic, Appalachian, Southern, Central Midland, North Central, Southwest, and Northwest.

❑ Although the U.S. has absorbed immigrants from many different countries, English is still the dominant and national language. Though bilingualism is increasingly highly valued, successful American citizens are expected to speak fluent MAE.

IMPLICATIONS FOR PROFESSIONALS

It is important to remember that people from different backgrounds often have cultural assumptions that differ from those of "mainstream" Americans. Again, it is crucial not to make judgments about which cultural attitudes are right or wrong. Much can be learned by interacting with others who have beliefs, ideas, and styles of living different from one's own. As previously stated, adapting a position of cultural relativism is encouraged.

School professionals need to have an understanding of issues such as the following so that they can interact with families in ways that are culturally appropriate:

❑ Addressing others by their first names, a common practice among American professionals, may be viewed as offensively over-familiar to some families. It is probably best to err on the side of being too formal when working with persons from different cultures. Professionals should use titles when addressing adults from other cultures.

❏ Persons from some cultures (e.g., Filipino) may ask personal questions such as "Are you married?" or "Why don't you have any children?" Professionals need to be aware that questions such as these are considered appropriate within some cultural groups.

❏ In many cultures, events are believed to result from one's fate. Because many Americans believe in their personal ability to shape and control their own future, they may be less tolerant of those who believe in fate or outside forces that they cannot control. Professionals should not label these persons as being "passive." It is important to be patient and open.

❏ It is considered rude in some cultures (e.g., Hispanic, Arab) to delve immediately into business without small talk and some conversational preamble. Professionals should take time to engage in preliminary courtesies.

❏ American professionals must remember that most cultures highly value the family unit Professionals must work with students and their families, rather than working only with students.

❏ In many cultures (e.g., Asian, Middle Eastern), elderly family members are highly valued and respected; their opinions carry more weight than those of younger family members. In these cases, professionals should defer to the oldest family members present in an interaction.

❏ Older immigrant parents often expect their adult children to provide for them in old age. For example, a Filipino mother may live in the home of her married daughter for many years. Professionals should be aware that disharmony and conflict may occur within families if children reach adulthood and do not care for their elderly parents.

❏ Differences in the value systems of older vs. younger family members may result in conflicts. Working adult children may be expected to give some of their earnings to the family. It is often best to engage the services of persons from the family's own culture to help resolve these conflicts.

❏ When making home visits, American professionals may be shocked to find large numbers of people sharing a single apartment or home. However, this is the norm in many countries. For example, in the Arab culture, there is no word for privacy; many individuals long for and expect a high level of closeness and physical proximity to one another.

❏ Some American professionals experience frustration when they discover that nontraditional forms of healing are being used by the family to help a child. Although school professionals may not feel that these treatment practices are appropriate, the beliefs of the family should be respected.

❏ Recommendations made by members of the family's cultural group may carry more weight than recommendations made by school personnel. Therefore, educational professionals should work in tandem with health practitioners that the family trusts.

❏ For many families from diverse cultural backgrounds, the past may be viewed as more important than the future. Spending money on a monument to an ancestor, for example, may be viewed as more important than using this money to meet the needs of children who require special education services. Professionals need to understand the importance of past events within the student's culture.

❏ Americans often view congenital anomalies (e.g., cleft palate) or syndromes (e.g., Down syndrome) as a mistake in the transcription of DNA during the process of meiosis. However, someone who believes in reincarnation might believe that the congenital anomaly or syndrome is the result of a family member's improper behavior in a past life. Thus, the disability is a punishment for sins. Professionals need to be aware that some parents view their child's congenital problem as the "cross they have to bear."

❏ Many American parents foster independence in children at an early age. Other cultures, however, do not prioritize early independence. Professionals must exercise caution in using terms such as "dependent," "immature," etc. because early independence may not be considered an important goal within a child's family.

❏ In the American culture, it is considered acceptable for females to ask direct questions when speaking with males. In some cultures, this practice can be highly offensive. For example, in areas of some Muslim countries, only males ask direct questions to other males. Female professionals, therefore, may require assistance from males when questions need to be asked.

❏ Because Americans are generally accustomed to equality between men and women, female professionals may be shocked and chagrined to discover that because of their gender, men from some cultural groups do not respect them and will not listen to their opinions and statements. It is important to be willing to allow a male professional to speak with these men, remembering that the most important goal of any interaction is ultimately the welfare of the child.

❏ American professionals may discover that certain adolescent immigrant students do not regularly use deodorant or bathe daily. It is important to gently and sensitively advise these students and their families about mainstream U.S. expectations, and to diplomatically discuss the social consequences of allowing one's natural body odors to remain uncovered. Speech-language pathologists and other professionals who are uncomfortable with these conversations should seek support from other school personnel such as physical education teachers or sports coaches.

❏ American professionals may find students from some cultural backgrounds to be quite "slow" in completing tasks or responding to messages. Although speed and efficiency are highly valued in the United States, American professionals need to realize that "speed" and "deadlines" are less important in other cultures. Families should not be made to feel inadequate if they are not as quick in meeting deadlines as might be expected.

❏ Some families will be upset if they are informed that a child with special needs lacks the skills required to attend or graduate from college. Professionals should be aware that families may remain in denial and may have difficulty accepting the school's recommendations.

❏ Professionals need to remember that, in many cultures, children are not encouraged to freely express their thoughts, opinions, needs, and emotions; for these children, conformity and respect for adults are key. Professionals must not misjudge these children as being insecure or as having expressive language delays simply because they display little verbal communication, especially in the classroom.

Profile _____

Brianda P. is a university senior who came to the U.S. from Mexico at 7 years of age speaking only Spanish. She was very shy when she started school in this country and it was difficult to get her to say anything in her first-grade all-English classroom. After being tested by several professionals, placement in a self-contained special education classroom was recommended for the "severe expressive language disorder" that was identified.

Brianda's mother did not feel that her child had a "disability" and refused to allow placement in a special education program. Instead, she fought with the school about what her child needed. Eventually, thanks to her mother's efforts, Brianda was placed into a bilingual classroom setting where support was available in Spanish. Brianda began to speak in the classroom and thrived in academic activities.

STUDY QUESTIONS

1. Choose three mainstream U.S. values that you consider important to maintain (e.g., the belief that men and women should have equal rights). Why are these values important to you?

2. Describe three stereotypes about mainstream Americans that you find particularly offensive. Why do these stereotypes offend you?

3. Describe four mainstream Anglo American communication behaviors that might be viewed as inappropriate by individuals from other cultural backgrounds. Why might these behaviors be viewed negatively?

MULTIPLE CHOICE

4. Which one of the following statements about mainstream Anglo European Americans is FALSE?

    A. Many are atheists or agnostics or claim to have "no religion at all."
    B. They believe that "children should be children" and allowed to develop at a relaxed pace.
    C. They value directness and assertiveness in communication.
    D. They value change and plan for the future.

5. Which statements about health care are TRUE?

   A. Anglo European American medical practitioners tend to separate illnesses of the body and mind.
   B. American medicine relies greatly on technology.
   C. Most Anglo European Americans believe that factors such as genetics, trauma, disease, and teratogens (e.g., toxins) can cause disabilities.
   D. Two rising health care concerns that are costing billions of dollars are the increasing number of adults with Alzheimer's disease and children with Autism Spectrum Disorder.

6. Which of the following statements is/are often made to "stereotype" Americans?

   A. Americans are rich.
   B. Americans are ethnocentric and do not know much about other countries.
   C. Americans are too strict with their children and need to allow their children much more freedom.
   D. Americans are superficial.

7. Which of the following communication behaviors do most Anglo Europeans view as being acceptable?

   A. Asking others personal questions about their age, salary, and marital status
   B. Standing approximately two feet apart during conversations
   C. Maintaining a manner of openness, friendliness, and informality during interactions
   D. Beginning a meeting or business interaction with lengthy, personal chit-chat to help all parties feel comfortable before business is addressed

8. An Anglo European American mother brought her 26-month-old son to you for an assessment. She stays at home to care for him, and he is her only child. He does not go to preschool. Her son has never produced any words and appears not to comprehend even simple requests and questions. Which of the following would be APPROPRIATE in your interaction with this mother?

   A. Being quite indirect and suggesting that the child will outgrow the problem if given more time
   B. Telling her that the communication problem may persist into adulthood and that, in the future, the child should be trained for a vocation that does not require a college education
   C. Recommending a preschool for several hours a day to increase his speech and language skills
   D. Telling her to present vocabulary drills several hours every day to build vocabulary

9. Which of the following are true?

   A. Anglo European Americans believe in maintaining traditions and living with an orientation to the past.
   B. Anglo European Americans' emphasis on indirectness and "saving face" may upset and alienate families from other cultures, who are accustomed to confrontation, honesty, and openness.
   C. Anglo European Americans believe in personal control over circumstances and in self-help; this could lead to conflicts with clients who have an external locus of control and believe in fate.
   D. Anglo European Americans value time, speed, and punctuality; they may feel frustrated when interacting with members of cultures that consider relationships and quality of life to be more important than getting things done quickly.

10. Jennifer V., an Anglo European American speech-language pathologist, has taken a job in an early intervention clinic in an area of the city heavily populated by immigrants from Asian and Hispanic countries. Which of the following could present possible conflicts between Jennifer's values and those of the families she is serving?

   A. Jennifer believes that early independence is important; children should be taught self-help skills as early as possible. Families may not prize early independence as much.
   B. It is normal and natural for young children to spend part of their time in day care apart from their families, so Jennifer encourages preschool attendance; families may not believe that this type of separation is a good idea.
   C. Jennifer believes that it is normal for elderly parents to be living under the same roof as their adult children; consequently, grandparents will be available to help children achieve specific speech and language therapy objectives.
   D. To Jennifer, families should be actively involved in their children's therapy and overall education; however, families may believe in leaving education and intervention to the "expert."

ANSWERS TO STUDY QUESTIONS

   4. B
   5. All of the above
   6. A, B, and D
   7. B, C
   8. C
   9. C, D,
   10. A, B, D

Chapter 4

Families from African American Backgrounds

Outline

Africandfrican Americans in the United States have had a profound influence on the American way of life. Although an increasing number of African Americans are finishing high school and obtaining college degrees, many continue to experience discrimination in a variety of social contexts. African American students who perform poorly in school are often mislabeled as having communication disorders and other disabilities based on culturally and linguistically biased assessment practices. Despite these concerns, the outlook for African Americans in the U.S. has improved in several areas as detailed in this chapter.

GENERAL BACKGROUND INFORMATION

❏ In the U.S. today, there are approximately 46.3 million African Americans (U.S. Census Bureau, 2017b). Half of the Black population is made up of Millennials (individuals born between 1982 and 2002) or persons younger than Millennials (Pew Hispanic Research Center, 2017). Over half of African Americans live in the south (Mental Health America, 2017).

❏ African Americans are unique in their history of immigration. Historically, some chose to enter the United States. However, most were forcibly taken from African villages (either by White slave traders or by Africans from other villages) and sold into slavery in the southern United States. Today, Black immigrants enter the United States each year from such areas as South and Central America, Africa, and the Caribbean.

❏ Although socioeconomic status (SES) plays an important role in individualizing experiences of middle- and low-SES African Americans, the set of cultural experiences that is common to many of them is the history of forced abduction from their homelands, slavery, and the racism and discrimination that still exist today (Goode, Jones, & Jackson, 2011; Paul, Norbury, & Gosse, 2018; Sue & Sue, 2016).

❏ Unfortunately, experiences of institutional racism and continued economic oppression in the United States still impact the lives of African Americans across the socioeconomic spectrum. Historical adversity, which includes sharecropping, slavery, and race-based exclusion from educational, social, health, and economic resources, translates into socioeconomic disparities experienced by African Americans in the U.S. (Mental Health America, 2017). For example, today, the annual median income of U.S. households is $55,775; the income for African American households is $36,544 (U.S. Census Bureau, 2017b).

❏ Whites and African Americans differ in their views relating to the amount of discrimination being experienced in the U.S. Whites tend to believe that discrimination is much less common than it actually is (Goode et al., 2011). A survey conducted in May, 2013 by the Pew Research Center (2013a) found that 88% of African Americans reported that discrimination against Blacks exists, but only 57% of Whites held this same opinion.

❏ Former President Barack Obama described incidences of racism that he experienced prior to becoming President. While he was standing in front of a hotel waiting for his limousine, for example, a White couple threw him their car keys, thinking that he was the valet (Obama, 2006).

❏ Some African Americans experience *colorism*, differential treatment based on skin color. For example, individuals with lighter skin are often viewed as more attractive and intelligent than those with darker skin (Kelly & Greene, 2010).

Profile

Shontal and Lakasha are two African American former students of mine. Shontal was slender, attractive, and had light skin. As a single mother of four girls, her life was not easy. But she was intelligent and hardworking, and I was so proud of her when I learned that she had been accepted into several graduate school programs. She got along well with and was accepted by White classmates.

Lakasha, her classmate, was also attractive but she was quite a bit darker than Shontal. Lakasha stood six feet tall, wore dreadlocks and bright African clothes and jewelry, and was much more outspoken than Shontal. Lakasha came to my office one day in sorrow and frustration. She shared how her White classmates were never overtly unkind to her, but she often felt left out of social events. Lakasha said that in many subtle ways, she knew she would never be like the White girls or fit in with them. She had even tried straightening her hair, but this did not help her fit in better with her White peers. When Lakasha spoke to my multicultural class about colorism in the African American community, she stated that the lighter your skin color is, the more attractive and prestigious you are considered to be.

❏ African American women represent 13% of the female population in the U.S. However, they represent 30% of all incarcerated women in the U.S. (American Civil Liberties Union, 2017). Stealing food, medicine, and other items needed by their children were often the crimes that led to incarceration.

❏ In early African religions, ancestors and spirits of nature were worshipped. Religion has traditionally played an important role in African American communities in the United States and it is integral to the lives of many African Americans today. African Americans often come from traditional Christian backgrounds, including the Baptist, Methodist, and Episcopal denominations.

❏ Of all the major racial and ethnic groups in the U.S., African Americans are the most likely to report a formal religious affiliation. The southern U.S. has the largest concentration of evangelical Protestant churches.

Profile

Miya, African American university senior

My parents are highly educated and don't speak African American English. African American women have to be very strong—as a woman, you must be a rock. My grandma was a single mom with seven children, and she packed a gun! Our discipline is harsh, but you know you are loved. Our philosophy was "Child talk back, you get a whuppin'." The family is the center of everything, and you never disrespect your elders. We rate ourselves on skin color; the lighter you are, the more attractive you are. In our families, everyone knows your business. It's important to be loyal to your posse. We don't trust White people, so White people should not expect us to warm up right away. We don't think that White people get us.

AFRICAN AMERICAN FAMILY LIFE

❏ Families from African American backgrounds may include blood relatives and others who are not blood relatives but have special caring relationships. Many African Americans have extended family networks that provide economic and emotional support.

❏ Fifty four percent of African American children live with a single parent, while 38% live with two parents (Pew Social Trends, 2015). Many more African American children are being raised by grandparents in today's society. More than 1.3 million African Americans age 45 and older are living with and raising grandchildren, and many of these grandparents live in poverty (U.S. Census Bureau, 2017b).

❏ Many African Americans place high value on developing children's awareness of members of both their immediate and extended families. They have pride in their African American heritage and cultural uniqueness.

❏ Rather than emphasizing the importance of individual effort and gain, many African American families emphasize group effort for the common interest and expect that those who succeed will share with the larger community. These families view collective responsibility, interdependence, and cooperation as important values.

❏ Most African American families value obedience to parents, older siblings, and other older persons. They place great emphasis on respect for elders, who are seen as having hindsight and wisdom. Most families expect young children to treat others well, to obey family rules, and to work hard in school.

❏ African American families tend to use an approach to child-rearing that is more authoritative than in some other groups. Many families make frequent use of disciplinary practices to teach children appropriate behavior (Goode et al., 2011; Ispa, Thornburg, & Fine, 2006; Sue & Sue, 2016). Mothers may be firm and physical in their discipline. Firm discipline accompanied by love and affection is common in many African American homes.

❏ Many African Americans believe that children must be loved, guided, protected, and disciplined; all responsible adults in many communities partake in the discipline and training of children.

❏ In many African American families, infants are nurtured warmly and affectionately; young children are given the opportunity to "be children" and to enjoy play.

❏ African American families tend to be flexible about family roles. Fathers and mothers share child-care responsibilities, and older siblings carry out household chores and help care for younger siblings.

❏ African American men are often accepting of "women's work" and willing to share responsibilities traditionally assigned to women, such as picking up children from school (Sue & Sue, 2016).

❏ In some African American families, a matriarch or grandmother figure takes much of the responsibility for raising more than one generation of children. This matriarch has a strong influence on the actions of family members.

Profile

Nikki, African American university senior

I come from a very conservative home; my dad was a minister. We spent all Sunday in church and also attended Wednesday night Bible study. Everyone in the neighborhood looked out for each other. If you were bad, the neighbors would tell your mom! We believe that children and young people should defer to elders—it is very disrespectful not to do this. It is shameful to put older people into skilled nursing facilities—the families should take care of them. Black women need to be strong. Mental health problems are a stigma in our community. I have been stigmatized for "talking White," which is seen as negative by some in the Black community.

EDUCATION AND LITERACY

❑ Education is viewed as an important and desirable achievement by many African Americans. Children in African American families are often taught that an education is something that no one can take away from them.

❑ Thankfully, the educational attainment gap between African Americans and Whites is narrowing. Today, 84.7% of the African American population age 25 and over has a high school diploma; 20.2% of African Americans age 25 and over have a Bachelor's degree, while 1.9 million have an advanced degree (U.S. Census Bureau, 2017b).

❑ The crisis in the education of African Americans has increased significantly in urban neighborhoods where public schools lack resources, experience overcrowding, exhibit a racial achievement gap, and have policies that fail to deliver adequate opportunities for success. In the view of some experts, some poorly performing schools serve as pipelines to prison for youths (Word Press, 2017).

❑ Some African American students experience barriers in the educational setting. For example, conflicts may occur because of differences between school values and peer group values (Ogbu, 1992; Tatum, 2013).

❑ Ogbu (1995) stated that members of involuntary minority groups (e.g., African Americans) who have a history of discrimination and suppression may be less likely to buy into majority group values and practices that uphold educational attainment as the surest route to personal and professional success.

❑ Researchers (e.g., Ladson-Billings, 1994; Sue & Sue, 2016; Tatum, 2013) frequently cite the fact that young African American males are at risk for disengaging from the educational process, especially during middle school and high school.

❑ Working hard in school is viewed by some as "acting White" or "being whitewashed." Peer pressure to avoid "acting White" may reduce students' motivation to do well in school.

❑ Some African American students communicate and interact in a style that is persuasive, animated, and confrontational. These individuals may feel uncomfortable in classroom settings where they are expected to sit quietly for long periods of time, to complete tasks independently, and to follow specific rules regarding how they interact with others (Sue & Sue, 2016).

Profile

Jonathan, African American university student

I was not around many African Americans as a kid. But when I went to high school, there were more Blacks. When I hung around with the White kids, my African American friends told me I was "whitewashed." My mom was always very strict about my behavior in public.

❏ Mainstream professionals may see the communication style of African American students as aggressive or even as unacceptable conduct and may inappropriately penalize the students. According to Monroe (2005), African American youth are 2-5 times more likely to be suspended from school and often receive harsher consequences for "misbehavior" than their White peers.

❏ Some African American students have difficulty in school because the language used in instruction and in books differs from the spoken language as it is used in their community. These children may use African American English (AAE) in their community and home, although school teachers conduct classes in Mainstream American English (MAE) and often expect students to use "standard English" at school.

❏ van Keulen, Weddington, and DeBose (1998) likened AAE-speaking students to second language learners in that these students have conversational language proficiency, but may struggle with the academic English used in textbooks.

❏ Children who speak MAE at home have congruence in the home language and the language in which books at school are written. AAE-speaking children who come from print-rich environments where parents model and reinforce emergent literacy skills will likely enter first grade equal to their MAE counterparts who have had similar experiences.

❏ The language of students who speak AAE is not represented in conventional storybooks and textbooks. This lack of congruence can cause AAE-speaking children to experience challenges when learning to read.

❏ Because of their language differences, students who speak AAE may struggle with reading, writing, and spelling. Learning to spell can be especially difficult (Harris & Moran, 2006). Learning differences resulting from lack of experience with the "school dialect" may be a factor contributing to the overrepresentation of African American students in special education. The overrepresentation of African American students in special education programs is well documented (Battle, 2012; Paul et al., 2018; Stockman, 2010; Terry & Connor, 2012).

❏ Terry and Connor (2012) discussed literacy achievement gaps between race and language minority children and mainstream children, acknowledging that differences between children's spoken dialects and the printed word may be a significant factor.

❏ However, metalinguistic knowledge (e.g., the ability to codeswitch) may also be a factor in children's literacy achievement. Children who have the ability to codeswitch easily between their dialect and MAE may develop better literacy skills than children who have weak codeswitching abilities.

❏ The overrepresentation of African American boys in terms of their classification as students with disabilities raises serious concerns, because these students often end up having limited access to the general education curriculum.

❏ Unfortunately, many of the schools attended by low-income African American students are quite dilapidated and segregated (Morris & Morris, 2013; Word Press, 2017). One third of all African American students attend schools that have minority enrollments of 90% or more. Low-income students and students of color are also more likely to have poorly trained teachers (Talbert-Johnson, 2004).

❏ Gifted and talented African American students may be under-identified in schools because of assessment procedures that do not adequately reflect the strengths of individuals from African American backgrounds. Traditional intelligence tests are notoriously biased against African Americans.

❏ A study by Mills (2015b) showed that African American school-aged children from low-income backgrounds who were in classrooms for the gifted had higher scores on a standardized test of vocabulary than peers in general education classrooms.

❏ Mills (2015b) suggested that performance on a standardized test of vocabulary can be used as a marker for identifying traditional giftedness in African American children and children from low-income backgrounds. These two groups of children have been shown to perform very well on standardized vocabulary assessments.

❏ Craig and Washington (2004b) discussed in detail the effects of poverty on the academic and language performance of African American students. They stated that African American children are more than three times as likely as their White peers to live in poverty; these children are also more likely to live in families in which parental education levels are low.

❏ According to Craig and Washington (2004b), poverty is a variable that is implicated in school reading failure for African American students. They stated that "...although poverty and its co-variables can have profound adverse effects on a child's well-being, recent research indicates that formal public preschool experience may mitigate some of these effects for literacy learning" (p. 234).

❏ Washington (2001) discussed the poor reading achievement of African American children in urban schools and stated that intervention efforts have traditionally focused on children in kindergarten through fifth grade. She suggested that prevention efforts must begin prior to kindergarten.

❏ Hale (2004) and Stockman (2010) recommended that linkages be created between preschools and kindergartens attended by African American children, with expanded training given to preschool teachers. This should help young African American children perform better in kindergarten.

HEALTH CARE AND DISABLING CONDITIONS

❏ Protective factors and strengths in the African American community include community support systems and extended family relationships.

❏ It is hypothesized that family and religious protective factors account for the fact that except for Asian Americans, African Americans have the lowest levels of heavy drinking and binge drinking of any ethnic group. Compared to 45.3% of White Americans, 40.6% of African Americans age 12 and over were treated for substance abuse in 2010 (Mental Health America, 2017).

❏ Many African Americans lack access to adequate health care and do not have medical insurance. The leading causes of death are heart disease, cancer, and stroke (Centers for Disease Control and Prevention, 2017d).

❏ The African American population tends to have a higher infant mortality rate than that of other groups in some communities. Lower income, less frequent prenatal care, poorer maternal nutrition, and other factors make it difficult for many African Americans to raise healthy children.

❏ Sickle cell disease, a hereditary disease of the red blood cells affecting Blacks worldwide, has been associated with sensorineural hearing loss.

❏ Approaches to health care vary depending on the income and/or educational level of individual families. Some African Americans, especially in the rural south, rely on home remedies or holistic health approaches in which herbs, roots, teas, and natural foods are used (Goode et al., 2011).

❏ Some low-income families do not understand or have access to the traditional health care system. Thus they may only receive care when they are seriously ill. Preventative health care may not be available or utilized.

❏ Major inner city areas of the United States are comprised primarily of African Americans. These areas have limited services, poor housing, unemployment, crime, poverty, overcrowding, and illegal drug activities. All of these phenomena have negative implications for health.

❏ African American children from low-income families are often exposed to harmful environmental pollutants such as lead, air pollution, and ambient noise. These exposures can negatively impact their health and, in turn, their academic performance in school.

❏ Many African American children under 6 years of age have an elevated level of lead in the blood, partly caused by high lead-levels in low-income housing. High lead levels in the blood have been linked to many learning problems and health risks (Battle, 2012).

❏ African American children who live in low-income housing may also be susceptible to asthma. If they experience frequent episodes of asthma, school attendance is likely to be affected.

❏ Some African Americans believe that disabling conditions are due to karma, fate or destiny, religious factors, natural life occurrences, and malevolent forces (Goode, 2010).

❏ African American families are often able to accept children who have disabilities. This acceptance may result, in part, from support within the extended family and strong ties with their churches .

Profile

      Latisha was a smiling, happy second grade African American girl who was referred to me for language testing. Her teacher said she was very "hyper" in the classroom, and that she showed signs of deficits in language and other skills. I assessed Latisha in a quiet room in a 1:1 testing situation. Latisha, though trying hard to be compliant, had difficulty focusing on the assessment tasks. When I analyzed my assessment results, it was clear that Latisha's expressive and receptive language skills were significantly below grade level. I found out that she was exposed to lead and had been diagnosed with pica. Latisha liked to eat dirt and lick furniture. In an effort to improve performance in school, our school team put together a comprehensive plan to address Latisha's health, behavioral, language, and overall academic challenges.

AFRICAN AMERICAN COMMUNICATION STYLES

❏ Approval and agreement between participants in a conversation may be expressed through touching or physical contact. African Americans often touch one another during interactions, but are less likely to touch White Americans. This is especially true of African Americans from lower socioeconomic backgrounds (van Keulen, Weddington, & Debose, 1998).

❏ Eye contact is used as a form of nonverbal communication. However, rolling of the eyes during conversation may be viewed as offensive.

❏ Some African American students make little eye contact with adults, who may view direct eye contact as disrespectful.

❏ African American students often speak in a manner that is animated, interpersonal, and confrontational. This manner of speaking contrasts with that of White students, who often speak in a manner that is dispassionate, non-challenging, and impersonal (Sue & Sue, 2016).

❏ Some African Americans may not observe traditional turn-taking rules during conversations. It is acceptable to interrupt if a participant feels a need to add valuable information. Abruptly changing the topic is also acceptable.

❏ Individuals are expected to participate verbally in conversations rather than remaining silent. Conversations may be quite competitive, with the most assertive participants doing most of the talking. Mainstream professionals must be careful not to label this behavior as "rude" or "lacking in pragmatic skills."

❏ Among many African Americans, charismatic speech with distinctive intonational patterns and rhythm is rewarded and valued. African Americans frequently speak with emotional vitality.

❏ African American culture encourages many communication rituals and distinctive styles that affirm cultural identity and allegiance to the group. One example is "call and response," in which the listeners echo part of the speaker's previous utterance. For example, in a church setting, the preacher might say, "And the Lord told Noah to build an ark." The congregation might respond "Build an ark."

❏ Battle (2012b) described the hyperechoic response, which is superimposed on top of the speaker's previous utterance. This confirms that the listener understands what was said and also predicts and verbalizes what the speaker's next words will be while the speaker is still talking. This type of response contrasts with Mainstream American English (MAE) rules about turntaking, where the listener is expected to refrain from talking until the conversational partner has completely finished her utterance.

❏ African American students' narrative styles often differ from those of mainstream White students who speak MAE (see Battle, 2012; Champion & Mainess, 2003; Gardner-Neblett,

Pungello, & Iruka, 2012; Mills, 2015a, 2015b; Mills, Watkins, & Washington, 2013; Wyatt, 2015). These differences can lead to incorrect judgments about the students' behavior. Some of the major research findings are summarized below:

1. African American children often produce a range of styles using sophisticated discourse techniques.

2. African American students often rely on gestures to accompany verbalizations or narratives.

3. When African American students tell stories, they may include personal judgments and evaluations about the characters. "Personal narratives may in fact be tall tales in which the events are exaggerated and embellished" (Mills et al., 2013, p. 213).

4. In mainstream school programs, students are expected to tell stories in a topic-centered style, characterized by topic elaboration, structured discourse on a single topic, and lack of presupposed shared knowledge. African American students often use a topic-associating style, characterized by presupposition of shared knowledge between the speaker and listener(s), structured discourse on several linked topics, and lack of consideration for detail. Unfortunately, examiners who expect students to use the topic-centered style may incorrectly view African American children as having language impairment.

Profile

Lautrell S., an African American college senior in my multicultural class, shared her story with the group. She stated that in her family, there was a lot of physical punishment. Her last spanking with a belt occurred when she was 13 years old. When Lautrell was 16, her mother would punish her for infractions by taking her bedroom door off its hinges. Lautrell's brother was born when their mother was 15 years old; at 42, Lautrell's mom is a grandma. When Lautrell speaks MAE around her African American friends, they say "How dare you talk white?" Lautrell has learned to successfully codeswitch in different speaking situations.

AFRICAN AMERICAN ENGLISH CONSIDERATIONS

African American English (AAE), the language spoken by some residents of the United States, has undergone many changes in nomenclature. AAE has been referred to as Black Dialect, Black English, Black English Vernacular, African American Vernacular, African American Language, and Ebonics. The changes in nomenclature have been due, in part, to an increasingly sophisticated understanding of AAE and to changes in sociolinguistic theory. Because it contains much similarity to MAE, AAE is considered by most experts today to be a dialect of MAE, not a separate language (Battle, 2012; Paul et al., 2018; Stockman, 2010). The extent to which African American English is used is influenced by a number of factors:

❏ Use of AAE is influenced by geographic region, socioeconomic status, education, gender, and age. For example, young boys use more AAE features than young girls (Battle, 2012). African Americans with higher educational levels tend to use AAE features less than those with lower educational levels (Craig & Grogger, 2012).

❏ Middle-SES African Americans generally use AAE less than working class African Americans, especially in formal settings. African Americans from low-SES backgrounds are more likely to use a higher percentage of AAE features.

❑ African American children from low-income homes use more "dialectal forms" than their peers from middle class homes. Again, the discourse of boys shows more evidence of use of these forms than that of girls.

❑ West African languages such as Yoruba have impacted modern-day African American English.

❑ Ivy and Masterson (2011) found that the writings of children who spoke AAE were characterized by the absence of such morphemes as:

Plural *–s* (We see chicken over there)

Third-person singular *–s* (She cook)

Possessive *–s* (Kenny bike)

Past tense *–ed* (Yesterday we show 'em)

Copula *is* and *are* (We having fun)

❑ Ivy and Masterson (2011) found that there was comparable use of AAE in spoken and written modalities among third graders. Eighth grade students, however, used more dialectal features in speaking than in writing.

❑ Terry, Connor, Petscher, and Conlin (2012) found that reading gains from first grade through second grade were closely related to increases in the use of MAE by African American children.

❑ Gatlin and Wanzek (2015) analyzed 19 studies consisting of 1,947 typically-developing African American students in grades K-6; these children all spoke AAE. Gatlin and Wanzek found that the more the children used AAE, the lower their overall literacy skills, especially in reading. This could not be attributed to the influence of poverty. Gatlin and Wanzek concluded that "...students who produce higher frequencies of nonmainstream dialect features in language tend to have lower scores on literacy outcomes, a relationship that appears to exist regardless of SES or grade level" (p. 1306).

Recent research thus indicates that the discrepancy between spoken AAE and oral and written MAE may contribute to a literacy achievement gap between AAE-speaking and MAE-speaking children. However, AAE-speaking children with highly developed codeswitching skills tend to have literacy skills that are more commensurate with current academic standards.

Tech Tie-In

 www.nbaslh.org, the National Black Association for Speech-Language and Hearing, is an excellent resource for information about African American English and other topics that directly impact service delivery to children in the African American community.

MISCONCEPTIONS ABOUT AFRICAN AMERICAN ENGLISH

There are numerous possible misconceptions about AAE that professionals must be aware of if they are to interact effectively with AAE speakers:

Misconception #1. All African Americans speak AAE.

Some African Americans speak AAE and some do not. Some codeswitch back and forth between MAE and AAE depending on context.

Profile

Dr. Ndidi Johnson is Chair of the Nursing Department in a university setting. She shared with me that she codeswitches between MAE and AAE, depending upon the situation. In Dr. Johnson's words, "When I'm at work, I speak White English because that's what I need to do. When I get home, I switch to Black English. [Linguistically], it's like wearing high heels all day— when I get home, I kick them off and put on a pair of comfortable tennis shoes."

Misconception #2. AAE is only spoken by African Americans.

AAE can be spoken by people of any ethnic and linguistic background. Non-African Americans may speak AAE if their primary peer group is composed of African Americans. For example, some Puerto Rican students in New York City speak AAE as do some White students in Oakland, California. In contrast, African Americans who are socialized primarily with Whites will generally speak MAE.

Misconception #3. AAE is a substandard form of Mainstream American English.

Historically, the language patterns of African Americans have been viewed as "deficient." A major premise of this view was that African Americans lacked the cognitive abilities necessary to learn the grammatical rules of the English language. Many viewed the language patterns of AAE speakers as "improper English." AAE is now recognized as a fully developed language system with its own structure and rules (Wyatt, 2015).

Misconception #4. AAE should be eradicated so that children can become proficient in MAE.

It is possible to learn Mainstream American English without eradicating African American English. Some experts believe that speakers of AAE should become "bilingual" or "bidialectal" so that they can speak both AAE and MAE fluently. In this optimal situation, students can preserve their culture, heritage, and community dialect while simultaneously learning the style of speaking required in school and in various types of social interactions.

Misconception #5. Speakers of AAE can be adequately assessed with standardized tests of intelligence, language, etc. if a representative sample is included in the norming population.

Many published assessment instruments used in schools were developed and standardized on student populations consisting primarily of White, middle class, monolingual English speakers. These tests, especially those designed to assess aspects of grammar and sentence production, have been criticized by numerous experts as being inappropriate for use with African American children and other cultural groups (Battle, 2012; Pindzola et al., 2015; Roy, Oetting, & Moland, 2013;

Oetting, McDonald, Seibel, & Hegarty, 2016; Stockman, 2010). Including a small sample of AAE speakers in the norming population does little to make tests appropriate for these students.

BIAS IN ASSESSMENT MEASURES

When AAE speakers are tested, it is critical to differentiate which aspects of their speech and language are reflective of AAE rules and which aspects are indicative of a disorder. It is illegal for speech-language pathologists in the public schools to enroll AAE speakers for "remediation" of speech-language "disorders" if the goal of intervention is to teach MAE grammar. An understanding of AAE and how it differs from MAE is critical if speech-language pathologists are to distinguish between a language difference and a language impairment in an AAE-speaking student. Important morphosyntactic and speech sound characteristics of AAE are presented in Tables 4.1 and 4.2 respectively. Additional examples of bias are as follows:

❏ *Bias in articulation and phonological tasks*

Most tests of articulation and phonology are normed on White children. The unique characteristics of AAE must be considered when assessing articulation and phonology. For example, on most articulation tests, the substitution of /f/ for the initial sound in *thumb*, would be considered an error. However, for AAE-speakers, this substitution is a dialectical difference, not a speech sound error.

❏ *Bias in sentence repetition tasks*

Examiner: "Repeat these sentences after me. Remember to say them EXACTLY like I say them!"

1. Neither child is using the swings.
2. They had been hungry.
3. She looks at the big, brown dog.

❏ *Bias in grammatical closure tasks*

Examiner: "I am going to say some sentences. I want you to fill in the word that is missing."

Demonstration item: A rose is a flower and a daisy is a flower.
                        Daisies and roses are both _____. (flowers)

1. Today I play the marimba; yesterday I _____the marimba.

2. I have a cat, and you have a cat; we have two _____.

3. Today Sue is going to the store; yesterday she _____ going to the store.

❏ *Bias in receptive grammatical tasks*

Examiner: "We are going to look at some pictures. Each page has three pictures. When I say a sentence, you point to the picture that goes with the sentence I say. Here's the first picture."

1. Show me, "The cats are playing in the garden."

2. Show me, "He played baseball."

3. Point to, "They have been painting the fence."

Table 4.1

Characteristics Of African American English Morphology and Syntax

AAE Feature/Characteristic	Mainstream American English	Sample AAE Utterance
Omission of noun possessive	That's the woman's car. It's John's pencil.	That *the woman* car. It *John* pencil.
Omission of noun plural	He has 2 boxes of apples. She gives me 5 cents.	He got 2 *box* of *apple*. She give me 5 *cent*.
Omission of third person singular present tense marker	She walks to school. The man works in his yard.	She *walk* to school. The man *work* in his yard.
Omission of "to be" forms such as "is, are"	She is a nice lady. They are going to a movie.	*She a* nice lady. *They going* to a movie.
Present tense "is" may be used regardless of person/number.	They are having fun. You are a smart man.	*They is* having fun. *You is* a smart man.
Utterances with "to be" may not show person number agreement with past and present forms.	You are playing ball. They are having a picnic.	You *is* playing ball. They *is* having a picnic.
Present tense forms of auxiliary "have" are omitted.	I have been here for 2 hours. He has done it again.	I been here for 2 hours. He done it again.
Past tense endings may be omitted.	He lived in California. She cracked the nut.	He *live* in California. She *crack* the nut.
Past "was" may be used regardless of number and person.	They were shopping. You were helping me.	They *was* shopping. You *was* helping me.

AAE Feature/Characteristic	Mainstream American English	Sample AAE Utterance
Multiple negatives (each additional negative form adds emphasis to the negative meaning.)	We don't have any more. I don't want any cake. I don't like broccoli.	We **don't** have *no* more. I **don't never** want *no* cake. I **don't never** like broccoli.
"None" may be substituted for "any."	She doesn't want any.	She don't want **none.**
Perfective construction; "been" may be used to indicate that an action took place in the distant past.	I had the mumps last year. I have known her for years.	I **been had** the mumps last year. I **been known** her.
"Done" may be combined with a past tense form to indicate that an action was started and completed.	He fixed the stove. She tried to paint it.	He **done fixed** the stove. She **done tried** to paint it.
The form "be" may be used as the main verb.	Today she is working. We are singing.	Today **she be** working. **We be** singing.
Distributive "be" may be used to indicate actions and events over time.	He is often cheerful. She's kind sometimes.	**He be** cheerful. **She be** kind.
A pronoun may be used to restate the subject.	My brother surprised me. My dog has fleas.	My brother, **he** surprise me. My dog, **he** got fleas.
"Them" may be substituted for "those."	Those cars are antiques. Where'd you get those books?	**Them cars**, they be antique. Where you get **them books**?
Future tense "is, are" may be replaced by "gonna."	She is going to help us. They are going to be there.	She **gonna** help us. They **gonna** be there.
"At" is used at the end of "where" questions.	Where is the house? Where is the store?	Where is the house **at**? Where is the store **at**?
Additional auxiliaries are often used.	I might have done it.	I **might could have** done it.
"Does" is replaced by "do."	She does funny things. It does make sense.	**She do** funny things. **It do** make sense.

Table 4.2

Characteristics of African American English Articulation and Phonology

AAE Feature/Characteristic	Mainstream American English	African American English
/l/ phoneme lessened or omitted	tool always	too' a'ways
/r/ phoneme lessened or omitted	door mother protect	doah mudah p'otek
f/voiceless "th" substitution at end or middle of word	teeth both nothing	teef bof nufin'
t/voiceless "th" substitution in beginning of a word	think thin	tink tin
d/voiced "th" substitution at the beginning, middle of words	this brother	dis broder
v/voiced "th" substitution at the end of words	breathe smooth	breave smoov
Consonant cluster reduction	desk rest left wasp	des' res' lef was'
Differing syllable stress patterns	guitar police July	**gui** tar **po** lice **Ju** ly

AAE Feature/Characteristic	Mainstream American English	African American English
Final consonant in verb may change when past tense ending is added	liked walked	li-tid wah-tid
Metathesis occurs	ask	aks ("axe")
Devoicing of final voiced consonants	bed rug cab	bet ruk cap
Final consonants may be deleted	bad good	ba' goo'
High front vowel substituted for mid-front vowel ("i" replaces "e")	pen ten	pin tin
b/v substitution	valentine vest	balentine bes'
Diphthong reduction	find oil pound	fahnd ol pond
n/ng substitution	walking thing	walkin' thin'

Note: Characteristics may vary depending on variables such as geographic region.

❏ *Bias in grammatical judgment tasks*

Examiner: "Tell me whether the following sentences are correct or incorrect."

1. Them girls is having a good time.

2. The boys is going to the party.

3. We don't have no time to talk to you.

Although the sentence examples above are "incorrect" according to the rules of MAE, they might not sound incorrect to speakers of AAE. Additional examples of language differences affecting sentence production are presented in Table 4.3.

FACTORS TO CONSIDER IN ASSESSMENT

❏ There are many considerations to keep in mind when assessing the speech and language of African American students. Professionals must be nonjudgmental, open, and knowledgeable about linguistic and cultural issues that can impact the evaluation of African American students.

❏ It is sometimes necessary to avoid asking personal and direct questions during the first meeting with African American students. Questions of this type may be viewed as offensive and intrusive. The question, "Can you tell me about your family?" may be too personal and therefore insulting to an African American student who does not know the interviewer.

❏ If an African American student feels intimidated by a school professional's questions, his responses may provide limited information, possibly causing the professional to conclude, inappropriately, that the student has limited expressive language skills.

❏ Mainstream clinicians must remember that African American students' pragmatics and narrative skills may differ markedly from those of MAE. Professionals must be familiar with the narrative strategies used by typical AAE-speaking children.

❏ With that in mind, researchers have recommended that oral narration may be an area of relative strength for African American children, and that assessment of narrative skills is ecologically valid (Gardner-Neblett et al., 2012). Narrative elicitation contexts that contain both audio and visual tasks are necessary to fully describe these children's narrative performance (Mills, 2015b).

❏ The Narrative Assessment Protocol (NAP) (Pence, Justice, & Gosse, 2007) has been shown to be a valid assessment tool for children who speak AAE, as have other assessments of narrative ability (Terry, Mills, Bingham, Mansour, & Marencin, 2013).

❏ The research of Mills et al. (2013) showed that evaluations during narratives are found in many African American homes. Fictional narratives from a wordless picture book may be the best context in which to elicit a story with evaluations from African American children.

❏ Other alternative forms of assessment (nonstandardized measures) that can be used to assess the presence of communication disorders in African American students include contrastive analysis, a description of the child's functional communication skills, and language sample analysis (Battle, 2012; Stockman, 2010).

❏ Professionals can administer a test created specifically for use with African American children. The Diagnostic Evaluation of Language Variation (DELV) is designed to be dialectically

Table 4.3

**Examples of Acceptable Utterances
by Speakers of African American English**

Mainstream American English	African American English
That boy looks like me.	That boy, he look like me.
If he kicks it, he'll be in trouble.	If he kick it, he be in trouble.
When the lights are off, it's dark.	When the lights be off, it dark.
It could be somebody's pet.	It could be somebody pet.
Her feet are too big.	Her feet is too big.
I'll get something to eat.	I will get me something to eat.
She is dancing and the music's on.	She be dancin' an' the music on.
What kind of cheese do you want?	What kind of cheese you want?
My brother's name is Joe.	My brother name is Joe.
I raked the leaves outside.	I rakted the leaves outside.
After the recital, they shook my hand.	After the recital, they shaketed my hand.
They are standing around.	They is just standing around.
He is a basketball star.	He a basketball star.
They are in cages.	They be in cages.
It's not like a tree or anything.	It not like a tree or nothin'.
He does like to fish.	He do like to fish.
They are going to swim.	They gonna swim.
Mom already repaired the car.	Mom done repair the car.

neutral with respect to AAE and can be used with children between 4 and 9 years of age (Seymour, Roeper, & de Villiers, 2004). When speech-language pathologists use this instrument, a child who speaks AAE can be identified as being at risk for a language impairment without being penalized for using features of AAE.

❏ McCabe and Champion (2010) recommended that dynamic assessment measures be used to assess children's ability to learn when provided with instruction; dynamic assessment is preferable to standardized tests for assessing the skills of African American children.

❏ Oetting, McDonald, Seidel, and Hegarty (2016) examined the sentence recall abilities of 70 speakers of AAE and 36 speakers of Southern White English. These skills were examined as a function of their dialect and clinical status ("typically developing" vs. "specific language impaired" [SLI]). These researchers found that when dialect-strategic scoring was used, sentence recall tasks were highly accurate in identifying subjects with SLI. Their results provide evidence that dialect-strategic scoring can be implemented to assess for the possible presence of SLI in children who speak AAE.

❏ When assessing speech sound production, it must be remembered that misdiagnosis is likely to occur if the determination of a speech sound disorder is based entirely on the results of formal articulation tests. These tests are often biased against African American children. It is important to examine the child's speech in everyday situations and to consider how others in the local community react to the child's speech.

❏ African American boys often demonstrate a high level of physical activity and may be mislabeled as having ADHD (attention deficit hyperactivity disorder). In one study, it was shown that African American boys were rated by teachers as having the most severe ADHD symptoms; White girls were rated with the least severe symptoms (Reid, Riccio, Kessler, DuPaul, Power, Anastopolous, Rogers-Adkinson, & Noll, 2000).

❏ In another study, African American girls were found to be 3.5 times more likely to score positive on screening measures for ADHD than were White American girls, and African American boys were 2.5 times more likely to score positive for ADHD than were White American boys (Reid, Casat, Norton, Anastopolous, & Temple, 2001). Behaviors that are viewed by White American teachers as "hyperactivity" in African American students may not be perceived in this way by teachers who are African American.

Profile

I was asked to evaluate the language skills of Poppy M., a second grade African American girl. Poppy was born two months prematurely and had a history of special needs (e.g., delays in language, gross motor skills, fine motor skills, and cognition). Poppy's file indicated that she also had ADHD, combined with behavioral issues. When my colleague and I attempted to assess Poppy, she spit on my colleague, bit her, and kicked her. When I assessed Poppy, she hit me and tried to pull my hair. She told me repeatedly that I was nasty. Despite our best efforts, we were not able to obtain a valid assessment of Poppy's language skills through formal or informal testing. Miss M., Poppy's full-time aide in the classroom, gathered a language sample of Poppy's utterances over a four-day period. My colleague and I obtained additional language samples in natural contexts as Poppy interacted with her teacher and others in the classroom. Based on an analysis of the results, it was evident that Poppy could benefit from language intervention. Because of her inability to focus attention and behave appropriately in the classroom, help from a behavior therapist was also recommended.

IMPLICATIONS FOR PROFESSIONALS

❑ Professionals should always address family members formally, using titles and surnames, unless specifically invited to do otherwise.

❑ Prior experiences of discrimination may result in issues related to a lack of trust between African American families and mainstream professionals. Historical and contemporary experiences of negative treatment have led to a mistrust of authorities, who are frequently seen as not having the best interests of African Americans in mind (Mental Health America, 2017).

❑ It is important to establish a good personal relationship with clients and families. I have found that a caring attitude, willingness to listen, and warm, personal touch can be extremely facilitative.

❑ Professionals should address students' needs with a family-focused approach to intervention. Families may be experiencing stress because of health and safety hazards, poverty, lack of access to medical care, etc. It is best to utilize the strong family support systems that exist within many African American families when helping them to achieve specific goals.

❑ Professionals may need to help low-income families navigate the community system by providing information about outside resources such as health organizations and legal sources of support.

❑ Resources available through churches and other religious organizations can often be used as allies in intervention. These resources are often more helpful than agencies that the family has never used. Church personnel frequently have an understanding of a family's dynamics and living conditions.

❑ For many African Americans, churches are places of religious, social, and even practical support. Research has shown that support systems connected with church help to promote resilience in African American undergraduate students who had been exposed to racism (Watkins, Labarrie, & Appio, 2010).

Profile

Erica, African American university senior

I grew up in generational poverty in Alabama, living in my grandma's house with her, my mom, her two sisters, my aunt, and her two sons. Growing up in Alabama, most African Americans affiliate with the church in some way whether or not they consider themselves to be Christians. My family and I attended church every Sunday for group worship and fellowship, and every Wednesday for Bible studies and church meetings. My church was an excellent resource which really helped me succeed. For example, they gave me a $400 scholarship to help with my community college education. Whenever we needed money, the church was a huge help in giving us money to pay our bills and buy groceries.

Church was a major part of our lives. Church activities usually lasted 8-10 hours on Sunday because breakfast was provided for struggling families. Sunday school was used for Bible study and extra tutoring for students who needed help with their public school homework. In the late evening we had a big dinner for everyone who wanted to stay and eat. I remember that the church was the first place where I was taught to say "please" and "thank you." People from church also helped me with correct grammar. When I was eight years old, my mom would not allow me to speak AAE anymore because she saw how it was negatively impacting my grades—especially in English and in all my writing assignments.

The church set up after school programs, and older high school students would help elementary children with their homework. I remember a wonderful tutor who worked with me free of charge for a year because I was failing math. Sometimes if families were struggling to find employment, all it would take to get a job was being seated in church next to a business owner. Contact information was exchanged and the parishioners set up a time to discuss potential employment opportunities. Church was a big deal for young adults like me because it was the only time we were exposed to working professionals like teachers, doctors, and lawyers. Community leaders often came and gave motivational speeches, encouraging us to get an education to gain a better future and quality of life. Luke 6:31 is a Bible verse that I find to be heavily instilled in most African American churches and communities; this verse is passed down from generation to generation. (Luke 6:31: "Treat others the same way you want them to treat you.")

❑ When working with families who are experiencing poverty, remember that poverty is not necessarily an indicator of dysfunction; many low-income families provide stable, loving environments for their children.

❑ Professionals should also remember, however, that because disproportionate numbers of African American families in the United States experience poverty, the need for educational services and rehabilitation often are viewed as less important than the need for food, clothing, shelter, and medical care. Professionals should not judge these families as being uncaring or indifferent if they place basic human needs above general or special education needs.

❑ African American parents often interact with their children through story-telling. Parents should be encouraged to stimulate their children's interaction with print by reading to them frequently.

❑ Britto, Brooks-Gunn, and Griffin (2006) studied African American children of mothers who were young and experiencing poverty. They found that the children's vocabularies appeared to be positively associated with a more interactive, maternal book-reading style that included behaviors such as encouraging children to participate, asking questions, and extending children's knowledge beyond the pages of the book. When parents provided high levels of guided participation and support during reading activities, children demonstrated greater expressive language use and school readiness than did children who received low levels of maternal engagement during reading activities. Thus, professionals should encourage parents to interact with children in ways that facilitate the development of school readiness.

❑ A longitudinal research study with low-SES African American mothers found that home visitors could be most supportive and helpful by gaining the mothers' trust gradually, being indirect (e.g., not giving commands or prescriptions), and modeling appropriate parenting and language stimulation strategies (Ispa, Fine, & Thornberg, 2006). The researchers found that it was more useful to make home visits over a period of time rather than just at one point in time.

❑ Some researchers have found that African American infants are more advanced in their motor development than infants from other ethnic groups; this is an important consideration when examining case history information relating to motor development (Carter et al., 2005).

❏ Educators should be flexible in identifying the special talents of African American students. Identification of students' strengths and limitations should be based, to a greater degree, on observations made by teachers and parents than on scores obtained from standardized tests.

❏ Among African Americans, the cultural emphasis on verbal expectations can lead some parents to perceive a language or articulation problem as a fluency problem. They hear a disruption in their child's speech and attribute it to abnormalities in the speech flow. Thus, it is important in these cases to carefully elicit parents' or clients' perception of the presenting communication problem in order to ascertain the precise nature of that problem (Robinson & Crowe, 1998).

❏ Because of the strong emphasis African Americans place on oral communication, they may feel the need to speak fluently, rapidly, and without struggle. This can cause some African Americans who stutter, especially males, to do everything possible to conceal their stuttering (van Keulen et al., 1998).

❏ Teaching styles that emphasize open affection, encouragement, and praise are highly effective with many African American children. These children may do their best work if they feel like they are in a community of learners that is like an extended family (Love & Krueger, 2005).

❏ When teaching African American students, professionals should remember that learning may be enhanced through the use of auditory and kinesthetic techniques in a high-energy, fast-paced atmosphere with a varied format.

❏ Because African American culture emphasizes cooperation and sharing rather than competition, cooperative learning activities benefit many African American students (Akella & Elimimian, 2012; Banks, 2013).

❏ African American students tend to be most responsive in educational situations in which the instructor is charismatic and encourages sharing, team work, and open discussions (Akella & Elimimian, 2012). They may be reluctant to participate in activities in which they are expected to sit still, be passive, and refrain from interaction.

❏ Professionals should be culturally responsive to their students, spending time to build relationships with them (Roseberry-McKibbin, 2015). When relationships are established, students are more likely to respond favorably. Students of color who have caring relationships with professionals are more motivated and perform better academically than students who do not.

Profile

I provided therapy for Trevon, an African American 13-year-old male with a history of sex-related crimes and violence. As a White female speech-language pathologist, I was concerned that Trevon would feel uncomfortable interacting with me. When I read about his background of severe physical and sexual abuse, I began to understand why Trevon acted out. During our sessions, I always let Trevon know how happy I was to see him. Because he had not yet learned to read many kindergarten-level sight words, I brought in a notebook that he could use to practice writing words. I asked Trevon who he admired and what his interests were. He said he admired Dr. Martin Luther King, and that he wanted to play football for the Oakland Raiders. I printed out some pictures of Dr. King and the Raiders, and Trevon chose some to glue onto the cover of his notebook. I helped him understand ways in which a good vocabulary helps professional football players. These discussions motivated him to develop better vocabulary skills.

When I found out that Trevon liked ballet, I talked to him about my own training in ballet and how Chicago football great Walter Payton used ballet to increase his flexibility. During breaks in therapy, I turned on music (e.g., Swan Lake) and we did barre exercises. I was deeply moved when I was told by the personnel at Trevon's special school that he greatly looked forward to seeing me—apparently, language therapy sessions were a highlight of his week.

On a rainy December day, I arrived at the school with Christmas presents for Trevon. I was told he had moved. I didn't even get to say goodbye (as so frequently happens with youth who are part of the juvenile justice system). Seeing my dismay, the vice principal promised to send my gifts to Trevon. Several years later, I found out that Trevon was thriving and doing well in a group home. It was very moving and uplifting to hear that Trevon was succeeding.

❑ Because African American students often prefer a field-dependent learning style, peer interaction and aspects in the surrounding environment should facilitate learning. A student might experience feelings of low self-esteem and mistrust if he or she is isolated from peers and not given opportunities to interact with others during instruction.

❑ Professionals should incorporate African American music, literature, art, and history into learning activities. Experiences of this type have been shown to enhance pride and to facilitate learning.

❑ Older students should read expository (informational) texts about role models such as Frederick Douglass and W.E.B. DuBois. Students can deepen their oral and written language skills by comparing and contrasting the viewpoints of these two African American intellectuals.

❑ Many African American students respond well to the spoken word and to the incorporation of movement and touch into learning activities.

❑ Sue and Sue (2016) recommended that students be encouraged to identify family sayings or Bible stories that instill hope. The writings of prominent African Americans can be used as well. I have used the sayings of Dr. Martin Luther King to build the vocabulary skills of African American students in therapy.

❑ Within the African American culture, the name given to a child is considered extremely important. Professionals should always ask students the name that they prefer to be called. If the pronunciation of the name appears unique to mainstream professionals, these professionals should make every attempt to memorize this unique pronunciation and use it appropriately.

Profile

An African American girl told a friend of mine that her name was La-a. The girl added that "The dash don't be silent." My friend was taught to call the girl "Ladasha."

❑ African American students who are accustomed to "call and response" may respond verbally in class to the teacher's question without first raising their hands. These students may be viewed as disrespectful, rude, and aggressive. Although "school rules" may need to be explained to these students, school professionals should be understanding when such behaviors do occur.

❑ Phrases such as "raise your hand," "take a seat," or "line up" are not necessarily familiar to African American students when they first enter kindergarten, especially if they have not attended preschool. Professionals can help these children adjust to the school setting by teaching the language and routines of the classroom (Roseberry-McKibbin, 2015).

❑ School professionals who feel that African American students are misbehaving when they communicate in a style that is confrontational and emotional should teach them that there is a "home way" and a "school way" of communicating.

❑ Professionals can teach the differences between "home talk" and "school talk" in a nonperjorative manner that helps African American students become bidialectal in both oral and written language. These students should be encouraged to codeswitch appropriately based on the context in which they are communicating.

❑ Most experts agree that it is not the province of school-based SLPs or special education teachers to provide services for "remediation" of AAE. It is important to remember that use of AAE is not a "disorder" and that students may not be enrolled in any type of special education program without evidence of a disorder or disability. However, experts over time have recommended that classroom teachers help these students learn MAE through dialect-focused instruction (Connor & Craig, 2006; Stockman, 2010; van Keulen et al., 1998).

❑ Connor and Craig (2006) suggested that professionals might help to increase students conscious awareness of code shifting by providing "explicit instruction in dialect awareness" (p. 782). This instruction can be provided in the classroom setting.

❑ Johnson, Thomas-Tate, Spence, and Connor (2011) obtained written language samples from 141 AAE-speaking students in grades two through four. They found that the more the students used AAE, the poorer their editing skills were on a writing task. Johnson et al. suggested that interventions that implement bidialectal education (explicit instruction in non-AAE grammatical features) may be useful in helping AAE users switch to MAE in academic settings.

❑ Pearson, Conner, and Jackson (2013) emphasized that highlighting correspondences between MAE and AAE at a metalinguistic level creates environments that support the academic achievement of students who speak AAE.

❑ Edwards and Rosin (2016) used the program Talking and Learning for Kindergarten (TALK; Edwards, Rosin, Gross, & Chen, 2013) with Head Start preschoolers who spoke AAE. The results of the study showed that a 28-hour summer program, which used contrastive analysis to highlight morphological, phonological, and pragmatic differences between AAE and

---

Tech Tie-In   *DYSA African American English (or Ebonics) in the classroom*

In this YouTube video, a fifth grade teacher from the Watts area of Los Angeles uses a fun, engaging game format to help African American students differentiate MAE from AAE. As Dr. Noma LeMoine, an African American researcher, states in the video, the goal of this teaching is not to devalue the students, but to support and affirm them as they become fluently bidialectal in AAE and MAE.

https://www.youtube.com/watch?V=xX1-FgkfWo8

MAE, was highly successful in enhancing children's awareness of MAE prior to kindergarten. The children also demonstrated significant improvement on three measures of phonological awareness— word completion, rhyming, and blending. A supplemental appendix in Edwards and Rosin (2016) includes the TALK program, a resource that can help young children increase their awareness of MAE features before they formally enter school.

❏ Teachers and other professionals should not overtly correct or criticize the oral language of students who speak AAE. However, professionals can use recasts and model MAE. For instance, if a student says, "Hey, he cool," the professional might reply, "Yes, he is cool. I think he is cool, too."

❏ Speech-language pathologists can provide in-service programs to enhance teachers' knowledge of specific ways to differentiate between a speech or language difference and a speech or language impairment in speakers of AAE. In this in-service, SLPs can share strategies for comparing and contrasting MAE and AAE. Such in-service programs are likely to result in fewer inappropriate referrals for speech-language and other special education programs.

Profile

Brianna, university graduate student

My dad is from Jamaica; he is one of 11 children. I'm one of five siblings. My father is a plumber who owns his own company, and my mom is a nurse. We definitely prefer White people to refer to us as African American instead of Black. It's extremely important to refer to people by titles, not first names! My family really values education, and my dad wants me to get my Ph.D. My mom grew up in a high poverty area in Louisiana; her mom cleaned houses for a living. My mom wanted to get out, so she went to school to become a nurse. When I spoke AAE, my family would say "Oh, Brianna, use your White girl voice." In a professional setting, if I used AAE, they'd say "You put that away." We did not go to the doctor for regular checkups and preventative care. Depression has negative connotations in my family. The attitude is "that's not a real disease."

A few years ago, I was pulled over by the police for driving too close to a truck. I was eating a snack, and the older White police officer said "Why are you continuing to eat?" He asked how much I had been drinking (which was nothing) and made me get out of the car. He shone a flashlight into my eyes and asked if I had been taking drugs. I told him no, and he said "Well…. we'll let you go with a warning."

CONCLUSION

The African American community in the U.S. has shown encouraging progress. An increasing number of students are graduating from high school and achieving personal goals. Members of this community, though, continue to experience challenges in their efforts to overcome poverty and discrimination. When general and special education personnel are serving African American students and their families, it is important to use nonbiased assessment instruments and to consider factors such as the use of AAE in both assessment and intervention. With support from families and school personnel, African American students who speak AAE can become confidently bidialectal and can succeed in school and beyond.

STUDY QUESTIONS

1. Briefly describe factors in the history of African Americans in the United States that have led to feelings of anger and mistrust toward White Americans.

2. List characteristics that are common within many African American families. What values do African American parents hold relating to child-rearing?

3. Describe educational barriers that African American students may experience when they attend traditional U.S. schools. In what ways has African American English been described as a barrier to achievement? Do you agree or disagree that AAE is a barrier?

4. Describe some alternatives to using traditional standardized tests with African American students who have potential language impairments.

MULTIPLE CHOICE

5. Many African American students respond best to intervention methods that:

    A. Require that they sit still and demonstrate "good" behavior.
    B. Incorporate many kinesthetic and auditory cues.
    C. Include African American music, history, and cultural materials.
    D. Allow students to receive individual therapy so that they get one-to-one attention from an adult.
    E. Are fast-paced and varied.

6. Which of the following are recommended as nonbiased, valid assessments of the communication skills of speakers of AAE?

    A. Language samples
    B. Narrative assessment
    C. Verbal portion of a standardized IQ test
    D. Norm-referenced tests standardized on a national sample
    E. Fill-in-the-blank expressive morphology tasks

7. Ganesha T., a 6-year-old speaker of AAE in first grade, has been referred by her classroom teacher for testing. The referral form says that "Ganesha is disruptive in class. I'm wondering if she needs therapy for her social communication skills." Which of the following indicate that Ganesha is manifesting a communication difference (not disorder) based on her cultural background?

A. When the teacher asks a question in class, Ganesha answers without raising her hand first.
B. When Ganesha tells a story, she assumes that the listener has enough background information to understand what she is talking about.
C. Ganesha looks down when she is talking to teachers and administrators (e.g., the principal).
D. Ganesha has difficulty sitting still and listening to the teacher lecture to a group of students.
E. Ganesha tends to talk loudly with her peers and (to the White teacher) appears to be "in your face."

8. On this same form, the teacher states that "Ganesha also has poor grammar. I'm concerned that this will interfere with her reading and writing." He gives several examples. Which one of the following utterances would NOT be typical for a speaker of AAE?

A. My daddy done buy the groceries.
B. They ain't no be gonna havin' a good time.
C. That might be my friend pencil.
D. We be readin' our book in class.
E. Those mice is gettin' chased by the cat.

9. Which of the following would be considered inappropriate in service delivery to African American students and their families?

A. Giving students nicknames to help them feel special (e.g., calling Ganesha "Nesha")
B. Calling family members by their first names to establish a cordial, comfortable relationship
C. Helping families develop strategies for reading and telling stories to their children
D. Asking for the parent's consent to conduct an assessment
E. Expecting the student to answer questions that can be answered by the parent

10. A teacher refers Treshaun, a kindergarten African American boy to you. The teacher has difficulty understanding the student's speech and reported that "he doesn't always pronounce his sounds correctly." Which of the following would NOT be typical for an AAE-speaking child and could be a sign of a speech sound disorder?

A. I'm gonna axe him to go.
B. We walkin' to the store.
C. The dentist cleaned mah teef.
D. The wed wabbit hop across the cage.
E. I tink he can come.

ANSWERS TO STUDY QUESTIONS

5. B, C, and E
6. A and B
7. A, B, C, D, and E
8. B
9. A and B
10. D

Chapter 5

Families from Hispanic Backgrounds

Outline
- General Background Information
- Hispanic Family Life
- Hispanic Education and Literacy
- Cultural Customs, Courtesies, and Beliefs
- Health Care and Disabling Conditions
- Hispanic Communication Styles
- Spanish Language Characteristics and Considerations
- Implications for Professionals

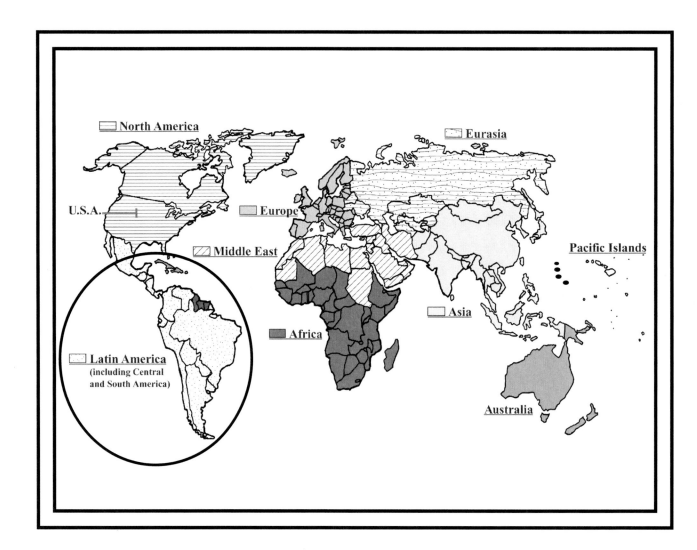

The Hispanic population is growing throughout the United States and is becoming increasingly more diverse. Many Spanish-speaking families are moving to areas in the U.S. that, until recently, had small Hispanic populations. Many school programs lack the resources necessary to identify and meet the learning needs of Spanish-speaking children with communication disorders and other disabilities.

The term **Hispanic** is used to refer to individuals who were born in or trace the background of their families to one of the Spanish-speaking Latin American nations or to Spain. Hispanics also come from Caribbean countries such as Puerto Rico and Cuba. Individuals from Mexican backgrounds constitute the largest portion of the Hispanic population.

Hispanics are an ethnic group rather than a "race." Most Hispanics are racially mixed and have diverse ancestral roots (e.g., African, Native Indian, and European).

Spanish is the language most often spoken in Mexico, Puerto Rico, Cuba, and throughout most countries in Central and South America (see Figure 5.1). Different dialects of Spanish, however, are used in different parts of the Spanish-speaking world.

Figure 5.1

GENERAL BACKGROUND INFORMATION

There is no one "Hispanic culture." Instead, there are different ethnic or cultural groups who speak Spanish. Some individuals from Spanish language backgrounds prefer to be called "Latinos" rather than "Hispanics." The term "Latino," refers to geography rather than language and is preferred by many individuals from South America, Central America, and the Spanish-speaking Caribbean countries. Others prefer a reference to their family's country of origin. For example, some Hispanics like to be called Cuban Americans, Mexican Americans, etc.

Many Hispanics are born in the United States; others immigrate for reasons such as family re-unification and economic opportunity. Individuals from Central and South America often come to the United States to escape from politically unstable situations in their native countries.

The information reported in this section, unless otherwise indicated, was compiled based on a review of the Pew Hispanic Research Center Report (2017), available at www.pewhispanic.org.

❏ Today, 55 million people or 17% of the American population are of Hispanic origin (National Hispanic Heritage Month, 2017).

❏ The U.S. Hispanic population growth has slowed down to a 2.8% growth rate in contrast to a 4.4% growth rate in 2007 and a 5.8% growth rate in the 1990s. At this time, Asians are the fastest-growing group in the U.S. and Hispanics are second. Sixty four percent of Hispanics in the U.S. are from Mexican backgrounds.

❏ The slowdown in growth has been driven by two large demographic trends: a slower rate of immigration and declining birth rates for Hispanic women living in the U.S. In the case of Mexico, there has been an increase in the number of individuals returning to Mexico since 2009.

❏ In California, in 2013, the number of Hispanics equaled the state's non-Hispanic white population. There were 15 million Hispanics and 15 million non-Hispanic Whites. Many Hispanics were young adults who were ready to start families, and in 2014 the Hispanic population became larger than the non-Hispanic White population in California for the first time since California became a state.

❏ Hispanics are the youngest racial or ethnic group in the U.S.; nearly 60% are Millennials or younger. About one-third of the Hispanic population is younger than 18.

❏ Hispanic children 5 years of age or younger are a very large and fast-growing segment of the U.S. population. Most are of low socioeconomic status (SES). Nearly 40% of children in Head Start in the U.S. are Hispanic (Mancilla-Martinez, Gamez, Vagh, & Leseaux, 2016).

❏ In terms of areas of residence, 27.1% of Hispanics live in California. Other states with high Hispanic residence rates include Texas, Florida, New York, and Illinois. Slightly over 40% of Hispanics live in the Western U.S.

❏ Multiple factors impact Hispanic children and families (Brice, 2013). One of these is poverty. Median annual personal earnings in 2014 were $22,400. At this time, approximately 23.5% of Hispanics were living in poverty.

❏ Consequences of poverty include poor housing conditions, educational and employment barriers, and health problems. Stresses caused by poverty can have a negative impact on the family life of Hispanics.

❑ According to current estimates from the U.S. Department of Labor, Hispanic farm workers work 42 hours a week and earn $7.25 an hour on average; however, this average varies depending on length of employment. The average annual income of crop workers is $10,000-$12,499 per individual. Thirty percent of all farm workers have total incomes below the poverty line (National Farm Workers Ministry, 2017).

❑ Many Hispanics deal with fear of deportation and undocumented status. This can make them more reluctant to become involved with agencies (e.g., schools, hospitals, clinics) that can help and support them. In the U.S., the antipathy toward undocumented immigrants along with racial profiling and the dramatic increase in border vigilance by the U.S. Border Patrol has exacerbated tension for many Hispanic residents.

❑ Even highly educated Hispanics report experiencing demoralizing situations in which their academic credentials are questioned or their qualifications are assumed to be less than they truly are.

Profile

Zenon Castillo, a Mexican speaker of Spanish, is an experienced public school psychologist with a Master's degree who just moved to a new school to work. He gave me permission to share the following from his latest Facebook status update:

Being at a new school is funny. I need a sign that says, yes I'm supposed to be here, no I will not hurt or kidnap the kids, no I will not steal your purse or flat out mug you, no I'm not hitting on you, I'm just introducing myself and observing that kid. No, I'm not the custodian. Oh! and no I will not jack your car. Have a great day!

❑ Despite numerous social and economic disadvantages, many Hispanics have benefited from improved educational opportunities, a strong work ethic, strong families, high labor force participation, and low reliance on welfare.

❑ Many Hispanics are Catholic. The church often plays an important role in their lives. Participating in church gives many Hispanics a sense of belonging to a community. It often offers them a sense of direction in their lives, and helps guide them in raising and educating their children successfully.

❑ Hispanics are becoming more prominent on the U.S. landscape today, especially in politics and entertainment. For example, Jennifer Lopez has become a cultural icon within the Hispanic community. Sonia Sotomayor's appointment by President Obama as a justice to the Supreme Court and Xavier Becerra's appointment as California's attorney general show that Hispanics are becoming increasingly more prominent in our government and legal system.

HISPANIC FAMILY LIFE

❑ Familialism is an important cultural value within the Hispanic community. Individuals tend to have a strong identification with and attachment to their nuclear and extended families and greatly value solidarity, loyalty, and reciprocity among family members. In the U.S., 46.1% of Hispanics are married (Pew Hispanic Research Center, 2017).

Immigrant Insight   Elizabeth, Spanish-speaking daughter of Mexican immigrants

When we came from Mexico to the U.S., I was four years old and still drank from a bottle. I spoke no English; when my mom dropped me off on the first day of kindergarten, I was terrified and crying because I didn't want to be separated from her. There were around 12 people living in my house growing up—uncles, their wives and children, my grandma, and my siblings and parents. My mom got pregnant with me when she was 15; I was born when she was 16. My dad has the last say in our home, and makes all the big decisions. I am educating myself for the sake of my family, and am the first person in my family to attend college.

❏ In some families, bearing children is viewed as the purpose of marriage. Children may be expected shortly after marriage. Large and extended families are common. Divorce is relatively uncommon due, in part, to the influence of Catholicism (Zuniga, 2011).

❏ In many families, the man is the authority figure and breadwinner and the woman cares for the family. However, these roles can vary if a woman needs to work outside the home. *Familismo* is important for most Hispanic mothers, who are the family's primary caretakers and nurturers.

❏ Many Hispanic children are taught to listen, obey, and not challenge authority. In some families, girls have restricted freedom and are taught that they need to be protected (Sue & Sue, 2016; Zuniga, 2011).

❏ Kayser (2012, p. 111) stated that "Girls have their role within the family. They may assume more responsibility around the house, and may be responsible for younger children. Boys may not have as much responsibility and may not be expected to care for their own needs until much later than what is expected of girls."

❏ Families may travel frequently from the United States to the home country to be with extended family members.

❏ Experiences associated with age are held in high regard, and children are expected to show respect for their elders, regardless of status or formal education. The advice of elderly grandparents, for example, is often solicited and followed because grandparents are integral and important family members.

❏ Parents may be indulgent and permissive with young children, especially infants, and often do not push them towards achievement to the extent that Anglo families do. For example, Hispanic preschool-age children may drink from baby bottles and pre-teens may sit on their mothers' laps. Direct physical closeness is the norm for many Hispanic families (Zuniga, 2011).

Immigrant Insight   Juanita, speaker of Spanish from Mexico, university senior

When I went to school in Mexico, they would shame you in front of your peers for wrong-doing. Many students drop out after sixth grade because after sixth grade, you have to pay for books and tuition—a lot of people can't afford it. My parents were supportive when I was in school, but they did not help me with my homework. We moved to the U.S., but visited Mexico last year. While there, I was assertive and spoke my mind at family gatherings. My relatives viewed me as disrespectful because, as a woman, I should know my place. Even my well-educated uncles expected me to stay in my place. My aunt in Mexico, who has a maid, spends 80% of her day in the kitchen. At meals, the man is always served first because he is the head of the house. The children are served second, and the wife/mom is served last. My dad definitely expected my mom to stay home and take care of the children, even though she worked some outside the home.

Recently (here in California) I moved in with my boyfriend and this has caused a huge uproar with my parents. There is a lot of drama and guilt! My dad threatened to take away my health insurance, saying "You don't respect yourself." My folks are worried about our family's opinion of me, and they are deeply upset that I don't care about what people think of me.

Profile

I worked with Carlos G., who was born to parents who came to Texas as refugees from El Salvador. Carlos was born with the umbilical cord wrapped around his neck, and he suffered from severe fetal anoxia. He experienced hydrocephalus and was eventually diagnosed with severe intellectual disability. Doctors told the parents that Carlos would never walk or talk, much less learn to read or write. His mother sought as many early intervention services for Carlos as possible, and Carlos did learn to walk and talk, albeit very slowly. However, his father did not participate in meetings and didn't carry out the recommendations made by professionals. The mother felt that she carried the entire burden of Carlos' rehabilitation. Eventually, the parents divorced.

As Carlos grew older, he received special education services in school and eventually learned to read and write at a basic level. I had the privilege of serving him and getting to know his mother. She loved Carlos deeply, and would not allow him to participate in field trips or to socialize with other students. She felt that social interactions caused too much stress for him. No effort was made in the home to help Carlos develop independent living skills. He was not taught how to catch a bus, order food in a restaurant, etc. His mother did everything for him, believing that this was the most loving course of action in light of his disabilities.

When Carlos was in tenth grade, he began manifesting symptoms of serious depression and mentioned suicide several times. He told the psychologist, "It would be better for me to die than for all these people to be working so hard for me." At his IEP meeting, 15 people were in attendance, including his mother. The meeting lasted for several hours. The team managed to persuade his mother to allow Carlos more social freedom and to allow school district personnel to teach the "basic life skills" he would need to support himself in a sheltered vocational setting. Because of my friendship with Carlos' mother and our mutually respectful relationship, I was able to talk with her about how her help over the years had prepared Carlos for greater independence. I emphasized that she deserved some time to pursue her own interests, including her relationship with her new boyfriend. We are now Facebook friends, and Carlos is a handsome and successful young man!

❏ In collectivist cultures such as the Hispanic culture, children participate in ongoing events through observation; keen perception is important, and children are expected to actively attend to what is going on around them. Collaborative engagement is important.

❏ Many children are raised to value cooperation within the family unit more than individual achievement. Family members help one another and work as a team to achieve common goals.

HISPANIC EDUCATION AND LITERACY

Immigrant Insight   Alexandra, female, speaker of Spanish from Puerto Rico

I am happy to be living here in the U.S. Health care here in the U.S. is far superior to that in Puerto Rico—there, you can wait days to receive health services in a hospital. One of my greatest challenges in coming to the U.S. was difficulty with English. When I first started going to school in the U.S., I was already written off as "going to fail" because my first language was Spanish. I was told that because I spoke Spanish, I must not be intelligent. Spelling has also been a struggle. I have often felt out of place and like I am not good enough.

❏ According to the Pew Hispanic Research Center (2017), 61.7% of Hispanics attained a level of education that did not extend beyond graduation from high school; 23.9% had a two-year college degree/some college, while 14.4% had a Bachelor's degree or a graduate degree.

❏ Teachers tend to be held in high regard. Educational professionals are viewed with great respect.

❏ Education is very important to families and is often viewed as the route to upward mobility. However, in many Mexican towns, education is only required up through sixth grade. Many parents are illiterate and are not able to help their children with homework.

❏ More than 70% of all migrant farm workers in the U.S. speak Spanish; they move frequently due to the nature of their jobs. If the family moves frequently, educational opportunities for the children may be sporadic and limited. These children often have gaps in content knowledge. Thirty two percent of migrant workers have less than a ninth grade education as compared to 3% of the American workforce as a whole (USDA Economic Research Service, 2012).

❏ Jackson, Schatschneider, and Leacox (2014) studied the growth of vocabulary skills in young Spanish-English children in migrant families. They stated that 50% of Latino fourth graders in the U.S. score at or below basic level in reading achievement, and that 75% of migrant Mexican mothers have less than a high school education.

❏ Mexican migrant children have fewer books in the home than other groups of children from Mexican backgrounds (Jackson et al., 2014).

❏ Wood, Diehm, & Callender (2016) compared Language Environment Analysis (LENA) data obtained from preschool-age Spanish-English bilingual children with that obtained from typically developing monolingual English-speaking peers. They discovered that the average number of conversational turns per hour was significantly lower in the homes of the Spanish-English bilingual children than in the homes of their English-speaking peers.

❑ Hispanic children are often sensitive to nonverbal indicators of feelings (i.e, field sensitive cognitive style) and learn best when interacting in situations where they experience warmth, responsiveness, and frequent attention. They often respond well to physical touch and affection.

❑ Women are expected to marry and bear children and may receive little encouragement to finish school or to pursue a career. Hispanic female university students have shared with me that relatives disapproved of their efforts to get a college degree.

❑ Students who immigrate to the United States may vary considerably in their school experiences and literacy skills. Many Hispanics in the United States have not had educational opportunities commensurate with those of Anglo Americans, and the academic underachievement of Hispanic students is a prominent national concern, especially as it relates to low literacy skills (Davison & Brea-Spahn, 2011; Iglesias & Rojas, 2012).

❑ Hispanic children with limited English skills often live in poverty. Their parents may have had limited schooling.

❑ The National Assessment of Educational Progress (NAEP, 2011) showed that 82% of Hispanic fourth-graders read below proficient level, with nearly 50% reading below basic level. This is a great concern, as reading is a fundamental necessity for success in today's society. Those with low reading skills face a host of problems into adulthood, and low literacy rates have been associated with higher rates of later incarceration.

❑ According to the One World Literacy Foundation (2017), two out of three students who cannot read proficiently by the end of fourth grade will end up in jail or on welfare. It is predicted that if a child is not reading proficiently in the fourth grade, he or she will have approximately a 78% chance of not catching up.

❑ Dropping out of school is common among Hispanic adolescents. The high drop-out rate of Hispanic students is a major national concern. Based on current statistics, it is estimated that 42% of Hispanic students will not graduate from high school on time (American Psychological Association, 2012).

❑ High school dropouts are 63 times more likely to be incarcerated than people with Bachelor's degrees or higher. One in six Hispanic boys will be incarcerated at least once in his lifetime (American Psychological Association, 2012).

❑ Possible reasons for the less-than-optimal educational attainment of Hispanics in the U.S. include: (1) culture shock and the differences between home and school expectations; (2) sporadic school attendance due to high family mobility; (3) poverty; and (4) fluctuating funding for programs designed to assist students learning English as a second language.

❑ Hispanic families often lack the social capital to help their children succeed. They do not know how school bureaucracies operate and do not have easy access to key people in decision-making positions (e.g., principals). In addition, Hispanic children are likely to attend underfunded, overcrowded schools with teachers who are inadequately trained to meet their needs.

❑ Hispanic students may be under-represented in gifted programs in schools because of cultural and/or linguistic bias in the assessment procedures used to determine giftedness.

Profile

Shawna, university senior, and tutor for students from Mexico

In my experience teaching English as a second language, Hispanic parents are extremely supportive of their children's education. But it is hard for them to complete homework; I have had adults bring me their children's first or second grade homework pages because they could not understand the language or format of the worksheets. I would have Mexican students disappear to Mexico for extended winter vacations. They would often go across the border on most weekends to shop, visit relatives, and for other activities. Many students also returned to Mexico during the summer and spent the entire summer with relatives there. While I am glad the children are getting great experiences and socialization in Mexico, they are not around on the weekends for classmates' birthday parties, and they aren't playing organized sports. Coming back to English schools is a big adjustment after spending the entire summer in Mexico; it can be tough for these kids to have such a split lifestyle.

Immigrant Insight

Sebastian S., university senior, speaker of Spanish, son of immigrants from Mexico

My dad came to the U.S. illegally from Mexico at 15 years of age. He had a second grade education, and became a gardener/landscaper. My grandpa told my mom after she completed 6th grade "You have to work—no more school." My mom worked two jobs; she was a factory worker during the day and a custodian at night. I was a latchkey kid who made dinner for my siblings. My parents couldn't help me with my homework, but they supported my education. The first time I saw a dentist, I was 12 years old. We would rather have the whole family eat than have one person get braces. Many Mexican immigrants speak an indigenous dialect, not Spanish. Mexicans often make fun of these indigenous people and put them down. Many Mexican immigrants are from rural areas and live in houses made of adobe and straw. There are very minimal services. One way speech-language pathologists can help these families is to make them aware of services that are available here in the U.S.

CULTURAL CUSTOMS, COURTESIES, AND BELIEFS

❏ **Allocentrism** (collectivism) is a fundamental Hispanic value that emphasizes the objectives and needs of an in-group rather than emphasizing competition and individualism.

❏ Families strive to be friendly, to welcome guests to their homes, and to offer refreshments.

❏ Many Hispanics have a flexible attitude about time and the importance of maintaining schedules. Thus, appointments are often not kept with the precision expected by school professionals. Hispanics tend to place greater value on interpersonal relations than on factors related to time.

❏ In traditional Hispanic culture, men are expected to be the dominant, strong, family providers (machismo). Women are expected to be self-sacrificing, nurturing, and submissive to men (marianismo). However, the degree to which these expectations are realized depends upon many variables such as age, level of acculturation, and whether or not women work outside the home (Sue & Sue, 2016).

❏ Girls are often encouraged to be modest and feminine. The sexual behaviors of adolescent females may be restricted, whereas male adolescents are afforded greater freedom (Sue & Sue, 2016; Zuniga, 2011).

❏ A strong Hispanic value is **personalismo**, or an emphasis on interpersonal relationships. Behaviors that convey *personalismo* include loyalty, honesty, generosity, hospitality, and willingness to help others.

❏ From the perspective of **personalismo**, many Hispanics will not engage in confrontations with others. They might say what they think the person wants to hear rather than being the bearers of bad news; they also might give ambiguous responses to avoid upsetting others.

❏ **Dignidad** (dignity) is important to Hispanics, who strive to present themselves with dignity, especially in public. *Dignidad* entails having a sense of pride and self-respect, which are often demonstrated through hard work and responsibility. It is shameful and humiliating to have one's dignity violated by another person.

❏ **Una persona bien educado** is one who has been taught skills in human relationships and who understands the necessity of treating each person with respect and dignity.

HEALTH CARE AND DISABLING CONDITIONS

❏ Although many residents of the U.S. are Hispanic, the quality of health care has not kept pace with population growth. In 2011, Hispanics were more likely to reside in counties that did not meet the ozone standard than non-Hispanic Whites (Center for Disease Prevention and Control, 2013).

❏ Many Hispanic families have limited access to health care. Lack of health insurance is especially acute, with 23.7% of Hispanics being uninsured (Pew Research Center, 2017).

❏ Unfortunately, exposure to pesticides in migrant Hispanic families puts both children and adults at risk for a host of health problems such as congenital birth defects, Parkinson's disease, asthma, and others.

Immigrant Insight   Ximena, American teacher of English and bilingual speaker
                             of Kichwa, Ecuador

Here in my indigenous community in the jungle of Ecuador, kids often don't have shoes to wear to school; they eat very little, and work very hard on their land. But they are happy! I live with a family of 10 children, and the father of the household recently showed me a black and yellow bird that had fallen out of its nest. It sang a long, shrill chatter and he explained to me that when a child isn't speaking, they will cut the tongue from that bird, who sings a lot, and feed it to the child to encourage speech.

❑ Among Hispanic children, there are several variables that have a major impact on health, growth, and development. Lead is often present in low-income housing areas. Many children are exposed to second-hand smoke. There may be high mobility, inadequate living space, and poor sanitary conditions. There are often environmental pollutants that impact these children. If their parents are migrant agricultural workers, they are at risk for pesticide exposure.

Profile

Sandra R., university senior

When I was growing up as the daughter of Mexican agricultural migrant workers here in California, we lived right by the fields. I remember my mom saying, "Shut the windows because the helicopters are spraying pesticides—stay inside!" My dad picked lettuce and strawberries. My mom had multiple miscarriages due to pesticide exposure from the fields. My parents would pull me out of school—sometimes for weeks at a time—to go back to Mexico. Migrant school helped me make up for some of what I had missed when we came back to the U.S.

❑ Families may believe in "curanderismo," a healing process believed to occur when folk medicine practices are used. Often these practices are more prevalent in groups with less access to modern health care (e.g., individuals who live in rural areas).

❑ Among some Hispanics, there may be resistance to institutionalization. Rather, individuals with illnesses or disabilities are likely to be cared for within the family.

❑ Families differ in their reactions to disabilities. In some families, a visible disability (e.g., cleft palate, cerebral palsy) is often attributed to an external, non-medical cause such as witchcraft. Some parents believe that a child's disabilities are punishment for their own wrongdoing (Zuniga, 2011). Many Catholic parents accept disabilities stoically, as part of a larger divine plan that is not comprehensible to humans.

❑ Families may have more difficulty accepting invisible disabling conditions such as learning disabilities or reading disorders than visible disabling conditions such as cleft palate.

❑ Families that greatly prize vitality and health may hide children with disabilities, limiting their opportunities for treatment. At the same time, family and friends may indulge these children, often not expecting them to participate actively in their own treatment and care.

❑ The roles of health agencies may cause confusion for family members. Families may prefer small clinics to large medical centers.

Tech Tie-In

Invisible America: The Migrant Story.

This touching video portrays the realities lived daily by children and their worker parents in America's migrant camps.
https://www.youtube.com/watch?v=l5QFm0qeAlk

❏ Some families turn to spiritualists to seek healing and dispel evil spirits. They may also seek out healers who are available in Mexican border towns (Zuniga, 2011).

Profile

I worked with Juan J., an attractive, courteous 10-year-old Hispanic fourth grader, who was referred for assessment by his classroom teacher because he was struggling academically. Psychoeducational testing in both Spanish and English revealed that Juan had a learning disability. At the IEP meeting, his mother was informed that special education services appeared to be necessary. She responded by saying, "Juan is just lazy—I know he can do the work. Look at him—he's a normal boy."

The team informed the mother that children with learning disabilities do not necessarily look different from classmates who do not have disabilities. Mrs. J. was visibly dubious about the conclusion made by the assessment team but signed the IEP and agreed to special education services for her son.

HISPANIC COMMUNICATION STYLES

❏ Many Hispanics utilize the social script of *simpatica*, which emphasizes positive personal interactions that convey empathy for others, emphasize harmony in interpersonal relations, and de-emphasize negative behaviors in circumstances of conflict. It is considered important to initiate conversations on a personal note before proceeding with business.

❏ Standing close and touching during conversations is acceptable. Hispanics tend to stand closer during conversation than Anglos and other groups. Some Hispanics feel insulted when someone steps away from them during conversation.

❏ Due to differences in cultural norms for physical distance or space (proxemics), some Hispanics view Anglos as being uninterested, aloof, or cold. In contrast, Anglos may view Hispanics as being too pushy or getting too close.

❏ Hispanic children may look away or lower their heads when talking to adults because avoiding eye contact is considered a sign of respect and deference; furthermore, sustained eye contact may be seen as a challenge to authority.

Immigrant Insight   Alfonso, male speaker of Spanish, Nicaragua

Americans are very direct in conversation. They lay out the facts in black and white. When I speak to my family in Nicaragua this way and am very direct, they don't like it. Nicaraguans become easily offended if you address issues in a forward or direct manner, so when I speak to them, I have to remember to say things very nicely and "speak to them with flowers."

❏ When Hispanic children converse with adults, they may show a reluctance to provide more information than is requested. Extending topics in this manner may be viewed as disrespectful to the listener.

❏ Children often learn through observation and hands-on participation rather than through verbal interactions with adults.

❏ In traditional families, when adults are talking, children are not to interrupt. They are not expected to participate in adult conversations, and they show respect for adults by considering themselves as "non-equals" during interactions. Parent-child conversation is not usually collaborative; rather, it tends to be directive.

❏ Children interact verbally more often with siblings or peers than with adults. Peers are considered equal partners in conversation.

❏ In many Hispanic homes, parents do not verbalize about ongoing events such as things that they are doing at the moment.

❏ Often, adults do not ask children to voice their preferences or to give their personal evaluations of situations. Adults usually do not ask children to foretell what they will do or to repeat facts.

❏ Many Mexican mothers regard themselves as "mothers" rather than "teachers" (García, Mendez Pérez, & Ortiz, 2000; Madding, 2000). My students and I have worked directly with Hispanic families in our community to promote literacy practices in the home. Anecdotally, we have noticed that parents are very enthusiastic about learning and applying information to help increase their children's oral and written language skills. The families usually express their gratitude for the information we provide, and are quick to apply it so that their children can have increased educational opportunities.

SPANISH LANGUAGE CHARACTERISTICS AND CONSIDERATIONS

Numerous dialects/varieties of Spanish are spoken in the United States (Gleason & Ratner, 2017). The two major Spanish dialect varieties in the U.S. are the Caribbean (e.g., Cuban and Puerto Rican) and southwestern (Mexican/Mexican American) dialects. However, many other dialects exist, and it is imperative to remember that the diversity among Spanish speakers is great. Some immigrants from Mexico speak Indian languages such as Zapotec (Lopez, 2012). Although Spanish is spoken in Spain and most of Central and South America, there are variations from country to country that are reflected in pragmatics, syntax, morphology, and phonology.

Individuals who speak Spanish have been exposed to a sound system that differs in many respects from the sound system of English.

❏ Although Spanish and English have many sounds in common, few of the consonants are produced in exactly the same way in the two languages. The bilingual stops /p/, /t/, and /k/ for example, are aspirated in word-initial position of English words, but this aspiration does not occur in Spanish. The Spanish /t/ and /d/ are dental sounds, produced by placing the tongue against the back of the upper front teeth. The English /t/ and /d/, however, are alveolar sounds, formed by placing the tongue on the ridge above the teeth.

❏ Phonemes are distributed differently in English and Spanish. Most English consonants, for example, can occur in the initial, medial, and final positions of words. In Spanish, however, /n/, /l/, /r/, /s/ and /d/ are the only consonant that can occur at the end of words. Because of this difference, individuals from Spanish language backgrounds frequently demonstrate difficulties producing consonants at the end of English words (e.g., deletion of word-final /t/).

❏ There are many dialectal variations in speech sound production among Spanish speakers in the United States and throughout the world. The replacement of /r/ by /l/ and the omission of word-final /s/, for example, are common in the speech of individuals from Puerto Rico and other areas of the Caribbean. These differences should not be viewed as evidence of a disorder.

❏ When assessing children in Spanish, professionals need to be familiar with the assimilation processes that affect speech sound production. Surrounding phonemes within a word or phrase influence how a particular sound is produced. In the phrase *los dientes,* for example, the /s/ at the end of *los* may become voiced because it precedes the voiced consonant /d/ in the word *dientes.* Assimilation frequently occurs across word boundaries in Spanish.

❏ The deletion of syllables from words is not necessarily the indicator of a disorder. Spanish speakers, for example, may say 'mijo' rather than "mi hijo" because consecutive identical vowels are typically produced as a single vowel.

Contact between cultures, economic variables, technology, and various other factors are influencing the Spanish language as it is used in the U.S. and around the world. Some words commonly used by Spanish-speaking populations in the U.S. have been "borrowed" from English. Words such as *rufo* (roof), *marqueta* (market), and *trábol* (trouble) are examples of words used by some Spanish speakers that would not be recognized as "good Spanish" by many Spanish speakers living outside of the United States. Many third-generation U.S.-born Hispanics do not speak Spanish at all.

Professionals must consider the individual student's background when evaluating language performance. The accent commonly heard among students learning English as a second language is to be expected and should not be viewed as evidence of a speech sound disorder. Rather, this can be viewed as transfer from Spanish. It is important for professionals who work with Spanish-speaking students to understand the speech and language differences commonly observed when these students learn English.

Information about speech and language differences commonly observed when Spanish speakers use English is presented in Table 5.1 and Table 5.2. Additional information about Spanish articulation and language differences, dialectal differences in Spanish vocabulary, idiomatic uses of language, and other factors that affect language production in English have been described by various authors (Gleason & Ratner, 2017; Brice, Gorman, & Leung, 2013; Goldstein & Guildersleeve-Neumann, 2012; Mattes & Saldaña Illingworth, 2009).

Profile

Rosa S., an 8-year-old girl from a migrant Mexican family, was being tested by the psychologist at the elementary school where I work. He noticed that she seemed to be unusually quiet, and he tried unsuccessfully for 15 minutes to encourage her to speak to him. Finally he asked her if anything was wrong. She responded by telling him that a snake had been found in her house and that snakes in the home are viewed in Mexico as a sign of bad luck. The psychologist sympathized with Rosa and said that luckily, in California, finding a snake was considered to be good luck. After several minutes of conversation about California's "good luck snakes," Rosa brightened considerably and was much more verbal in the testing situation.

Table 5.1

**Language Differences Commonly Observed
Among Spanish Speakers**

Language Characteristics	Sample English Utterances
1. Adjective comes after noun.	The house green is big.
2. "s" is often omitted in plurals, possessives, and regular third person present tense.	We have five plate here. The girl book is brown. The baby cry.
3. Past tense -ed is often omitted.	We walk yesterday.
4. Double negatives are used.	I don't have no more.
5. Negative imperatives may be used; no is used instead of don't.	No touch the hot stove.
6. "No" may be used before a verb to signify negation.	The kid no cross the street.
7. Superiority is demonstrated by using more before an adjective in a similar manner to the use of mas in Spanish.	This cake is more big.
8. The adverb often follows the verb.	He drives very fast his motorcycle.
9. Postnoun modifiers are used.	This is the book of my sister.
10. Articles may be used with body parts.	I bruised the knee.
11. "Have" may be used in place of the copula when talking about age.	I have 12 years. (Instead of I am 12 years old.)
12. Articles are often omitted.	Papa is going to store.
13. When the subject has been identified in the previous sentence, it may be omitted in the next sentence.	Mama is sad. Lost her purse.
14. There may not be noun-verb inversion in questions.	What this is? (instead of What is this?)

Table 5.2

Articulation Differences Commonly Observed Among Spanish Speakers

Articulation Characteristics	Sample English Patterns
1. /t, d, n/ may be dentalized (tip of tongue is placed against the back of the upper central incisors).	
2. Final consonants are often devoiced.	dose/doze
3. b/v substitution	berry/very
4. Deaspirated stops (sounds like speaker is omitting the sound because it is said with little air release).	
5. ch/sh substitution	chew/shoe
6. d/voiced th, or z/voiced th (voiced "th" does not exist as a distinct phoneme in Spanish).	dis/this, zat/that
7. t/voiceless th (voiceless "th" does not exist as a distinct phoneme in Spanish).	tink/think
8. Schwa sound is inserted before word initial consonant clusters.	eskate/skate espend/spend
9. In *Spanish* words can end in 10 different sounds: a, e, i, o, u, l, r, n, s, d	may omit other sounds at the ends of words
10. When words start with /h/, the /h/ is silent.	old/hold, it/hit
11. /r/ is tapped or trilled (tap /r/ might sound like the tap in the English word "butter").	
12. There is no /j/ (e.g., judge) sound in Spanish; speakers may substitute "y."	Yulie/Julie yoke/joke
13. Spanish /s/ is produced more frontally than English /s/.	Some speakers may sound like they have frontal lisps.

Spanish has 5 vowels: a, e, i, o, u (ah, eh, ee, long o, oo) and few diphthongs. Thus, Spanish speakers may produce the following vowel substitutions:

14. ee/ih substitution	peeg/pig, leetle/little
15. eh/ae, ah/ae substitutions	pet/pat, Stahn/Stan

IMPLICATIONS FOR PROFESSIONALS

❑ Professionals may need to include the entire family in meetings or procedures relating to an individual student and should encourage active family participation.

❑ Professionals should use formal titles to show respect when interacting with Hispanic adults. Adults should be addressed with the formal *you* (*Usted*) rather than the less formal *you* (*tu*). It is acceptable to use *tu* with children.

❑ Professionals should attempt to communicate with both parents in meetings. However, it is important to understand that in many families, the father is the spokesperson and the primary decision maker.

❑ Professionals will more readily gain the trust of family members if they have a humanistic orientation during meetings rather than a task orientation. Informal, friendly chatting can set the stage for work to be done. Discussing business immediately or appearing hurried may be considered rude. For this reason, professionals may need to set aside extra time for the meeting to accommodate Hispanic families.

❑ Relationships are very important to Hispanic families; they may care more about the professional's personal qualities (e.g., approachability, respect for the family) than about the professional's technical qualifications.

❑ Some Hispanic families may be uncomfortable collaborating with professionals because these families do not see parent participation as necessary. Out of respect for the professionals' expertise, they may prefer to leave decisions to school personnel. Thus, professionals should make sure that families truly understand their role in assessment and treatment plans. Family participation should always be strongly encouraged.

❑ Professionals should be aware that families may have difficulty coming to school for meetings because they work in jobs that do not allow time off. Some parents work multiple jobs.

Profile

Elisa P., university senior

My parents came to the U.S. from Mexico. My mom has a second grade education, and my dad has a sixth grade education. They worked in the fields picking lettuce and strawberries. There were nine people living in my home. My mother was not able to help me with my homework. She worked in the fields and got off work at 7 o'clock in the evening, so she couldn't go to school conferences. It was very hot, hard work. Field workers have to work even when it's raining—except if it is raining very hard—and there are many injuries from workers slipping in the mud. My mom got up between 3 o'clock and 5 o'clock in the morning and would get home at 7 P.M. and need to care for the family. I have worked in the fields in 100 plus degree weather just to help my mom. We wear scarves over our noses and mouths so we won't breathe in as many pesticides; this also helps prevent sunburn. My dad no longer works in the fields; he manages a restaurant now. He told my siblings and me "Go to school, or work in the fields for 25 years." I am the first in my family to attend college.

❑ As a sign of respect, parents often do not openly disagree with professionals or question statements made during meetings. They, however, may not follow suggestions that they consider to be inappropriate. Professionals may need to confer with parents to identify specific concerns that they have.

❏ Professionals should define terms such as "language impairment" and "learning disability" to ensure that parents understand their meanings. Otherwise, the parents may think professionals are talking about intellectual disability or mental illness. As one Colombian immigrant told me, "In my country, children are normal, lazy, crazy, or retarded."

❏ Families may appear passive about accepting treatment for a child's condition if they believe that the condition is the result of external forces, as discussed previously. Professionals must work within the framework of the family's culture to foster confidence and trust.

❏ Professionals should openly state their expectations and explain the importance of maintaining schedules. Otherwise, families may be late for or miss appointments because they have a different perspective about time and/or lack of understanding about the importance of schedules. As a clinician, I try to emphasize the fact that I want the family to have the full meeting time that they deserve. If they are late, they will not receive all the meeting time that they deserve.

❏ Professionals need to remember that there may be child-rearing norms among some Hispanic families that do not fit the Anglo American mainstream time line for developmental milestones. For example, some Puerto Rican children are not weaned off the bottle until three years of age, and some Mexican American preschool-age children still use pacifiers or bottles. These children should not be labeled "immature" or "delayed."

❏ Because of the relaxed attitude toward child rearing, some parents may be resistant to the concept of early intervention, believing that children will eventually "catch up" to their peers. Professionals should explain that early intervention often results in improved performance in elementary school and beyond.

❏ Because of the primary importance of the family, children may be kept home from school to tend to sick family members, help meet the family's financial needs, attend a family function, etc. Professionals must help these families to understand U.S. laws about school attendance and the high value that is placed on attendance in American schools.

❏ If families are grieving about a child's disability, they may find comfort at a local church. Professionals should consider presenting this option when appropriate.

❏ Professionals may need to assist families so that they can be assertive in obtaining needed services (e.g., educational, medical).

❏ Be mindful of the child's and family's privacy when choosing other family members or friends to act as interpreters. Families may not share needed information if they are worried about confidentiality.

❏ Professionals should be willing to accept offers of gifts, food, or drink because some Hispanic families may be insulted if these offers are refused.

❏ Professionals should not try to move away if clients choose to sit or stand close to them.

❏ As with any cultural group, gathering detailed background information is critical, especially regarding patterns of language use at home (Riquelme & Rosas, 2014).

❏ Standardized tests often require children to name pictures; however, many Spanish-speaking children will provide functions for objects rather than names. Clinicians may need to rephrase questions or present prompts to elicit appropriate responses.

❑ Because some Hispanic children feel that it is rude to extend a topic when talking to an adult, professionals need to be careful that they do not judge these children as having limited expressive language skills. Many standardized tests have tasks that require verbal elaboration (e.g., "Tell me all you can about a horse.") These types of tasks may be biased against Hispanic children who consider this type of verbal elaboration to be rude.

❑ Professionals need to be extremely careful when using standardized tests with Hispanic children because of the bias inherent in these measures. Dialectal variations and individual differences in the amount of exposure that children have had to English and Spanish make it difficult to make educational decisions based on test norms.

❑ There are new tests and measures created specifically for Spanish-speaking children. For example, a text dedicated to the topic of assessment of Spanish-English bilingual preschoolers describes 37 specific assessments for this population to effectively differentiate a language difference from a language impairment (Barrueco, Lopez, Ong, & Lozano, 2012).

❑ When assessing Spanish-speaking children for the possible presence of a language impairment, an important preliminary first step is to determine proficiency in English as well as Spanish. The Spanish-English Language Proficiency Scale (SELPS) has been used successfully for this purpose. (Smyk, Restrepo, Gorin, & Gray, 2013).

❑ The SELPS can be helpful in determining English proficiency for sequential bilingual children between 4 and 8 years of age. It is not intended to diagnose language impairment, but can be used as a screening tool of English language skills to determine whether a child has sufficient skills to be further tested in English (Smyk et al., 2013).

❑ The Bilingual Communication Assessment Resource (BCAR), created by Mattes and Saldaña-Illingworth (2009), includes a variety of practical, easy-to-implement, informal Spanish language assessment tasks, protocols, questionnaires and other resources that can be adapted quite easily for use with different Spanish dialects. Specific guidelines are described for implementing assessment strategies based on an analysis of the student's language usage history, and family background.

❑ The Bilingual English Spanish Assessment (BESA) provides reliable assessment of language development in Spanish-English bilingual children ages 4:0-6:11. It was designed for bilingual clients and normed on a national sample that included 16 dialects. The goal of the BESA is to help speech-language pathologists differentiate language impairment from limited English exposure in young Spanish-speaking children (Peña, Gutiérrez-Clellen, Iglesias, Goldstein, & Bedore, 2014).

❑ Professionals must also remember that many Hispanic students have stronger vocabulary skills in English in some areas and stronger vocabulary skills in Spanish in other areas. The students, for example, may know school vocabulary in English and home vocabulary in Spanish. Professionals can dual-score vocabulary tests, using both Spanish and English responses to achieve a total score for the test (conceptual scoring).

❑ Some Hispanic children may not perform well on tasks that require repeating facts or foretelling what they will do in the future. They may have little experience with these activities in the home.

❑ In addition, Hispanic children may remain silent when interacting with unfamiliar adult professionals who are attempting to assess and/or treat them. It is important not to misinterpret the children's silence as being indicative of a language impairment.

❑ Experts recommend the use of information from parent interviews and language samples when assessing Spanish-speaking children for possible communication disorders. These methods continue to be widely viewed as the "gold standard" when attempting to distinguish communication differences from impairments in Spanish-speaking children, especially because research shows that parent reports about their children's language abilities are accurate and helpful (Ebert, 2016; Fiestas, 2017; Guiberson, Rodriguez, & Dale, 2011; Jacobsen & Walden, 2013; Mancilla-Martinez et al., 2016).

❑ When conducting parent interviews to ascertain the language skills of young children, professionals may consider utilizing the Fundación MacArthur Inventario del Desarrollo de Habilidades Comunicativas: Palabras Enunciadoes (IDHC: PE; Jackson-Maldonado, Bates, & Thal, 1992). Research shows that this measure continues to be valid and reliable for use with Spanish-speaking children and families (Jackson-Maldonado, Marchman, & Fernald, 2013).

❑ Other measures that are shown to be effective and valid in the assessment of Spanish-speaking children are the Spanish Ages and Stages Questionnaire:3 (ASQ:3; Squires & Bricker, 2009) and the Spanish Preschool Language Scale:4 (SPLS:4; Zimmerman, Steiner, & Pond, 2002) (Guiberson et al., 2011).

❑ Ebert (2016) cautioned that when conducting parent interviews, professionals should be aware that developmental questions related to parent-child interaction may conflict with European-American cultural values. For example, because many Hispanic parents do not engage in child-directed play, questions about this might be culturally incongruent for them.

❑ Ebert (2016) also stated that when professionals gather case histories from Hispanic parents, it is best to be specific. For example, rather than saying "Does anyone in your family have a speech-language problem?" it is better to say "Does an aunt, uncle, parent, sibling, or grandparent have any problems with speaking, listening, reading, or writing?" Specific questions will elicit more accurate answers.

❑ When distinguishing between language difference and impairment in Spanish-speaking children, grammaticality measures have been shown to be useful. Frequent difficulty with specific structures has been shown to be an indicator of a possible language impairment. For example, difficulty acquiring participles and structures that are linked to the verb system is a hallmark of language impairment in Spanish-speaking students. Students with disorders often omit clitics. When referring to combing hair, for example, the child may omit *me* from the phrase *me peino* (*I comb myself*) (Jackson-Maldonado, 2012).

❑ Spanish-speaking children with language impairment also have significant difficulties with article production in spontaneous speech and on elicited tasks. For example, a child may use a feminine article with a masculine noun (*la niño* instead of *el niño*) or omit articles entirely (Jacobsen & Walden, 2013; Restrepo & Gutiérrez-Clellen, 2012).

❑ When testing Spanish-speaking children for the possible presence of a language impairment, it is useful to employ conceptual scoring, by giving credit for responses in either language.

❑ Gross, Buac, and Kaushanskaya (2014) administered standardized vocabulary measures in English and Spanish to Spanish-English speaking children between 5 and 7 years of age. The researchers discovered that when conceptual scoring was used, fewer children achieved vocabulary scores that fell below the average range. They concluded that conceptual scoring reduces the likelihood that typically-developing bilingual children will be identified as having vocabulary deficits.

❏ Evaluating children's language skills through language sampling has been empirically shown to be valid for Spanish-speaking children (Washington & Iglesias, 2015).

❏ In a recent study, Guiberson (2016) found that assessing young Spanish-speaking children's language during play activities can be an especially valid and reliable way to evaluate language skills. In this study, parent-facilitated semi-structured play activities were shown to be a useful way to gain information about children's communication development.

❏ Parents may believe that an all-English program is superior to bilingual programs that enhance Spanish skills. It is therefore important to emphasize to parents that initial literacy instruction in Spanish often enhances future academic success.

❏ Unfortunately, many Hispanic students are placed into all-English classrooms with no support in Spanish; this can be detrimental to their learning and progress. Language loss in Spanish is a major issue for these students, especially as they get older. Students who have limited opportunities for continued use of Spanish are likely to become less proficient in the language over time.

❏ Professionals should do as much as they can to promote bilingual education opportunities for Hispanic students. Ideally, Hispanic students, especially those with language impairment, should receive bilingual instruction that maintains and promotes their Spanish skills while helping them learn English. Bilingual Spanish-English preschool experience is especially helpful.

❏ Mendez, Crais, Castro, and Kainz (2015) examined the effectiveness of teaching vocabulary to low-SES preschool Spanish-English children in two conditions: monolingual (English) and bilingual (English and Spanish). The group that was taught vocabulary in both Spanish and English showed far greater gains in Spanish and English vocabulary than the group that was taught in English only.

❏ Spanish-speaking children with language impairment generally benefit from a bilingual approach to intervention in which support is available in both Spanish and English (Gutiérrez-Clellen, Simon-Cereijido, & Sweet, 2012; Kohnert, 2013; Kohnert & Derr, 2012; Mancilla-Martinez et al., 2016). It is not optimal to provide intervention only in English. Activities that support the development of Spanish vocabulary and phonological awareness facilitate growth in both Spanish and English.

❏ Parents should be encouraged to speak the language in which they feel most comfortable. When interacting with students at home, parents who speak English with limited fluency should continue to use Spanish. Building children's Spanish skills in the home has many cognitive, linguistic, and social benefits.

❏ It is better for children to hear fluent Spanish than "broken" English. Interacting in Spanish in the home reduces the likelihood of language loss and consequent negative cognitive and linguistic effects.

❏ Vocabulary, Oral Language, and Academic Readiness (VOLAR), a program presented in Gutiérrez-Clellen, Simon-Cereijido, and Restrepo (2013), includes vocabulary and oral language intervention activities for bilingual Latino preschoolers. This program can be used by both bilingual and monolingual speech-language pathologists working in collaboration with bilingual teachers or assistants. The manual includes lessons that correspond to preschool-level books that are commercially available in both Spanish and English. Lessons are presented in both languages. Parents can present activities from VOLAR at home to promote their children's Spanish and English development.

❏ Because migrant Hispanic children tend to have few books in the home and are read to less frequently than other groups (Jackson et al., 2014), it is important for professionals to help these families gain access to reading materials. Professionals should make efforts to collect books that can be given to these families in addition to encouraging use of the public library. (Roseberry-McKibbin, 2018).

❏ In addition, professionals should suggest language development activities for the home that are concrete and relevant to the interests and communication needs of children. By providing information to parents on a CD or DVD, they will be able to review the suggested strategies at home. Appropriate YouTube videos may also be beneficial (Roseberry-McKibbin, 2013, 2014).

❏ Parents should be encouraged to engage children in songs, rhymes, riddles, oral history, proverbs, and folklore in Spanish. Wood et al. (2016) stressed that professionals should find innovative approaches to helping parents minimize gaps (in early language development) between Spanish-speaking preschoolers and their monolingual English-speaking peers. Short videos of therapy activities, for example, can be used to show parents how to teach specific language skills to their children at home (Palafox, 2017).

❏ Bitetti and Hammer (2016) found that positive benefits were observed even if Hispanic parents engage in reading activities with their children only once a week. In addition to encouraging home reading activities, Bitetti and Hammer recommended that parents engage their children in story-telling interactions to promote narrative development.

❏ Because many parents now have devices such as iPhones, they can purchase inexpensive book apps to read and discuss with their children. For example, *Miss Spider's Tea Party* in Spanish is a charming, inexpensive app that can be used again and again by parents and children.

❏ Professionals must bear in mind that families may leave the U.S. for a month at a time or more to celebrate important family events and holidays. If families are of migrant status, they will also be highly mobile. "If your client is part of the migrant program, you will see them in August, not September, you'll see them in October, but not November and December" (personal communication, D. Gutierrez, 2/18/13).

❏ In therapy, Hispanic students may respond better to cooperative, group learning activities than to individualistic, competitive learning activities. Many perform best in cooperative learning situations in which they experience warmth and enthusiasm.

❏ It is recommended that students eight years and older participate in cognate instruction. For example, a geometry teacher can point out pronunciation and spelling similarities in curriculum vocabulary terms such as *angle (angulo), sphere (esfera),* and *parallel lines (lineas paralelas)*. A geography teacher can highlight such cognates as *gulf (golfo)*. In this way, students can consciously apply their knowledge of Spanish vocabulary when reading and learning in English.

❏ Some parents are fearful about having their young children away from home and, therefore, may not show an interest in preschool programs. Encourage these parents to make observations in the classroom or to volunteer as helpers. Such participation is likely to reduce their reluctance to send their children to preschool. In addition, immigrant parents whose children are already attending preschool can be effective recruiters (Kummer, 2012).

❏ Professionals need to make sure that any relevant paperwork is translated into Spanish. If caregivers are nonliterate, interpreters can be utilized to explain the purpose of the paperwork and what needs to be done.

❑ Research has shown that when pediatricians are involved in encouraging literacy-related activities at home with infants, Hispanic mothers are responsive and willing to engage in promoting early emergent literacy behaviors in their children (Maxwell, 2012a).

❑ Diener, Hobson-Rohrer, and Byington (2012) utilized the program, *Reach Out and Read (ROR),* to promote literacy development. Hispanic parents were given books and literacy instructions by pediatricians and other medical personnel at well-baby checks. Parent compliance with ROR was very high, and follow-up measures showed that in elementary school, even at-risk children who had participated in ROR had higher print and phonemic awareness skills and better reading fluency scores than students who had not participated in the program. Thus, school professionals should consider working with pediatricians to help promote literacy skills in families.

❑ Efforts should be made to incorporate Hispanic literature into the instructional program; students respond well to books written by Hispanic authors.

❑ Hispanic students are likely to benefit from interactions with older Hispanic mentors and from friendships with other Hispanic students who have high academic ideals.

By incorporating the Hispanic student's language and culture into the educational curriculum, school professionals are better able to provide the comprehensible input necessary for these students to succeed in the classroom. Our efforts to meet the needs of the rapidly growing Hispanic student population will require collaborative efforts between parents, school professionals, and members of the Hispanic community. Progress is being made, but much more needs to be done to ensure that students from Hispanic backgrounds receive appropriate instructional services and enhanced opportunities for future success.

Profile

Jorge, a 17-year-old high school sophomore, had a documented bilateral 50 dB sensorineural hearing loss. His family moved to California from rural Mexico when Jorge was 16 years old. In Mexico, Jorge had not learned sign language or lipreading, and he had never used hearing aids. The school district tested Jorge's hearing and informed his parents that he would need hearing aids to function effectively in school and in a vocation.

Jorge and his family were angry because of the school district's "interference," and denied that the hearing loss existed. Thus, Jorge received no additional assistance and was performing poorly in high school. The speech-language pathologist contacted Jose R., a Mexican professional from the State Department of Vocational Rehabilitation, who himself had come from a migrant Mexican family. Mr. R. met with Jorge and his parents, and found that they actually knew about Jorge's hearing loss but denied it, believing that the hearing loss meant that they (the parents) had sinned against God. The parents felt that Jorge's "defect" was punishment for their sins. They had accepted their fate and believed that no intervention was appropriate.

Mr. R. arranged a meeting with Jorge's family and the local priest to discuss the situation. After this meeting, the priest assured the parents that Jorge's hearing loss was not an indication of sin on their part. The parents then informed the school district that they would permit the use of hearing aids. Jorge was subsequently fitted with aids and his academic performance improved markedly.

STUDY QUESTIONS

1. Describe three ways in which cultural expectations within the Hispanic culture differ from cultural expectations within the mainstream Anglo culture in the United States (e.g., degree to which punctuality is important). How might these differences impact service delivery to Hispanic students and their families?

2. Traditional language assessment measures are often biased in favor of mainstream Anglo students. Describe two nondiscriminatory strategies, recommended by researchers, that can be used to conduct language assessments with Hispanic students.

3. Describe health considerations that are relevant to many Hispanic families in the U.S.

MULTIPLE CHOICE

4. Unfortunately, Hispanic students often experience academic difficulties and fail to complete high school. Which of the following are possible reasons for this failure?

   A. Fluctuating funding for programs designed to assist students in learning English as a second language
   B. Sporadic school attendance due to high family mobility
   C. Culture shock and other differences in home and school expectations
   D. Negative effects on learning that have resulted from bilingualism

5. Which of the following recommendations reflect "best practice" for professionals who work with Hispanic children and their families?

   A. Tell parents that children do best in school if their parent speak English only when interacting with them at home.
   B. Encourage parents to teach their young children basic concepts and to read to them in the early years (e.g., before kindergarten).

   C. Rely on nationally normed language tests to ensure that language skills are measured precisely when differentiating language differences from disorders in Spanish-speaking children.
   D. Encourage Hispanic students to be assertive in the classroom (e.g., raise their hands, interact with teachers).
   E. Let family members know the importance of being punctual for scheduled school meetings.

6. A teacher has referred a Spanish-speaking child to you for assessment. In the teacher's words, "This child has trouble pronouncing his sounds in English. I think he may need speech therapy." Which of the following English productions are indicative of a speech sound difference rather than a disorder?

   A. My tum (thumb) got cut when I was eskating (skating) wit (with) my friends in de (the) park.
   B. The pawk (park) had a bun (bunch) of dwied (dried) gwass.
   C. Dere (there) was a leetle peeg (little pig) in de (the) park and I wanted to as' (ask) if I could pet it.
   D. Lat (that) TV tow (show) is not bunny (funny).

7. Which one of the following general statements is NOT true about Hispanics in the U.S.?

   A. Most Hispanics have strong family values.
   B. Most Hispanics receive welfare services because poverty impacts so many of them.
   C. Most Hispanics are Catholic.
   D. Young Hispanic children tend to interact more often with other children at home than with adults.
   E. Hispanics may experience inadequate medical care because they frequently do not have health insurance.

8. Many Hispanic families do not:

   A. Emphasize education for girls
   B. Respect and listen to older family members
   C. Emphasize cooperation and the welfare of the whole family
   D. Question statements made by professionals

9. A large number of bilingual Hispanic preschoolers have been referred to you because of "suspected language impairment." What is important to remember as you assess these children?

   A. Assessing their grammatical skills in Spanish is not a good idea, as recent research has shown that grammatical performance (especially use of articles) is not a reliable indicator of language impairment.
   B. The SELPS can be helpful in determining English proficiency for sequential bilingual children between 4 and 8 years of age.
   C. Research has consistently shown that parent report of children's language skills is an accurate indicator of the presence of language impairment.
   D. Hispanic children who are hesitant to respond to questions asked by the speech-language pathologist during the initial testing session are likely to have expressive language disorders.
   E. Standardized Spanish tests of language ability are generally valid and reliable for Hispanic children because most of these tests account for dialectal differences.

10. In terms of intervention with bilingual Spanish-speaking children who have language impairment, we know the following:

   A. We definitely want to encourage continued development of Spanish skills at home and school.
   B. Most Hispanic parents are not open to using CD programs, YouTube videos, and other forms of "technology," so only traditional methods of teaching should be recommended for use at home.

C. When teaching vocabulary, professionals should be aware that the teaching of English and Spanish cognates (e.g., *angle vs. angulo*) may cause confusion and reduce learning.

D. Research has shown that literacy development can be promoted at home by working with pediatricians and other medical personnel to provide parents with books and information about reading.

E. Encouraging parents to observe young children in preschool helps them to understand how these programs benefit children.

ANSWERS TO STUDY QUESTIONS

4. A, B, and C
5. B, D, and E
6. A and C
7. B
8. A and D
9. B and C
10. A, D, E

Families from Asian Backgrounds

Outline

Asian Americans are the fastest growing racial group in the United States. Individuals who are classified as "Asian" come from three primary geographic regions:

East Asia:	Japan, Korea, China
Southeast Asia:	Philippines, Laos, Cambodia, Thailand, Indonesia, Singapore, Myanmar (Burma), Vietnam, Malaysia
South Asia:	Sri Lanka, Pakistan, India

Many Asians in the United States came from countries in the Pacific Rim, which includes all nations and regions touching the Pacific Ocean. Although most countries in Asia are small in physical size, some (e.g., Japan) have large populations. As shown in Figure 6.1, China is the largest country in Asia.

Figure 6.1

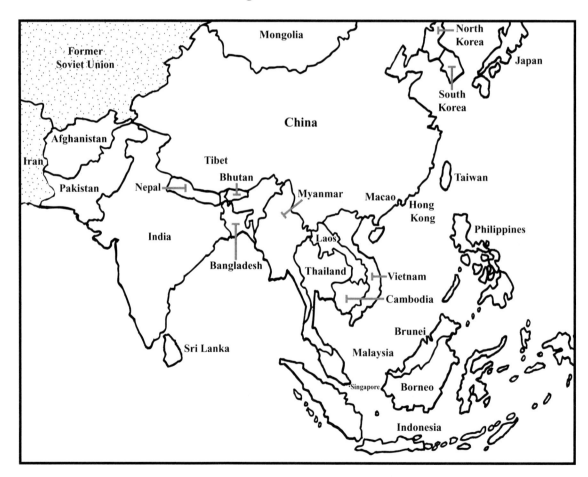

Immigrant Insight   Nancy, female, speaker of Vietnamese, university senior, daughter of immigrant parents from Vietnam

My father was the oldest of seven siblings. He was forced to leave his village as a young man and to live in a labor camp with no job, possessions, or money. He tried to flee four times, and was caught and tortured each time. Eight years after being placed into the camp, he escaped and a warrant was issued for his arrest. In the meantime, he had met my mother and they had several children. They were forced to flee from Vietnam in the middle of the night with two babies. They spent 45 days in a tiny, rickety boat with no food or water. They were often attacked by pirates. Finally they landed in Hong Kong where my mom gave birth to another child.

My family spent three years in a refugee camp, living together in a room with one bunk bed for the whole family. My father cooked daily for 300 people in the camp. He eventually passed successfully through an interview process and was sent to the Philippines to learn English. About a year later, he and the rest of my family were accepted for entrance into the U.S. My dad says that the happiest day of his life was the day they landed in San Francisco. I was born one year after they arrived here.

There are six people in my family, and we lived on welfare in a one-bedroom duplex; we received food stamps. My father worked two jobs. During the day he worked in a bread factory, and at night he washed cars. My parents spoke no English, and we had no medical care for a long time.

I didn't go to preschool; I started kindergarten speaking only Vietnamese. Because I didn't understand what the teacher was saying and could not follow her instructions, she often sent me to the time-out corner. I was bullied and called "the free lunch kid." I skipped lunch a lot because it was so upsetting to be bullied like that in the cafeteria. My oldest brother did not go to college so that he could work and earn money for us through helping my father with his landscaping business. My mother works at a nail salon. Throughout my life, I have served as an interpreter for my parents. I've translated at doctors' visits, food stamp offices, parent-teacher conferences. Because of the sacrifices my parents have made, I am absolutely driven to succeed.

When I was six years old, my dad asked me to teach him English. I remember that well, and it was what first triggered my interest in education which eventually led me into the profession of speech-language pathology. My advice to speech-language pathologists is that if you are working with refugee families, remember that they may not remember details about their children's case histories. Their primary concerns were about survival, food, and having a roof over your head. In my community, there is no focus on children's developmental milestones. It is ideal to use a Vietnamese interpreter whenever possible because families will relate best to someone from their community.

GENERAL BACKGROUND INFORMATION

Unless otherwise noted, information in this section has been compiled from the following sources: Cheng, 2012; Chhuon & Sullivan, 2013; Pew Research Center, 2017b; Sue & Sue, 2016; U.S. Census Bureau, 2017a.

❑ Asian Americans have the highest-income and are the best-educated racial group in the U.S. The estimated number of Asians in the U.S. is currently between 21 and 22 million. California has the largest Asian population, followed by New York. Seventy-four percent of Asian adults in the U.S. are foreign born.

❏ The largest number of Asians in the U.S are from Chinese language backgrounds. The following is a ranking of Asian groups from high to low based on population size in the U.S.: (1) Chinese, (2) Filipino, (3) Indian, (4) Vietnamese, (5) Korean, and (6) Japanese.

❏ The median annual household income for Americans in the general public is $49,800. The median household income for Asians is $76,260. However, median household income varies greatly by Asian group. For example, Asian Indians' median income in 2015 was $103,821; for Bangladeshi, it was $49,515.

❏ The median age for the U.S. population as a whole is 37.8 years old; for Asians, the median age is 34.0 years old. Almost 25% of Asians are under the age of 18.

❏ In terms of regional dispersion in the U.S., 47% of Asians live in the West, with 11% living in the Midwest, 21% living in the South, and 20% living in the Northeast.

❏ Asians in the United States are often referred to as the "model minority." The "model minority" belief can cause many problems such as the following:

1. Asians may be targets of resentment because they are put into an uncomfortable comparative position with other ethnic groups.
2. Social problems such as gang membership among Asian youth, poverty, substance abuse, domestic violence, and mental illness may be ignored, making it difficult for Asians to receive help in dealing with these problems.
3. The needs of Asian students often go unrecognized and, consequently, unmet by the educational system. This can contribute to a higher dropout rate. Whereas Asian students are typically overrepresented in programs for the gifted, they may be underrepresented in special education programs. Asian students with disabilities are less than half as likely as other groups to be identified with learning disabilities and cognitive impairments (Office of Special Education Programs [OSEP], 2011). Asians are one third as likely as African Americans to be in programs for students with learning disabilities (Kirk, Gallagher, Coleman, & Anastasiow, 2012).

Immigrant Insight   Ntsais, female, speaker of Hmong, university senior, daughter of immigrant parents from Laos

My mother had me when she was 13 years old. She was a grandma by the time she was 30. In the Hmong culture, getting married is extremely important! My parents do not like my white boyfriend; they really frown on any public displays of affection! It is shocking to my parents that I am 22 years old and not married. In my family, my dad makes all the major decisions. The males eat first. My sisters and I do all the chores. Before my brothers were born, we were looked down upon as a family because we were "all girls." After the boys were born, we got more respect. I have to take time out of my schedule to help my brothers with their homework and translate for my parents in different situations because they don't speak English.

❏ Common religions in Asia are Buddhism, Taoism, and Confucianism. Confucianism is especially prevalent in China. Other religions include Animism (all forms of spirit worship, including the spirits of nature), Hinduism, Islam, and Shinto.

❏ Some Asian cultures (Korean, Chinese, Vietnamese) are rooted in civilizations that are over 4,000 years old.

❏ Many Southeast Asians are Buddhist, and some groups believe in astrology, shamanism, ancestor worship, and the use of fortune tellers.

❏ Residents of the Philippines are primarily Roman Catholic. However, some Filipinos are Protestant. In the Philippines, as in other Asian countries, religion is actively intertwined with everyday life.

❏ The majority of Asian Indians are Hindus. Indian Hindus regard the cow as sacred and pure because it gives milk, one of the purest substances. Most Hindus, therefore, do not eat beef.

❏ The caste system is a unique feature of Hindu life. There are four castes, with Brahmins being the highest caste and Sudras being the lowest caste or "menials."

❏ As stated by Cheng (2012, p. 49), "Postindependence reform abolished the caste system legally, but, in practice, it still lingers. Most Indians in the U.S. came from the Brahmin group. As such, they represent a people of considerable wealth who place a very high value on education and professional careers, particularly those in science and medicine."

❏ While individual families differ, even today there are lines of division between Brahmin Indians and those of lower castes.

❏ Intermarriage between castes is often frowned upon by Indians. Persons who marry into a lower caste may be disowned by their families.

❏ Indians with lighter skin are often perceived by their ethnic peers as more attractive than Indians with darker skin.

Immigrant Insight   Noma, female, speaker of Nepali, daughter of immigrants from Nepal, university senior

My family and I are Brahmin Indians. When we lived in Nepal, it was greatly frowned upon to entertain members of lower castes in your home. Because we were in refugee camps and everyone was struggling to survive, we would sometimes bring lower caste fellow refugees into our home in order to help and support them. Other Brahmin Indians viewed us very negatively for this and we were looked upon with suspicion a lot. If you entertain a Christian in your home, this can also cause your Brahmin friends to reject you. Generally people do not marry outside of their caste; the consequences are quite severe in terms of possibly being rejected by both families.

ASIAN FAMILY LIFE

❏ The family is the basic societal unit and the central focus of an individual's life. Extended families, with several generations living under the same roof, are quite common. Filial piety is a strong value for most Asian families.

❏ In terms of the importance of being a good parent, 50% of the general public said this was one of the most important things in their life as compared to 67% of Asians. Thirty-four percent of the American general public viewed having a successful marriage as "very important" compared with 54% of Asian Americans (Pew Research Center, 2017b).

❏ Most, but not all, Asian cultures are patriarchal; women derive their status through their roles as wife, mother, and daughter-in-law. Fathers may hold the highest authority in the family. Eldest sons also frequently have high positions of respect. Some families value boys more than girls and stress education more for boys.

❏ Interdependence and conformity are often emphasized in Asian families. Family support and maintenance of social harmony are seen as lifelong obligations. Each individual family member views himself or herself as part of the larger social structure of the family.

❏ In many traditional Asian families, extramarital sex is unthinkable. Children who are born out of wedlock may be viewed as a disgrace and rejected by the entire family on both sides (S. Nguyen, personal communication, 2/23/16).

❏ As stated earlier, role relationships within hierarchies are often considered important, especially in Confucian families. Individuals within the family are expected to fill their roles according to gender, age, and position. For example, wives may submit to husbands, younger male children may submit to older male children, and female children may submit to everyone.

❏ In Confucian Asian families, each individual child is a developing part of a continuing family lineage. Children are encouraged to defer to adults and other authority figures. Respect for elders is expected.

Immigrant Insight   Jennifer, female, immigrant from Japan, university senior

I was born in Japan. My father had nothing to do with me, and my mother felt forced to give me up for adoption because she was an unwed minor (17 years old) and I would have brought shame on the entire family. My mom's father would have lost his job and the whole town would have turned their back on them. My adoptive parents wanted me to go into the medical field, and to marry a doctor or pharmacist. They want me to marry a Japanese man to keep the pure breed alive. If we had received a C or worse in school, the whole family would have found out. My adoptive mom beat me a lot with a broom, slipper, or anything else available.

Tech Tie-In

Gran Torino: Next Door (Hmong Documentary) Part 2 of 2
https://www.youtube.com/watch?v=xC2zoxES45U
Gran Torino is a touching movie about a Hmong community in the U.S. This informative and moving YouTube video summarizes some challenges experienced by members of the Hmong culture.

❑ Many Asian mothers treat their infants in a way that Americans would consider "spoiling." For example, infants are carried frequently; if they are away from a caregiver and begin crying, they are attended to immediately. Most are breast-fed on demand around the clock.

❑ Children may sleep in their parents' beds for the first several years of their lives. Parents often believe that this is the best way to create a confident, secure individual (Chan & Chen, 2011).

❑ In many Asian families the children learn to rely heavily on nonverbal cues from their caregivers. Adults may model or demonstrate a particular action as a child watches, and there may be little emphasis on verbal communication.

❑ Some Asian parents hand feed their children to ensure that they get enough to eat. When these children come to preschool, they may not know how to feed themselves and may need to be shown (Hwa-Froelich & Westby, 2003).

❑ Many Asian adults do not create learning situations for their children; rather, children are responsible for learning culturally valued behaviors through observing and being with adults during the course of a day.

❑ Hwa-Froelich and Westby (2003) reported that Asian caregivers in their study did not show love for children by playing with them but rather by taking care of their needs (e.g., dressing, feeding, bathing the children).

❑ Some families believe that learning through exploration is unnatural. If children express curiosity and engage in active exploration, they are viewed as ill-mannered. Children should be self-restrained and quiet, not spontaneous and exuberant.

❑ The viewpoint that children "should be seen and not heard" is common. Talking at the family dinner table is generally viewed as impolite. Many Asians believe that "a quiet child is a good child."

❑ Parents often control the direction of a conversation, the length of time children can talk, and the topics discussed.

❑ The child's individual growth and development are not viewed as a priority in many families; Neither self-realization nor self-expression are viewed as priorities.

❑ If a child behaves badly, the entire family may lose face. Children are expected to work toward family goals and not engage in behaviors that would bring dishonor to the family.

❑ Children may be strictly controlled and punished physically (Chan & Chen, 2011).

❑ Children may continue to reside in the home until they get married, even if they have reached adulthood. Older siblings commonly care for younger siblings.

❑ Among the Hmong and some other Asian groups, it is common for girls to marry between 13 and 16 years of age.

❑ Marriage may be a concern of the entire family rather than a private matter between the two people involved. Divorce is often viewed as being unacceptable. For example, divorces are not permitted in the Philippines, although annulments are possible.

❑ In some groups, the whole family's reputation may be in danger if a young woman has a boyfriend before she is married.

❑ Among some Asian groups, women bring honor to themselves and their families by bearing sons. Sons may be more highly valued than daughters.

Profile

Ameet Singh (not his real name) was referred to me by his kindergarten teacher, who was worried about his behavior, language, and overall lack of engagement in classroom activities. Ameet came from a Hindi-speaking home, so I engaged the services of a Hindi-speaking interpreter to screen his language and cognitive skills. Ameet would not look at the interpreter or talk to her; he showed her the same hostile behavior he had directed at other adults at the school site. I met with Mrs. Singh and spoke with her extensively. Mrs. Singh revealed that Ameet had never been to preschool, and that he only went to temple when accompanied by his family. He had never been in the care of anyone other than family members. Mrs. Singh indicated that she wanted Ameet to spend his time with family members and that he should never be alone with strangers (e.g., day care providers or preschool teachers). Not wanting to mislabel Ameet as "special ed," my colleagues and I decided to give him time to develop and acclimate to being away from his family and to being in a school environment. Ameet struggled in kindergarten, but ended up performing quite well in subsequent grades. He did not have a language impairment, intellectual disability, or autism spectrum disorder. He merely needed time to adjust to a formal school setting.

Immigrant Insight   Felipe, male from the Philippines, speaker of Tagalog

In my school in the Philippines, physical punishment was seen as appropriate for infractions. I remember being told to hit myself with a book and repeat over and over, "I will never forget to do my homework." Teachers checked on personal hygiene and general cleanliness. When the teacher entered the room, we would stand and greet him or her with a formal, ritualized phrase.

I have never been comfortable with Americans' lack of respect for authority. I was unsettled by how my American high school classmates challenged their teachers. I believe Americans do not show proper respect to the elderly. People here tend to speak as though everyone was equal. In the Philippines, there is a defined hierarchy. Everyone knows their place and understands how to properly address people who are older. I cannot get accustomed [here in the U.S.] to children addressing adults by their first name or talking back.

EDUCATION AND LITERACY

Because I was raised in the Philippines from age 6 through age 17, I learned much about the Asian educational system. Additional information for this section was obtained from interviews with individuals from Asian cultures, especially recent immigrants, and a review of the research cited.

❏ Sixty-one percent of recent Asian immigrants between 25 and 64 years of age have a college degree. In the general U.S. population, 28% have a college degree as compared to 49% of Asians. Seventy percent of Asian Indians have a Bachelor's degree or higher (Pew Research Center, 2017b). Asians are more likely than non-Hispanic Whites to hold at least a Bachelor's degree.

❏ Refugees from some Asian countries tend to have limited literacy skills. For example, many Hmong students in the U.S. enter school preliterate and without any school experience (Vang, 2005). Many Laotian students need to be convinced to remain in school until they graduate (Cheng, 2012).

❏ Many Asians have great respect for people who work hard in school. Education is viewed as a means of advancement for the individual and represents honor for the family. Immigrant Asian parents commonly view education for their children as a way out of poverty.

❏ The question "Does hard work equal success?" was answered "yes" by 69% of Asian Americans while 58% of the general American public responded "yes" (Pew Research Center, 2017c).

❏ In Asian families, the greatest tribute that children can pay to their parents is successful academic achievement. Asians have high expectations for their children's educational attainment. Children are expected to succeed academically and to have a good career (particularly in the technical fields or hard sciences; medicine is especially valued). Such success is evidence of a good family upbringing (Sue & Sue, 2016).

❏ Abboud and Kim (2007, pp. 1-2) stated that "The role of Asian children in the family is clear-cut and two-fold: Respect your elders and obey your parents. Study hard and do well in school to secure a bright future." Asian children in the U.S. may perform better academically than their non-Asian counterparts because non-Asian children often divide their time between many activities, while Asian children focus more single-mindedly on their school work.

❏ Abboud and Kim (2007) also pointed out that many American non-Asian parents try hard to boost their children's self esteem, while Asian parents praise their children less frequently. Asian parents may show that they are proud of their children's efforts yet unsatisfied with their performance. Some Asian parents believe that criticism is more effective than praise in changing children's behaviors (Sue & Sue, 2016).

❏ Many Asian parents see themselves as active agents in their children's learning and work diligently at home with their children. However, other parents may see school work as the "school's job" because of the high level of respect that they have for teachers.

❏ A study by Hwa-Froelich and Westby (2003) found that the goals considered important by Head Start teachers are not necessarily considered important by parents. The Southeast Asian parents' goals for their children were not oriented toward developing self esteem and independence. Rather, a primary goal for the Southeast Asian parents was that their children be respectful and obedient when interacting with authority figures. They believed that both respect and listening were more important than learning. In fact, some parents viewed the teachers as if they were "royalty."

❏ Some Asian families prefer to keep children who do not perform well out of school because poor school performance will cause the entire family to lose face (Hwa-Froelich & Westby, 2003).

❏ Students and their families often accord teachers great respect. In some Asian countries, teachers are revered as much as doctors.

❏ In some schools students are expected to stand up and bow when the teacher enters the room. Students sit down only when given permission to do so.

❏ Some Asian schools rely heavily on rote learning and memorization. Conformity may be considered more important than creativity.

❏ In some Asian schools, corporal punishment is acceptable. Teachers may physically discipline children whose behavior, performance, or both do not conform to expected norms. In the Filipino schools I attended as a child, teachers carried big sticks and were not reluctant to use them.

❏ Many Asian students are accustomed to authoritarian teachers. Asian students are expected to maintain a proper social distance from their teachers.

❏ Teachers in Asia often lecture to students without offering opportunities for discussion of the information presented. Thus, many Asian immigrant students consider it rude to volunteer or to ask questions in class. In U.S. schools, Asian students may take fewer risks, participate less, and hesitate in response to questions.

❏ Asian students are unlikely to correct a teacher or to hear a teacher admit that an error was made. Students tend to avoid eye contact with teachers because direct eye contact is considered rude.

❏ Some Asian schools do not provide textbooks to individual students. Students are expected to copy information from the blackboard or to take oral dictation. When I attended schools in the barrios of the Philippines, we copied everything from the blackboard and were not given textbooks.

Profile

A former college student of mine was from a Chinese immigrant family. The student, Misono, was very bright and hardworking; she was clearly going to be an excellent speech-language pathologist. Once, in class, she shared that her family had originally expected her to be a pharmacist. Her decision to major in speech-language pathology led to a considerable amount of family conflict. Her mother was especially disappointed, cried a great deal, and continually pressured Misono to change her mind and major in pharmacy. Misono shared that her mother "backed off" when she told her that speech-language pathologists' salaries had risen and, although not commensurate with those of pharmacists, would provide Misono with a good living.

CULTURAL CUSTOMS AND COURTESIES

❏ Hospitality and courtesy are highly valued. Many Asians bow slightly when greeting others.

❏ Among some groups, dating is not permitted and premarital sex is frowned upon.

❏ Modesty in dress and appearance is highly valued; some American clothing may be considered immodest and revealing.

❑ Modesty and humility are highly valued; "blowing your own horn," on the other hand, may be viewed as arrogant and unseemly. In Japan, it is said that "the nail that sticks its head up gets hammered down."

❑ Other important personal qualities for many Asians include self-restraint, self-sacrifice, inner strength, perseverance, and patience.

❑ Authority figures of any kind generally should not be questioned.

❑ Hierarchical relationships tend to be viewed as important, especially for Chinese individuals who are from Confucian backgrounds. Conventions can be based on age, gender, social status, etc.

❑ Many Asian groups show reverence for the elderly. Asians therefore approach old age with self-respect, dignity, and pride. In addition, the number of grandchildren one has may be viewed as a measure of one's success in life.

Immigrant Insight   Phuong, female, speaker of Vietnamese, Vietnam

We came to the U.S. for freedom. When I was 12 years old in Vietnam, I couldn't go to school because we couldn't afford it. I began a job sorting and carrying fish at 3:00 A.M., and helped my mother cook and sell the fish.

People who worked for the government could execute and put you in jail without any reason at all. Patrolmen would make up reasons to arrest people and throw them in jail. My mom was put in prison for 3 years for no reason. After she was released, she sent me to America with my relatives. We were on a boat with 51 people for days until an American ship rescued us. There is a lot of freedom in America, and it is a lot cleaner. The quality of life is better, with bigger homes and more food.

HEALTH CARE AND DISABLING CONDITIONS

❑ Asians often consider only physical disabilities to be worthy of treatment.

❑ Many Asians believe that children who are "disabled" will show physical evidence of that disability. Conditions that are not visible (e.g., stuttering, language impairment) are believed to result from "not trying hard enough." Because of these beliefs, parents may not see any need for therapy or rehabilitation.

Immigrant Insight   Fidela, 24, university senior, speaker of Laotian,
                            daughter of Laotian immigrants

I was in a car accident in college. My parents sent me a spiritual care package with a bottle of holy water to splash on myself. They sent my Tweety Bird pajamas from when I was a little girl and they had tied white strings around the sleeves for faster healing. I am under a lot of pressure to get married. My mom reminds me, "Your eggs are dying."

❏ Hwa-Froelich and Westby (2003) found that Southeast Asian parents in their study believed that learning problems were associated with fate, stubbornness, or laziness. When students did not perform as expected in school, strict discipline was used to force these students to study longer and work harder. Some parents referred to learning problems as the child's "fate" or as the result of "being born under bad stars." All of the Southeast Asian parents preferred administering physical punishment to their children over losing face; none of them wanted their children to repeat a grade.

❏ Hwa-Froelich and Westby (2003) also found that the Southeast Asian parents in their study viewed students with severe physical conditions such as blindness or deafness as a potentially shameful burden on the family. These children were not viewed as capable of doing anything useful.

❏ Some Asians define the causes of health-related problems and disabilities in spiritual terms. For example, problems may be attributed to spoiled foods, demons or spirits, or a bad wind. Others feel that disabling conditions occur because of one's "fate" and that nothing can or should be done to interfere.

❏ Some families believe that congenital defects and disabilities result from sins committed by parents or possibly even remote ancestors. As a result, the child may be looked upon as an object of shame for the entire family and consequently isolated from society.

❏ If a child needs special education or underperforms academically in school, the parents often feel ashamed and perceive the child's difficulties as a sign of their own personal failure (Cheng, 2012).

❏ To "save face," some families hesitate to seek medical or other care for children with disabilities. Some Asians believe that caring for children with disabilities is the responsibility of the family rather than the school or other agencies.

❏ Among Asian Indian Americans, disability may be viewed as a stigma, and those with disabilities are often marginalized (Cheng, 2012). For example, Asian Indian parents of students with disabilities such as autism spectrum disorder (ASD) may feel sidelined and isolated by parents of typically-developing children, who have high aspirations for their children's achievement and are not aware of ASD. Asian Indian children with ASD may not be welcome in social circles or invited on play dates (Mahendra, 2012).

❏ Health practices may involve acupuncture, herbs, massage, and baths in hot springs. People may visit religious shrines or temples to seek healing.

Immigrant Insight   Yuki, male, immigrant from Japan, speaker of Japanese

I am embarrassed to say that in Japan, it is considered very bad to have a disability. Our culture is centered on collectivism, so everyone is expected to contribute equally to society. People with disabilities are given no voice and are kept at home with their families because it is believed that they have nothing to contribute. It is common for them to be mistreated and neglected. I have never heard of a speech-language pathologist before.

Profile

      Melanie, an 8-year-old Filipino girl, was born with a cleft palate. She had undergone several surgical operations, but her speech continued to be affected by hypernasality and poor articulation. The surgeon had recommended pharyngeal flap surgery for Melanie to resolve the velopharyngeal incompetence that was causing her hypernasality, but the family refused the surgery. At the triennial IEP meeting, I informed Melanie's parents that her speech had become more intelligible as a result of treatment, although she still exhibited hypernasality.

      I expressed the concern that further therapy to modify Melanie's resonance would not be effective unless she had pharyngeal flap surgery. The father was very angry and refused to allow Melanie to come back for more speech therapy. He smiled as he left, however, and thanked me and the speech-language pathologist at the school site for the work done with Melanie over the past three years.

ASIAN COMMUNICATION STYLES

❏ Many Asian languages have formal rules of communication propriety based on the relative status of each of the participants in the interaction. Personal questions Americans might find offensive (e.g., "How old are you?" or "Are you married?") are considered appropriate as a means of ascertaining each conversational participant's status.

❏ Smooth and harmonious interpersonal relationships are a high priority. Asians may therefore avoid public confrontations and open competition.

❏ Many Asians are indirect in their communication, giving the impression that they are evasive and noncommittal. Much information is conveyed nonverbally through subtle gestures, postures, positioning, facial expressions, eye contact, and silence. This is typical in many Asian countries and should not be labeled negatively.

❏ Direct eye contact may be considered an open show of rudeness or challenge between individuals who are conversing. Interrupting a conversation may also be considered impolite.

❏ Many Asians believe that it is inappropriate and offensive to display anger publicly or to contradict others. Rather, it is considered proper to keep one's outward composure, no matter how one may feel inside.

❏ A polite smile, nod, or response of "yes" may simply be an acknowledgement that the client has heard a message. It may not indicate agreement with the comments. When asked to do something, Asians often give a positive response in an effort to be polite. However, they may not follow through.

❏ Smiling does not necessarily imply happiness or pleasure; it can connote many positive or even negative emotions. Some Asians smile or laugh in situations when they are embarrassed. "Saving face" or avoiding public embarrassment is very important.

❏ Many groups (e.g., the Japanese and Indians) value silence and think that Westerners are verbose. Silence may be used to avoid expressing disagreement.

❏ Among some groups, it is considered unacceptable to touch others on the head.

❏ Some groups, such as the Japanese, are accustomed to more personal space than that commonly experienced during interactions with Anglo Americans. It is important not to violate space boundaries.

❏ Among many traditional Japanese, honorifics and formalities are the norm. Such formalities might seem excessive to Americans.

ASIAN LANGUAGE CONSIDERATIONS

❏ The five most commonly spoken languages in the United States are English, Spanish, Chinese, Tagalog, and Vietnamese (Accredited Language Services, 2017).

❏ Many Asian languages have numerous dialects that may or may not be mutually intelligible; for example, there are over 87 dialects in China and the Philippines (Nations Online, 2013). Most dialects spoken in the Philippines are mutually unintelligible.

❏ The Indian constitution recognizes 15 major languages, but India has over 700 dialects. Hindi is recognized as the national language, although many Indians do not speak it. British English has been a major influence in India.

❏ Kannada is another major language of India. English is the official language of education and the government.

❏ Students from countries such as Vietnam and Cambodia may speak French in addition to their primary language.

❏ Some groups have politeness conventions that dictate the use of certain word forms depending upon the relative status of the participants in the interaction. For example, Japanese has more than 100 words for "I" and "me" that are selected based on one's social status and the status of his or her conversational partner.

❏ Politeness conventions are so important in Japan that business etiquette training is provided to enhance the skills of Japanese businesspersons in building corporate images (Dunn, 2013).

❏ Vietnamese, Chinese, and Laotian are tonal languages. Each tone change is phonemic in nature and represents a meaning change. For example, in Mandarin, the word "ma" can mean *mother, horse, scold, flax,* or *curse* depending on the tone used.

❏ Mandarin has four types of tones that affect meaning. These are referred to as **tonemes**. Cantonese has seven tonemes; Northern Vietnamese has six tonemes; Central and Southern Vietnamese each have five tonemes.

❏ Japanese, Khmer, and Korean are not tonal languages.

Tech Tie-In

Detailed descriptions of Asian languages can be found at http://www.nationsonline.org/oneworld/asian_languages.htm

❑ Written Asian language systems vary widely. The Vietnamese, for example, use a modified Roman alphabet whereas the Chinese use symbols to represent concepts.

❑ When stating their names in writing, the last name precedes the first name in most Asian cultures (see Table 6.1).

❑ Chinese, Vietnamese, and Laotian languages are basically monosyllabic.

❑ The Hmong language has only recently developed written forms. Very few people have received formal Hmong literacy instruction.

❑ Some languages (e.g., Indonesian, Japanese, Tagalog) do not have specific gender pronouns such as *he* or *she*.

❑ The prosody or intonation of an Asian-born speaker of English may sound very "choppy" and monotonous to the ears of those born in the U.S. Some speakers sound nasal when speaking English.

It is difficult to provide generalities about Asian speakers' English language patterns because of the variety of languages and dialects spoken by this population. However, some of the commonly observed characteristics of the English of Asian speakers are listed in Table 6.2 and Table 6.3 based on information reported in the literature (Chan & Chen, 2011; Cheng, 2012).

IMPLICATIONS FOR PROFESSIONALS

Much diversity exists among Asian populations. Among the cultural variables that may be important to consider are the following:

❑ Many Asian Americans prefer to be referred to by their country of origin (e.g., Vietnamese American, Filipino American).

❑ Shaking hands with someone of the opposite sex may be considered unacceptable.

❑ Use of one's left hand to touch someone or to hand something to someone may be frowned upon. Some Asians consider the left hand to be unclean.

❑ The older members of the family should be addressed first, as a sign of respect.

❑ Because of the high value Asians place on education, they greatly respect educated professionals. They may even revere the professional as an "expert" and therefore hesitate to volunteer opinions or responses. Also, Asian individuals may agree to carry out recommendations yet have no intention of actually doing so.

❑ As stated, when family members say "yes," they may mean "I hear you" rather than "I agree." Professionals need to encourage open communication as much as possible. When interacting with Filipino families, first impressions are extremely important. If the professional appears aloof or rude during the first meeting, Filipino families will remember this and may lose trust in the professional. Smooth interpersonal relations characterized by sensitivity to and concern for others are extremely important in establishing relationships (R. Dimaano, personal communication, 3/15).

❑ Many American professionals treat a child's mother as the family expert and decision maker. However, in some Asian families, especially those who are Confucians, it is believed that husbands should be dominant and wives should be subordinate. Thus, professionals may need

Table 6.1
Information About Asian Family Names

Characteristics of names most often given to members of various Asian populations are summarized below.

Cambodian:	Names consist of two parts. Family name precedes personal name. Middle names are rare.
Chinese:	Names consist of two parts. Family name precedes personal name. Most Chinese names consist of only one syllable. Common Chinese names: Chan, Chang, Chin, Chung, Lee, Liu, Lum, Tang, Wong, Woo, Yang
Hmong:	Most names consist of two parts. Family name precedes personal name. Common Hmong family names: Chang, Chue, Fang, Her, Khang, Kue, Lor, Lee, Moua, Thao, Vang, Vue, Xiong, Yang
Indonesians:	Names consist of two parts. Many are polysyllabic and thus quite lengthy by American standards (e.g., "Pranawahadi"). Many Indonesians have Muslim names.
Japanese:	Most names consist of two parts. Family name precedes personal name. To be polite when interacting with an authority figure, "san" is added to the end of the individual's last name. Japanese names often consist of more than one syllable. Common Japanese surnames: Kawaguchi, Nakamura, Tanaka, Watanabe, Yamamoto
Koreans:	Most names consist of a family name that precedes a two-part personal name. Common Korean surnames: Kim, Park, Lee
Laotians:	Family name precedes personal name. Names may consist of more than one syllable, and some are quite lengthy by American standards (e.g., Souphanouvong).
Thais:	Personal name precedes the surname. Some names are quite long (e.g., Suvarnarami).
Vietnamese:	Names consist of three components: family, middle, and given names. The family name is followed by the middle name and personal name respectively. The name, Nguyen Van Thieu, for example, begins with the family name "Nguyen" and ends with "Thieu," the name that the individual is called by family members and friends. Approximately 52% of Vietnamese individuals have the family name "Nguyen"; 31% have the family name "Tran." Other common family names are Pham, Le, Ngo, Do, Dao, Vu, Hwang, Dang, Dinh, and Duong.

Table 6.2

Language Differences Commonly Observed Among Asian Speakers

Language Characteristics	*Sample English Utterances*
Omission of plurals	Here are 2 piece of toast. I got 5 finger on each hand.
Omission of copula	He going home now. They eating.
Omission of possessive	I have Phuong pencil. Mom food is cold.
Omission of past tense morpheme	We cook dinner yesterday. Last night she walk home.
Past tense double marking	He didn't went by himself.
Double negative	They don't have no books.
Subject-verb-object relationship differences/omissions	I messed up it. He like.
Misordering of interrogatives	You are going now?
Misuse or omission of prepositions	She is in home. He goes to school 8:00.
Misuse of pronouns	She husband is coming. She said her wife is here.
Omission and/or overgeneralization of articles	Boy is sick. He went the home.
Incorrect use of comparatives	This book is gooder than that book.
Omission of conjunctions	You _____ I going to the beach.
Omission, lack of inflection on auxiliary "do"	She _____ not take it. He do not have enough.
Omission, lack of inflection on forms of "have"	She have no money. We _____ been the store.

Table 6.3

Articulation Differences Observed Commonly Among Asian Speakers

Articulation Characteristics	*Sample English Utterances*	
In many Asian languages, words end in vowels only or in just a few consonants; speakers may delete many final consonants in English.	ste/step ro/robe	li/lid do/dog
Some languages are monosyllabic; speakers may truncate polysyllabic words or emphasize the wrong syllable.	efunt/elephant **di**versity/diversity (emphasis on first syllable)	
Possible devoicing of voiced cognates	beece/bees luff/love	pick/pig crip/crib
r/l confusion	lize/rise	clown/crown
Omission of /r/	gull/girl	tone/torn
Reduction of vowel length in words	Words sound choppy to Americans.	
No voiced or voiceless "th"	dose/those zose/those	tin/thin sin/thin
Epenthesis (addition of "uh" sound in blends, ends of words)	bulack/black	wooduh/wood
Confusion of "ch" and "sh"	sheep/cheap	beesh/beach
/ae/ does not exist in many Asian languages	block/black	shock/shack
b/v substitution	base/vase	Beberly/Beverly
v/w substitution	vork/work	vall/wall

to defer to husbands when decisions regarding a child (e.g., placing that child into special education) are to be made.

❏ Because most Asians are very family oriented, the whole family may need to be a primary source of authority in decisions. This includes decisions about whether or not a child will receive intervention.

❏ It may be considered disloyal or disgraceful to the family for parents to openly discuss a child or family-related problem such as a disability. For many Asians, public discussion of family problems is considered to be a source of embarrassment and an indication of the family's failure. Professionals need to be sensitive when asking personal questions and discussing areas of concern.

❏ Because not all Asian homes emphasize development of verbal skills in infants and young children, families may be surprised if recommendations are made for early intervention. As stated previously, infants and young children are often taught through nonverbal cues and demonstrations. Thus, professionals may find that recommendations for early language intervention are not greeted with enthusiasm.

❏ Professionals should emphasize that early language intervention will boost academic achievement in the later years. Professionals can demonstrate how building oral language in the early years will support written language development and consequent academic success during the school years.

❏ In a recent study in Shanghai, China, it was discovered that parents were responsive to and benefitted from feedback about the frequency with which they interacted with their young children (Zhang et al., 2015). For many families in the study, this feedback was successful in modifying the behavior of adult caregivers to benefit children's language development.

❏ Early intervention professionals often utilize play therapy with children, emphasizing exploration and independence. This may run directly counter to an Asian family's cultural practices, which emphasize quietness, conformity, and respect. Many Asian parents do not play with their children (Hwa-Froelich & Westby, 2003).

❏ Asian parents may be shocked when asked to participate in the development of remediation plans. Out of respect for teachers and the school, these parents may have a policy of noninterference and deference. They may be unfamiliar with and confused by legislative policies that emphasize parental rights and responsibilities. Formal requests for parent participation may be interpreted as indications that the child's difficulties have exceeded the professionals' intervention capabilities (Chan & Chen, 2011). In these cases, cultural mediators, or persons from the family's community, can be helpful in providing information to parents about American educational policies and practices.

❏ Because Asian children are often quiet and respectful, learning problems are sometimes overlooked or may be inappropriately attributed to limited proficiency in English.

❏ It was emphasized by Hwa-Froelich and Westby (2003) that for American professionals, children's independence is the paramount goal. However, because of the interdependence of their members, many Asian families do not share the goal of helping a child to be as independent as possible.

❏ American professionals should not be shocked if they find out that young children sleep in the same bed as their parents; this should not be viewed as unnatural or as a sign of immaturity.

❏ As stated previously, in Confucian Asian families, each individual child is a developing part of a continuing family lineage—a continuation of his ancestors. Thus, a family may reject a diagnosis of any type of disability because the entire family lineage would be disgraced. They might, therefore, refuse special education services for a child.

❏ In these cases, children with special needs might be served through other models, which will be described in later chapters (e.g., classroom modifications, non-special education supports). In this way, the family can save face and the child's needs can still be addressed.

❏ In some Asian countries, there is limited tolerance for children with disabilities (Roseberry-McKibbin, 2013). Professionals should reassure families that in the U.S., disabilities are not considered shameful and that there are laws, agencies, and services to support children with disabilities and their families.

❏ In some Asian countries (e.g., Malaysia), it is considered rude to say "yes" when first offered an item or service; to be polite, one should first say "no." The person who made the offer then tries to persuade the other person to accept it. Thus professionals may need to offer services many times before these services are accepted.

❏ In traditional Asian cultures (especially Chinese, Japanese, and Korean), it is very important to give and receive things with both hands. To give or receive things with one hand may be viewed as a sign of laziness or disrespect. So for example, when handing a form to a client to sign, it would be ideal to hand it to the client with both hands (A. Chun, personal communication, 2/28/17).

❏ Families may offer gifts in exchange for professional services and may feel offended if professionals do not accept these gifts.

❏ Professionals should dress formally, even when making home visits, because informal dress may be seen as a sign of disrespect.

❏ Some parents believe that English as a Second Language or bilingual education classes are inferior to monolingual English classrooms. Professionals should provide parents with information about bilingual programs of instruction and emphasize that bilingualism is a great asset in today's increasingly global economy.

❏ Many Asian parents urge their children to control their feelings, especially if the feelings are negative (e.g., anger). They are not to verbalize these feelings, or punishment may ensue. This clashes directly with the American value of "letting it all hang out."

❏ Many Asian immigrant parents believe that children in the U.S. have too much freedom and are consequently disobedient, disrespectful, and uncontrollable. Some parents fear that their own children will begin to behave in this manner. To reduce their fears, students can be taught "home talk rules" and "school talk rules." For example, a professional might say "At school, adults expect you to raise your hand, speak out in class, and look them in the eye. At home, it is important to be silent and not look adults in the eye." In this way, Asian students will be given two sets of behaviors from which to choose depending on the circumstances.

❏ The informal atmosphere in American schools may be disconcerting to some Asian students and parents. In addition, many Asian parents do not emphasize extracurricular activities such as after-school sports because studying and getting good grades are viewed as far more important.

❏ Many Asian parents are not familiar with after-school clubs and activities (Cheng, 2012). They may not be enthusiastic about these extracurricular activities because the activities "interfere with studying." Professionals should consider recommending extracurricular activities that increase children's oral and/or written language skills. These activities will help parents develop an understanding of the relationship between enhanced language skills and academic success.

❑ Parents often expect students to bring home large amounts of homework. Professionals may be asked to account for "too little" homework.

❑ Some immigrant Asian students are not accustomed to being called upon in class and may feel uncomfortable speaking up or even reading in front of the group.

❑ Students may appear to have "expressive language problems" because they have been taught to be quiet and respectful and to accept direction from authority figures.

❑ In some Asian families, girls are socialized to grow up to become willing workers, submissive daughters-in-law, and obedient wives. Wives expect to count on their husbands and sons for their future security (Chan & Chen, 2011).

❑ Thus, some Asian girls may appear to be especially "passive" to American professionals. It is important to refrain from viewing the passive behaviors as indicators of a language impairment.

❑ Professionals should gently ease students into tasks that require them to express opinions, form judgments, and solve problems. Such activities may be a new experience for students who had been taught to sit quietly and to defer to adults in all settings.

❑ Due to the group orientation of many Asian cultures, cooperative learning activities can be beneficial (Yeh et al., 2002).

❑ The expressive language skills of Asian students are often difficult to evaluate because these students tend to be quiet in classroom situations. Written homework assignments and portfolio assessment (described in a later chapter) might be a more valid means of evaluating their academic progress than analyzing oral expressive language skills (Yeh et al., 2002).

❑ The concept of winning a game may be unfamiliar to some Asian students. These students may feel uncomfortable competing with others.

❑ Students from Hindu Indian backgrounds may feel uncomfortable if pictures of beef are used in the educational program or if beef snacks are served.

❑ To ensure that culture-fair assessment procedures are used, Cheng (2012) recommended: (1) interviews with family members, (2) multiple observations over time in various settings, (3) collecting narrative samples using wordless books, and (4) dynamic assessment procedures. These procedures are superior to standardized, formal tests when assessing students with possible language impairment.

❑ Pua, Lee, and Liow (2017) conducted a study in Singapore with preschool children who spoke English, Malay, and Mandarin. It was found that preschool teachers' reports of potential language difficulties in these children were both reliable and valid sources of information that could be useful in distinguishing language difference from language impairment. The researchers concluded that subjective teacher ratings of language skills such as vocabulary may be an effective method of screening bilingual preschoolers for language difficulties.

❑ To, Stokes, Cheung, and T'sou (2010) conducted a study on the use of narrative assessment with Cantonese-speaking children. They studied typically-developing subjects and those with language impairment (LI). The findings were that narrative assessment can be reliably and validly standardized for use with Cantonese-speaking children. The researchers also discovered that when using narratives, Cantonese-speaking children with LI showed limited ability to present as many ideas as typically-developing peers. Children with LI also used nonspecific terms (e.g., "The girl did the leg of the cat" rather than "The girl bandaged the leg of the cat.").

❑ Rezzonico et al. (2016), in a study of bilingual Cantonese-English preschoolers, showed that there is a possible transfer in narrative abilities between the two languages. This study provides further support for the utility of narrative assessment measures in differentiating language difference from language impairment in children who speak Cantonese.

❑ Pieretti (2011) found that Hmong English Language Learners (ELLs) who were struggling with literacy in first grade benefitted from intense, short term response to intervention that focused on increasing phonological awareness skills. Contextualized, language-rich oral narratives were helpful in increasing reading ability and classroom participation.

❑ Lam and Sheng (2016) recommended that Mandarin-speaking students who are at risk for slow vocabulary development in English be explicitly taught morphological rules such as appropriate use of the English –er suffix (e.g., *teacher, painter, dancer*). This instruction is likely to be helpful because the morphological systems of Mandarin and English are so different.

CONCLUSION

It is imperative for school professionals to develop an understanding of Asian cultural groups and the beliefs they have about educating children with disabilities. It is especially important to be sensitive to cultural rules of interaction that influence behavior in social contexts. By learning about Asian cultures, school professionals will be better prepared to interact with families from Asian backgrounds and to develop appropriate educational programs for students who need special education intervention.

STUDY QUESTIONS

1. Why are Asians often called the "model minority?" Describe problems that this label creates for them.

2. Compare and contrast mainstream U.S. beliefs about causation of disabilities and the need for intervention with the beliefs commonly held within Asian countries.

3. You will be meeting with the family of a well-behaved 3-year-old Southeast Asian girl who is not yet able to speak. Your assessment results indicate that she has a language impairment. Describe what you will need to remember as you prepare to talk with her family about this in a culturally sensitive manner.

MULTIPLE CHOICE

4. Which one of the following is FALSE?

    A. Japan, Korea, and China are in East Asia.
    B. Sri Lanka, Pakistan, India, and Saudi Arabia are in South Asia.
    C. The Philippines, Laos, Cambodia, Thailand, Indonesia, Singapore, Burma, Vietnam, and Malaysia are in Southeast Asia.
    D. Most Indians are Hindus.
    E. The Asian American population in the U.S. is now over 10 million.

5. Which of the following statements describe communication styles observed frequently among Asian cultures:

    A. Personal questions (e.g., asking one's age) are considered highly inappropriate.
    B. Direct eye contact may be considered an open display of rudeness or challenge between individuals who are conversing.
    C. Periods of silence during a conversation are considered awkward and should be avoided if at all possible.
    D. Many Asians avoid open competition and public confrontation.
    E. To maintain harmony, many Asians will not outwardly express their feelings of disagreement.

6. A teacher refers a child to you for assessment. This student recently moved to this country from China. Which of the following would indicate a communication difference, not a disorder?

    A. Omission of articles (e.g., "Little dog is playing in water.")
    B. Difficulty with consonant clusters
    C. An *a/ae* substitution (e.g., substituting "block" for "black" by saying, "The sky gets <u>block</u> at night.")
    D. Substitution of /r/ for /n/
    E. Substitution of /t/ for /k/ (e.g., *tat* for *cat*)

7. Which statements about Asian education are true?

    A. In Asia, teachers are often formal and tend to maintain a distance from students.
    B. Teachers are not highly respected.
    C. Some Asian parents see themselves as active agents in their children's learning and work diligently at home with their children.
    D. Teachers in Asian schools tend to discourage rote learning and memorization so that divergent thinking and creativity can be promoted.
    E. Many Asians believe that the greatest honor children can bestow on their parents is academic achievement.

8. Which of the following beliefs or actions would suggest a professional's lack of "cultural awareness" during interactions with the parents of an Asian child?

    A. The professional is aware that Asians often agree to recommendations out of respect, although they have no intention of following through on these recommendations.
    B. The professional assures parents that to prevent stress in the home environment little homework will be given.
    C. The professional is direct and forthright when informing the family that the student has a communication disorder.

  D. When making recommendations, the professional speaks in a stern voice to earn the respect of the parents.

  E. At a meeting, the professional speaks to the father first.

9. Xin Ren, an 11-year-old Chinese immigrant, is referred to you because the fifth grade teacher suspects that she might have language impairment. The teacher reported the Xin Ren has difficulty expressing herself in class and that "After eight months in the U.S., I think she should be doing better." The teacher listed specific difficulties that the student is experiencing. Which of the following listed behaviors might be cultural signs of a communication difference rather than evidence of a disorder?

  A. Xin does not make eye contact with the teacher, preferring instead to look downward.

  B. Xin does not volunteer in class, remaining quiet and nonparticipatory.

  C. When asked to critique an author's statement, Xin says "I don't know—the author is the expert."

  D. A, B

  E. A, B, C

10. You are working with several preschools in your area, conducting assessments when teachers refer children for special education evaluations. A teacher approaches you about Nigam, a 3-year-old Indian boy who has just started preschool. She says that he is "such a cute little thing, and I can tell his parents really are involved. But he seems so immature, and I think his parents baby him. I wonder if I should talk to a psychologist or occupational therapist?" Which of the following teacher's concerns could be due to cultural differences rather than immaturity or a specific delay?

  A. Nigam has difficulty feeding himself and expects the preschool teacher to feed him at snack time.

  B. Nigam is physically injurious to other children, bumping into them and sometimes hitting them.

  C. Nigam has difficulty buttoning his jacket, coming expectantly to the teacher and standing in front of her with his jacket open.

  D. A, C

  E. A, B, C

ANSWERS TO STUDY QUESTIONS

  4. B
  5. B, D, and E
  6. A, B, and C
  7. A, C, and E
  8. B, C, and D
  9. E
  10. D

Chapter 7

Families from Native American Backgrounds

Outline
- General Background Information
- Native American Family Life
- Native American Education and Literacy
- Cultural Customs, Courtesies, and Beliefs
- Health Care and Disabling Conditions
- Native American Communication Styles
- Native American Language Considerations
- Implications for Professionals

In recent years, indigenous groups living in the United States have become more vocal about the terms used to describe them. Use of the terms *Indian* and *American Indian* have declined in favor of terms such as *Native American* and *Native American Indian*. The use of the word "Indian" is viewed by many as pejorative.

The term **Native American** is used in this book when referring to indigenous populations. It is important for readers to understand that the Native American population is quite diverse. There are approximately 565 separate and distinct Native American tribal entities with distinct languages and cultures in the United States. These groups differ in many of their customs, beliefs, and values.

GENERAL BACKGROUND INFORMATION

Unless otherwise indicated, information in this section was compiled from data reported in the following sources: National Conference of State Legislatures, 2016; National Congress of American Indians, 2017; U.S. Census Bureau, 2016.

- ❏ There are 6.6 million members of the Native American population; they make up almost 2% of the total population in the U.S. The projected Native American population is projected to grow to 10.2 million by the year 2060.

- ❏ The state with the highest number of Native American individuals is Alaska, followed by Oklahoma, New Mexico, South Dakota, and Montana.

- ❏ There were 326 federally recognized reservations in 2016, and there were 567 federally recognized tribes. At this time, there are 567 federally recognized American Indian and Alaska Native tribes and villages.

- ❏ The median age for the U.S. population as a whole is 37.8 years, while the median age for the Native American population is 30.2 years.

- ❏ Youth under the age of 25 make up 42% of the Native American population, while youth under the age of 25 make up 34% of the U.S. population. There is a large "bubble" in the 15-19 year age group in the Native American population.

- ❏ In the U.S., 63% of the population own their own home as compared to 53.1% of Native Americans.

- ❏ The median income for U.S. households is approximately $55,775; the median household income for Native Americans is $28,530. Approximately 27% of Native Americans live in poverty compared with 14.7% of the U.S population as a whole.

Tech Tie-In

The Bureau of Indian Affairs website has comprehensive information about Native American history, language, culture, and contemporary issues facing this population today. The website is http://www.bia.gov.

❑ There are various names for Native Americans (e.g., First People). Some prefer to be called Native American Indians (NAmI). The term "Native American" became widely used in the 1970s, and has gradually expanded to include all Native peoples of the U.S. and its trust territories. Many Native Americans prefer to use terms specific to their tribe (e.g., Dineh, Cherokee, Yurok, or Navajo).

❑ Historically, most Native Americans lived in nations that were made up of tribes and clans. When Europeans came to North America, millions of Native Americans were slaughtered or died of disease and/or starvation.

❑ Some Europeans deliberately gave Native Americans smallpox-infested blankets. Buffalo were exterminated so that Plains Indians would starve to death. Native Americans were constantly forced to move (Dapice, 2006).

❑ To early Whites living in North America, the extermination of Native Americans was perceived as an easy way to deal with the Indian "problem"—that is, Native Americans stood in the way of Whites' free reign over the land and its resources (including gold).

❑ By the end of the 18th century, the population of Native Americans may have decreased to 10% of its original number.

❑ Like other indigenous peoples, Native Americans have a history of widespread trauma and injustice that has led to emotional wounding across generations (Westby & Inglebret, 2012). This has been described as "soul wounds" that are related to behavior dysfunction and substance abuse (Sue & Sue, 2016). Intergenerational grief is a common phenomenon.

❑ Many Native American children were, in the past, removed from their families and forced to attend government-run boarding schools, where a major goal was to eliminate the children's language and culture. Children also lived with non-Indian families; they were removed from their own families for eight years in order to become "civilized."

❑ These children were often punished severely for speaking their native languages. In addition, they were forbidden to dress in traditional clothing and were forced to wear school uniforms instead.

❑ After the enactment of the Indian Child Welfare Act in 1974, boarding schools began to close. Children were allowed to return home.

❑ Because of the cultural genocide caused by forced boarding school attendance and other factors, there have been renewed efforts to preserve Native American culture and family unity. Today, many Native American tribes are attempting to revitalize their languages, cultures, and traditions (Gaskell, 2012; Inglebret, Banks-Joseph, CHiXapkaid, & Pavel, 2016; Joe & Malach, 2011; Leedom Shaul, 2014; Westby & Inglebret, 2012).

❑ Over half of Native Americans now live away from their tribal lands. However, most return home to participate in cultural or spiritual activities, visit family, and attend celebrations (U.S. Department of the Interior Indian Affairs, 2017).

❑ On March 1, 2013, the U.S. federal Advisory Council on Historic Preservation (ACHP) formally endorsed a plan to support the United Nations Declaration on the Rights of Indigenous People. The goal of this plan is to promote better protection and stewardship of Native American sacred sites and historic properties, helping to ensure that Native American cultures survive and thrive (Donaldson, 2013).

❑ Poverty is endemic among Native Americans. Many reservations are located in remote, geographically barren parts of the U.S. Employment opportunities are virtually nonexistent. The poverty rate among Native Americans is double the U.S. average. However, younger Native Americans are making greater use of technology to learn about employment opportunities.

❑ Most Native American spiritual traditions emphasize a universal spirituality that is integral to all of life. Native Americans believe that all things, supernatural and natural, are interconnected. For example, the Lakota Indians use the term *mitakuye oyas'in*, which means that everything that has ever been or will be created is related. This includes Father Sky, Mother Earth, and all persons, animals, plants, and minerals.

❑ Members of many tribes believe in one Creator or Great Spirit. They have great respect for Mother Earth (Chamberlain & Roseberry-McKibbin, 2008).

❑ Whereas Anglo Americans have been most concerned with harnessing and controlling nature, Native Americans have attempted to live in harmony with nature. For example, they look to the land to provide treatment for diseases (e.g., using herbal remedies).

❑ Historically, Native Americans did not believe in private or individual ownership of land, but rather viewed (and continue to view) themselves as caretakers of it. Today, most tribes teach respect for the land and forbid destruction of their ancestral lands. For many Native Americans, everything relates to relationships to the land.

❑ Many Native Americans hold dual citizenship status with their own tribal nations and the U.S.

NATIVE AMERICAN FAMILY LIFE

❑ Close-knit, extended families are common. Members of the extended family often care for children and provide long-term nursing care for elderly family members. Many families are headed by a single adult female.

❑ For many Native Americans, family ties are more important than anything else, including money, school, and prestige.

❑ Each family member is expected to support others in the family. Working members of the family may be expected to care for brothers and sisters, elderly parents, and even more distant kin.

❑ Often, grandparents and other elders are in positions of authority and assume more responsibility for the training of children than either the mother or father.

❑ Many Native Americans are married via tribal customs that are not perceived as "valid" in the eyes of the American government. Thus, persons married in this way may experience barriers in accessing mainstream U.S. government services for themselves and their children. In these situations, some Native Americans marry again in a "mainstream" ceremony that is sanctioned by the U.S. government. This helps them to access needed government services.

❑ Because the family is so close-knit, many Native Americans do not leave their children in the care of people outside the family or tribe. Some families never use baby-sitters or day-care workers. Recent data indicates that 59% of Native American children in the U.S. do not attend preschool (Maxwell, 2012a).

❏ Native Americans tend to be affectionate with their children. Touching and closeness are integral in parent-child relationships (Joe & Malach, 2011).

❏ Children are often accorded great respect and given individual responsibility. They may even be allowed to make decisions for themselves about matters that other cultural groups tend to view as being too important to be left to a child or young adult.

❏ Between parents and children, there may be tolerance for mistakes, and little censure or punishment. A high level of independence is often permitted and even encouraged. Professionals from the majority culture, who value "taking charge," may see this as permissive and even neglectful (Sue & Sue, 2016).

❏ Native American children are encouraged to master self-care skills at an early age; children who help around the house are praised.

❏ Many Native Americans do not shower babies with compliments because such behavior draws attention that is believed to be harmful (Joe & Malach, 2011).

❏ In many tribes, there is a high fertility rate and a large percentage of out-of-wedlock births (Sue & Sue, 2016). Professionals must be careful when they describe the birth of a baby as "out of wedlock." As previously stated, in many tribes, men and women are married in tribal ceremonies that are not officially recognized by the United States government. Thus, the marriage "exists" by tribal standards but not by technical legal standards as mandated by mainstream society.

❏ Before Europeans came to North America, Native Americans valued all members of their families and communities as gifts from the spirit world. Violence was virtually nonexistent within families.

❏ Unfortunately, it is common for Native American families today to experience family violence, incest, homicide, and suicide within the family. Child abuse has become more prominent. These phenomena are manifestations of racism, internalized oppression, historical patterns of trauma, the impact of poverty, and other problems (Bureau of Indian Affairs, 2013).

Profile

I have had the privilege of working for the last five years with Sally D., a Yurok Native American Indian who is the lead teacher of our school's Head Start program. Sally is retiring, and I asked her what she will do in her retirement. A gifted teacher with a compassionate heart, Sally shared that she is going to try to start a library on her large Yurok Indian reservation up in northern California near the Oregon border. She shared that poverty, alcoholism, and domestic violence are prevalent on "the rez," and she hopes to begin making a difference for the children. We will be working together for the next several years, with me having the privilege of encouraging literacy through a children's book drive that I have sponsored for the past few years. I will bring free books to Sally's home here in the Sacramento area of California, and she will bring them to the reservation, create a library, and start a reading program. Though the focus is on children, I will be providing free books for teens and adults as well. It is exciting to be part of a project that works to incorporate literacy into the lives of Yurok families.

NATIVE AMERICAN EDUCATION AND LITERACY

❏ Educators continue to be concerned about the high dropout rate and low high school graduation rate of Native American students (Cerecer, 2013). At this time, 82.7% of the Native American population has at least a high school diploma, GED certificate, or alternative credential in comparison to 87% of the overall population. However, 19.1% of Native Americans have a bachelor's degree or higher in comparison with 30.6% of the U.S. population (U.S. Census Bureau, 2016).

❏ Many Native American students work at expected levels until they reach the fourth grade, where a pattern of decline and truancy begins to develop.

❏ Around seventh grade, achievement may dramatically decline because students who work hard in school are accused of "acting White" by their peers (Sue & Sue, 2016). By tenth grade, many Native American students are, on average, three years behind their peers (Powers, 2005).

❏ Some Native American young people can find jobs on the reservation, so they see no need for "White man's education." Becoming more educated may run counter to in-group values and create pressure for those who desire a higher or more formal education. In addition, there may be suspicion of "White man's educational system" (Tunison, 2013).

❏ In addition, children who are used to having large extended families around them may feel isolated when they "break out" and go to college. Relatives may view them as trying to break away from their culture. These factors make it even more challenging for young people to obtain a higher education.

Profile

Irene, Native American child care provider, Orangevale, California

I was blessed to be very gifted in art. I got a scholarship to attend university and get a Ph.D. in art. I moved away from my family and started my university art program. I loved it but was so homesick for my family that I dropped out of the program and went back to the reservation to be with my family. I became a child care provider, and have been doing this work for over 25 years now.

❏ Students may miss school because of traditional family obligations. Some also move on and off of reservations regularly. Sporadic attendance can cause them to fall behind academically and can create a conflict between family loyalties and school expectations.

❏ Many Native Americans value patience and the ability to wait quietly. Native American students are often thought to have a reflective rather than impulsive learning style. Thus, in school, the continuous flurry of activities according to a rigid schedule can cause confusion for these students.

❏ In many Native American tribes, an emphasis is placed on learning through observation. Children tend to refrain from performing skills until they have a thorough understanding of what to do.

❏ Native American students are often viewed as lacking motivation because of their reluctance to compete with peers in the classroom. Competitive behavior is considered to be an unacceptable expression of individuality and may be looked upon as an effort to show one's superiority (Sue & Sue, 2016).

❏ Information is often passed down from one generation to the next by story-telling (Inglebret et al., 2016). Some Native American groups had no system for writing down information until recently. Reading, therefore, is often not culturally reinforced and oral story-telling is emphasized over reading books.

❏ White-Kaulaity (2007) reported that nobody read to her on the Navajo reservation where she lived as a child; she emphasized that many Native Americans "...are masters of oral literacy. Unless there is a specific purpose, they choose not to bother with print literacy" (p. 560). She stated that to her grandmother, reading was a sign of laziness because, unlike household chores, reading does not require any overt physical activity. Moreover, reading and writing are often viewed as activities that produce no practical, visible, or tangible results.

❏ Some Native Americans consider reading and writing to be "White man's" activities. In many Native American communities, the oral tradition is far more valued.

❏ Paradis, Genesee, and Crago (2011) described language practices among the Inuit families of Canada. Inuit mothers often do not converse with their babies. Children's needs are met silently, and children are expected to look, listen, and observe. Children interact primarily with their peers. Listening to adults is emphasized more than speaking.

❏ Parents don't often read books with their children, and book-reading by older children may be frowned upon because the child is just sitting around instead of developing physical strength and prowess. Activities that strengthen the body and teach the child about the physical world are much more valued than literacy activities (Paradis et al., 2011).

CULTURAL CUSTOMS, COURTESIES, AND BELIEFS

❏ The tribe and reservation provide many Native Americans with a feeling of comfort and security. People see themselves as an extension of their tribe, so tribal connections are important.

❏ Many Native Americans judge each other and themselves in terms of whether or not their behaviors and actions benefit the tribe as a whole. Personal accomplishments are rewarded if they are of benefit to the tribe.

❏ It is considered culturally unacceptable in some tribes to seek outside assistance when a family is in need; the extended family is supposed to provide everything that is needed.

❏ Many Native Americans are taught not to interfere in the affairs of others (Joe & Malach, 2011). Thus, they may not give advice or information unless it is specifically asked of them.

❏ Most groups teach their younger members to show respect for authority and for the elderly, who are regarded as valuable sources of knowledge and experience (Westby & Inglebret, 2012).

❏ Happiness and harmony among individuals, society, and nature is emphasized (Chamberlain & Roseberry-McKibbin, 2008).

❏ Anglo American society emphasizes competition and winning. Native Americans believe in doing their best, but they do not want to stand out as being "superior" to others. As previously stated, Native Americans strive to avoid competing with peers.

❏ Native Americans are often reluctant to exalt themselves above others in their community; high achievers may downplay or even mask their talents in order to be accepted. Bragging about oneself and one's abilities is considered rude.

❏ A core value among many Native Americans involves The Circle of Life, which is believed to consist of the basic elements of life (earth, wind, fire, water). Nature's resources are viewed as gifts to be honored.

❏ Spiritual practices are such an integral part of everyday life that, in many Native American languages, there is no word for "religion." Some Native Americans practice a combination of Christianity and tribal ceremonies.

❏ Many tribes emphasize generosity in the sharing of resources, possessions, and self. Honor and respect are obtained through sharing and giving rather than through accumulating material goods.

❏ Many young Native Americans experience conflict between the old and new ways of doing things. They may feel that they are on a "bridge between two worlds." Parents and grandparents often hold beliefs that are rejected by the "younger generation" because of their desire to assimilate into White culture. This can lead to pain, frustration, and conflict within families.

❏ Ceremonies and traditional activities have an important place in the lives of many Native Americans. Some activities are highly spiritual, while others are social and recreational. Activities might include Pow Wows, giveaways, rodeos, and competitive dance contests.

❏ The establishment of human relationships is considered to be far more important than adherence to schedules. Punctuality and planning may be de-emphasized and even viewed negatively.

❏ Native Americans believe in being flexible, having a sense of humor, and accepting changes calmly and gracefully. James (2007) shared that the Native American concept of balance in life includes the famous saying, "If you are riding a horse and it dies, get off the horse."

❏ Native Americans are often encouraged to focus on the present moment rather than on the future.

Profile

As a part-time itinerant speech-language pathologist in the public schools, I have been providing speech and language intervention to "Sammy," a 15-year-old biracial White and Native American student. Sammy attends a high-security school because he had sexually molested young children. Sammy himself had experienced multiple episodes of sexual abuse from a young age. His father was recently released from prison after serving time for assault with a deadly weapon. Both of his parents have a history of drug and alcohol abuse.

When Sammy was born, he failed the universal newborn hearing screening, but his parents failed to follow through on recommendations that were made for further testing. At two years of age, it was determined that Sammy had serious hearing difficulties and that he would benefit from cochlear implants. He received a cochlear implant in his right ear, but his left ear remained unaided.

At this time, Sammy is a ward of the state. Neither of his parents want to care for him because they are afraid that he might harm his younger siblings. Restorative justice is emphasized in the school program, and he receives services from social workers and other mental health care professionals.

Sammy's speech is highly unintelligible and his language skills are approximately equivalent to those of an 8-year old. During his therapy sessions, he is always a sweet and hardworking student. When Sammy turned 15 a few months ago, I asked him what he wanted for his birthday. I knew that he would get nothing from his parents and hoped that his guardians at the group home would do something to celebrate. I bought him a blue Nike hoodie at his request. It was very rewarding and touching to see the huge smile on his face when I gave him his gift.

Although Sammy urgently needed a cochlear implant in his left ear, his parents did not sign the necessary papers. I talked with the school principal several times about this topic. The principal discussed this matter with Sammy's probation officer. After threatening legal action, the probation officer was able to get the parents to sign the necessary paperwork.

Sammy's speech and language skills are improving. Recently his mother reported that she can now understand Sammy's speech when he talks to her on the telephone.

Sammy told me that he wants to be an automobile mechanic. It is possible that he will be mainstreamed part time into a public high school so that he can take auto shop classes. Knowing that he may be attending a public high school soon, Sammy is especially motivated to work hard in therapy with me to improve his speech and language skills. Working with Sammy has been inspiring and a great gift to me.

HEALTH CARE AND DISABLING CONDITIONS

❏ In the U.S. as a whole, 9.4% of persons do not have health insurance. In contrast, over 21% of Native Americans lack health insurance. Thus, the number of uninsured Native Americans is more than double that of the general U.S. population (Centers for Disease Control and Prevention, 2017b; U.S. Census Bureau, 2016). If a Native American is not a member of a federally recognized tribe, it can be very challenging to obtain health services.

❏ In some tribes, medicine people serve a dual role as religious leaders and doctors for physical illnesses. Many medicine people believe in treating the whole person, not just the affected part of the body.

❏ There is a lack of effective, comprehensive health and prevention programs for Native Americans, although the Indian Health Service (IHS) has attempted to provide as many health services as possible. Because many Native Americans live in urban areas, they have limited or no access to IHS services. Some Native Americans have two residences—one on the reservation, and one in an urban area where health care is more accessible.

❏ Most Native American health facilities are difficult to staff. They are located in isolated rural areas on or near reservations.

❏ A major variable contributing to health problems among Native Americans is the housing on reservations. Many families live in government housing that is poorly insulated. Other families live in mobile homes or tar-paper shacks. Often, three generations live together under one roof.

❏ Some of the most common health problems experienced by Native Americans are obesity and diabetes, stroke, heart disease, cancer, and cirrhosis of the liver. Other health problems common among Native Americans include gastrointestinal disease, malignant neoplasms, and tuberculosis.

❏ In the early 21st century, Native Americans had the second highest infant death rate in the U.S. Their infant death rate was 48.4% higher than the infant death rate among White mothers (Center for Disease Prevention and Control, 2011).

❏ A high incidence of alcoholism among Native Americans is a well-documented phenomenon. Alcohol use often starts when Native Americans are young teenagers.

❏ Almost half of Native American deaths are due to cirrhosis of the liver. In fact, the number of alcohol-related deaths is five times greater among Native Americans than among Americans as a whole.

❏ The incidence of Native American babies born with Fetal Alcohol Syndrome (FAS) is much higher than the incidence within the general population; approximately 20% of Native American babies are born with FAS.

❏ Among many Native Americans, alcoholism is related to poverty, lack of education, unemployment, poor living conditions on reservations, social pressure, and hopelessness about life (Sue & Sue, 2016).

❏ Anxiety and depression also contribute to substance abuse, and diagnostic rates of these problems in Native American youth equal or exceed rates in youth of other racial groups (Listug-Lunde, Vogeltnz-Holm, & Collins, 2013).

❏ There have been some recent efforts to educate Native American youth about safe sex practices and issues relating to the misuse of drugs (Kenyon & Hanson, 2012; Kulis, Dustman, Brown, & Martinez, 2013; Leston, Jessen, & Simons, 2013).

❏ Unfortunately, Native American women are often physically and sexually abused beginning early in life. This has been linked to stressors associated with economic and social marginalization and with changes in traditional roles for men and women (Sue & Sue, 2016).

❏ Suicide occurs more frequently among Native American youth than among individuals from other groups (D'Oro, 2011). Native American young men who are on the journey from adolescence to adulthood are especially at risk.

❏ Conditions such as substance abuse, diabetes, and heart disease occur more frequently in families who experience high levels of poverty (Westby and Englebret, 2012).

❏ Leading causes of death among Native Americans include 1) heart disease, 2) cancer, and 3) accidents (unintentional injuries) (Centers for Disease Control and Prevention, 2017).

❏ Higher than average prevalences of certain health conditions associated with communication disorders are reported for the Native American population. Otitis media, bacterial meningitis, fetal alcohol syndrome, and cleft lip and palate, for example, are all more prevalent among Native American than among other groups.

❏ Most tribal lands are located in remote rural areas of the U.S.; they lack public transportation systems, making it difficult for persons with disabilities to function independently.

❏ Healing and purification ceremonies are quite common among many tribes (Joe & Malach, 2011). Many of the herbs used by Native American medicine men have been shown to have true healing properties.

❏ Some Native Americans accept a child with a disability as the Great Spirit's gift; others may believe that the disability resulted from witchcraft or moral transgressions.

❏ Many Native Americans believe that thoughts, words, and actions have the power to bring about misfortunes such as disabilities, serious illnesses, or even death. Allison and Vining (1999, p. 198) stated that "Out of this basic belief comes the assumption that parents and family members have a clear and ever-present responsibility for causing and preventing serious illness and disability in children."

❏ Some Native Americans believe that a child is born with a disability because that child has made a choice prenatally to be disabled. Other beliefs about what causes disabilities have been described in the literature (Joe & Malach, 2011; Paul et al., 2018; Sue & Sue, 2016; Vining, 1999; Westby & Inglebret, 2012) and include the following:

1. Events and experiences encountered by the Holy People
2. Traditional teachings not being honored
3. Curses placed on the child
4. Taboos violated by parents (e.g., the mother viewed a solar or lunar eclipse during pregnancy)

❏ Many Native Americans are unaware of services provided by speech-language pathologists and may have their own ways of treating communication disorders. Individuals from the Navajo tribe, for example, often believe that certain types of communication disorders can be treated by performing rituals such as breaking a pot over a child's head, having a child eat roasted corn with straight kernels, or holding a purification ceremony (Vining, 1999).

❏ For many Native Americans in the U.S. and Canada, speech-language services are hard to access for a variety of reasons. Native Americans may live in remote places. Jurisdiction is an issue—who pays for the services? Lack of access to services of health care professionals overall is a serious issue for many Native Americans ((Kay-Raining Bird, 2011; Listug-Lunde, Vogeltanz-Holm, & Collins, 2013).

Profile

A young girl from the Cherokee tribe was referred to the early intervention team after enrolling in a local preschool. The child had been born with cerebral palsy. The team head arranged to visit the family at home to talk about services for the child (speech, occupational, and physical therapy). Upon visiting the home, the team leader found that the family expressed gratitude for the child's cerebral palsy. The mother shared that this condition was a gift from the Great Spirit to help her become a more patient person. She added that she had also been given the opportunity to appreciate every minor development her child made. The family stated that they would like to postpone rehabilitative efforts until their daughter was in kindergarten.

NATIVE AMERICAN COMMUNICATION STYLES

❑ Respect is highly valued; one way of signifying respect for another person is to avoid eye contact by looking down.

❑ The Navajo culture values an introspective, quiet demeanor, which may seem "withdrawn" to mainstream Americans (Owens, 2016).

❑ Children's communication with adults is respectful and discrete, with little eye contact. A child who makes eye contact may be considered defiant, disrespectful, or rude.

❑ Native American mothers, especially those in the Navajo population, may be silent during interactions with their infants. As mentioned previously, Inuit mothers in Canada are also silent with their infants, expecting them to learn by listening, watching, and observing (Genesee et al., 2011).

❑ In many families, adults either do not carry out verbal exchanges with infants or they respond to infants' vocalizations as if these vocalizations carry no meaning.

❑ Most children are taught that one learns more by listening and observing than by speaking (Tsethlikai & Rogoff, 2013).

❑ Native American etiquette requires a lapse of time between the asking and answering of a question. Some Native Americans believe that an immediate answer to a question implies that the question was not worth thinking about. People who answer a question quickly or interrupt someone else may be considered immature.

❑ Children often do not answer a question unless they are confident that their answer is correct.

❑ Parents often feel that their children's auditory comprehension skills are more advanced than their expressive language skills.

❑ Children are generally discouraged from speaking the tribal language before they are capable of correct articulation. Opportunities for oral practice in the language may be limited.

❑ In many Native American tribes, silence is valued. Among some Western Apache Indians, children may be rebuked for "talking like a White man" if they speak English or talk too much in the village.

❑ Children do not express opinions on certain subjects because they first need to earn the right to express such opinions.

❑ In many groups, it is considered inappropriate for a person to express strong feelings publicly. Adults usually express grief around outsiders only during official mourning ceremonies.

Tech Tie-In

In a YouTube video, Terry Teller expresses the importance of preserving the Navajo language. He talks about how technology can facilitate this preservation. https://www.youtube.com/watch?v=ScL4l0RzMHs

NATIVE AMERICAN LANGUAGE CONSIDERATIONS

❏ There are approximately 296 Native American languages in North America, and dialectal variations exist within each of these languages.

❏ Twenty seven percent of Native Americans 5 years of age or older speak a language other than English at home, compared with 21.5% of the population as a whole (U.S. BOC, 2016).

❏ Six general "families" of Native American languages are Eskimo-Aleut, Algonquin, Penutian, Na-Dane', Macro-Siouan, and Aztec-Tanoan. Some of the most commonly spoken Native American languages in the U.S. are Navajo, Teton Sioux, Cherokee, and Dinneh.

❏ There has been much concern about the decline of indigenous languages—not only in the U.S., but also in Canada, Australia, and New Zealand (Loakes, Moses, Wigglesworth, Simpson, & Billington, 2013). Thus, efforts are being made to maintain and revitalize these languages (Kay-Raining Bird, 2011; Leedom Shaul, 2014; Westby & Inglebret, 2012). In schools on some reservations, there are immersion preschools to help young Native American children learn the native language.

❏ The importance of language within culture was described by Kay-Raining Bird (2011, p. 121):

> Language is a central and integral component of culture. For both individuals and communities, cultural experiences are mediated by, framed within, and to a certain extent formed by the languages we speak. Clearly, language loss negatively impacts cultural integrity, and efforts to stem the tide are critical to the well-being of Indigenous communities.

❏ Many Indian languages have no word for time, contain no future-tense verbs, and are based almost entirely on the present tense.

❏ Many Native American languages contain fewer vowel sounds than English. The English sound system is often difficult for students to master.

❏ Native American languages contain some sounds that do not occur in English. For example, there may be voiceless stops in combination with velar fricatives, ejectives (sounds made with a glottalic egressive airstream), and implosives (sounds made with an ingressive glottalic airstream).

❏ Navajo belongs to the Athabaskan language family, one of the most widespread indigenous language families on the North American continent. Navajo itself is spoken primarily in the Four Corners region of the U.S. Southwest, where the Navajo Nation encompasses parts of New Mexico, Utah, and Arizona. North of Mexico, there are more speakers of Navajo than any other indigenous language.

❏ The Navajo language is a complex language with many different vowel sounds and tones. Most English speakers find that Navajo is a difficult language for them to speak with correct pronunciation (Benally & Carey, 2013).

❏ Among the consonants, the glottal stop is one of the few sounds that is common to most Native American languages. In addition, many vowels are nasalized.

❏ There are other differences between Native American languages and Mainstream American English (MAE) that make MAE difficult for Native Americans to master. For example, word order may change, even in the same language, depending on the speaker's intended meaning. Pronoun deletion is also common.

❑ Harris (1998), in her extensive description of the Navajo language, details other differences, such as the language's absence of gender and its intricate verb system. Professionals should be aware that Native American students learning English may struggle in school because Native American languages are so different from English.

It is beyond the scope of this book to describe the characteristics of all the Native American languages spoken in the United States. Consultation with native speakers is important in situations where a problem is suspected. For more specific information about Native American languages, see Westby and Inglebret (2012).

IMPLICATIONS FOR PROFESSIONALS

❑ In order to gain increased knowledge about Native American cultures and languages, professionals should work closely with Native American community mentors and attend appropriate cultural events. It may be especially helpful to work with elders.

❑ Many Native Americans believe in taking life as it comes and accepting all circumstances; professionals should not interpret this as passivity and as resistance to change.

❑ If a member of an urban-dwelling family needs health care that can only be obtained on a reservation, the entire family must relocate, sometimes resulting in a situation in which children miss school for a period of time.

❑ Pow-wows are sacred and often honor elders and ancestors. Thus parents may remove their children from school to take them to pow-wows, ceremonies, and events considered important within the culture.

❑ Some tribal groups are forced to constantly choose between White people's modern medicine and traditional Native American approaches. This can cause uncertainty and guilt for some tribal members.

❑ It is often appropriate to consult with an Indian medicine person before recommending a therapeutic intervention or medical procedure.

❑ Professionals should not be surprised if grandparents show up for conferences instead of parents.

❑ To maintain pride, some families are reluctant to take advantage of aid and services that are available, such as health care, welfare, legal aid, and counseling. Well-founded mistrust of the "establishment," including government agencies, may also contribute to their reluctance to accept assistance. Part of this mistrust stems from the aforementioned historical forced placement of children into boarding schools.

❑ Because of their history of being forced into boarding schools, some Native Americans are distrustful of the educational system or the professionals who work within it. Professionals will need to work hard to gain their trust, as many Native Americans have had bad educational experiences within mainstream schools.

❑ In a similar vein, when families do seek health care or services such as speech-language remediation, they may be slow to open up to professionals. Professionals should take time to build trust (Sue & Sue, 2016). At the beginning of meetings and visits with families, it is important for professionals to engage in small talk to establish rapport with family members.

❏ When professionals introduce themselves, it is appropriate to tell the family what geographic location they are from. Because land is so important to Native Americans, they are interested in the professional's geographic roots.

❏ Some Native Americans are unwilling to discuss family affairs freely. They may believe that words have power to hurt as well as heal, so they feel that if they even discuss a disabling condition, the discussion itself may lead to problems for the person or the family as a whole.

❏ It is critical to reach out to the families, both immediate and extended (especially the grandparents), of Native American students. One should not attempt to treat the student in isolation. Many Native American families view rehabilitation as a family-centered rather than client-centered affair.

❏ Professionals should be flexible when scheduling meetings. It is also important for Native Americans to understand that schools within the United States are "time-oriented" institutions with schedules that professionals need to maintain. Developing an understanding of our time-dominated mainstream social system is critical.

❏ Professionals should address all family members during meetings, rather than addressing only the parents.

❏ If families feel that personnel are hurried, they may not discuss their true concerns. Allow plenty of time for meetings so that families will not feel rushed.

❏ As a sign of respect, family members may avoid eye contact with school professionals and refrain from asking direct questions.

❏ Native Americans may nod and smile when professionals make recommendations, but this does not necessarily mean that they will comply with the suggestions. They may be acting politely because of their respect for professionals, even if they do not intend to follow through on suggestions. Professionals must work hard to make sure that their suggestions are culturally appropriate. As previously mentioned, Native Americans from the community can facilitate communication between school professionals and parents.

❏ Professionals should always ask families to share concerns that they have regarding the use of interpreters; families may be uncomfortable using interpreters selected by school professionals.

❏ Parents of Native American children with disabilities may not be aware of the support and services their children are entitled to receive. They may need help in advocating effectively for their children.

❏ Support groups should be provided when possible. The traditional group approach to problem-solving in some tribes fits ideally with the support group concept, and professionals can take advantage of this.

❏ Some families (e.g., Navajo) do not attach great importance to developmental milestones. They feel that children will develop individually at their own pace. Thus, during the gathering of the case history, professionals may find that parents/caretakers are unable to provide details about children's acquisition of specific skills.

❏ Research relating to the acquisition of gross motor developmental milestones indicates that Native American infants may develop specific skills (e.g., walking) later than infants from other ethnic groups (Harris, 1998). Professionals must keep this in mind and avoid labeling these children inappropriately as "delayed."

❏ Efforts should be made to preserve students' traditions. For example, native styles of dress should be accepted as much as possible within the school setting.

❏ Students may experience conflicts in educational situations in which they are asked to complete culturally inappropriate activities (e.g., dissecting animals in traditional biology classes). Professionals should give Native American students alternate assignments in these situations.

❏ School professionals need to be aware that certain markings or objects (e.g., amulets) may be placed on Native American students during sacred ceremonies. It is important to learn about these customs so that students are not criticized or punished for culturally appropriate behavior.

❏ When professionals arrive at the home for a previously scheduled meeting, they should make sure that the family is ready for their visit. If family members are involved in a religious ceremony or some other activity, they may not wish to be interrupted.

❏ During home visits, professionals should not assume that they can choose where to sit. They should ask the family if there is a place to sit. In the home, it is customary to address all who are present.

❏ Professionals may be offered food or coffee in the home. If the professional chooses to refuse these offerings, an explanation should be provided (e.g., "I have just finished eating.").

❏ Some studies have shown that Native American students tend to perform better on tests of spatial ability and visual skills than on tests of verbal and/or auditory skills (Harris, 1985; Harris, 1998; McAvoy & Sidles, 1991). Professionals should be aware of this in assessment situations.

❏ Certain pictures, toys, dolls, and animals may be viewed as causes of evil or bad luck by members of specific tribes. The family should be consulted to make sure that the materials used in assessment and intervention are appropriate.

❏ As stated, it is culturally appropriate within many Native American groups for children to avoid eye contact with adults. Professionals should not misinterpret this as evidence of shyness, immaturity, rudeness, or a deficit in pragmatic language skills.

❏ Native American students often respond well when professionals attempt to strengthen interpersonal relationships with them. Strong relationships between students and professionals promote a feeling of belonging and may help students negotiate cultural discontinuities between home and school. Personal warmth may be especially effective.

❏ Tsethlikai and Rogoff (2013) examined incidental recall of a folktale told to 91 nine-year-old Tohono O'odham Native American children. It was found that cultural engagement significantly predicted incidental story recall for all children, including those who overheard it and those who were directly told the story. Some children recalled the story well by just listening and overhearing it, showing that the Native American emphasis on learning by listening can be applied to story-telling/recall situations.

❏ Native American students may be incorrectly diagnosed as having language impairments if they do not interact with adult examiners or if they give limited responses. These behaviors, however, are often culturally appropriate for situations in which children are asked to respond to questions from an adult authority figure.

❏ Costa-Guerra and Rhein (2011) conducted a study with Tewa and Deneh parents of children with language impairment. They found that, within this population, use of nonspecific vocabulary, having a short mean length of utterance, frequent pauses in connected speech, and failure to initiate conversations may be typical language behaviors rather than indicators of a language impairment.

❏ During assessment and intervention, silence is often a culturally appropriate response. Remember, students are taught to reflect before answering a question. Students should not be penalized when they fail to respond immediately to questions directed toward them. It might be best to start off with closed questions that are easy for children to answer, and then progress to more open-ended questions as the students become more comfortable.

❏ Scores on formal tests may fall "below the norm" because of a variety of factors. Low parental education, poverty, nonstandard English usage, lack of facility with English, poor health and nutrition, limited experience in taking formal tests, and other factors are likely to influence the test performance of Native American students (Harrington & Pavel, 2013). This is especially true when taking tests that emphasize auditory and verbal skills (Robinson-Zañartu, 1996).

❏ Many Native American children will not respond to a question if the answer is something that the person asking the question already knows. The child, for example, might not respond to the test question, "What color is a banana?" Assessment personnel may incorrectly conclude that the child has limited knowledge of basic vocabulary.

❏ To assess Native American students in a nonbiased manner, dynamic assessment strategies are recommended (Long, 2013). Language samples, portfolios, narrative assessment, and questionnaires are also helpful in collecting nonbiased assessment data (Westby & Inglebret, 2012). Table 7.1 lists patterns of narrative discourse that are typical in Native American student populations.

❏ In terms of intervention, Native American students tend to have strengths in the visual modality and often learn quickly by observing the behavior of others. Professionals can make use of these strengths to enhance learning. For example, colorful visual aids can be used to complement material delivered auditorily.

❏ Many Native American children are "whole-to-parts learners" (Long, 2013). They perform best if they see the whole, or "big picture" first; then they can begin to understand individual and discrete parts of the whole, using simultaneous rather than sequential processing.

❏ In addition, most Native American students are "hands-on" learners. They benefit best from experiential teaching. They tend to have strong spatial skills and have been described by some Native American professionals as being strongly "right brained" (S. Gaskell, personal communication, 3/22/17).

❏ Many Native American students perform more readily when learning activities are presented in a group situation. Individual instruction may, therefore, be less effective than group instruction. Cooperative learning situations are ideal for many Indian students (Inglebret et al., 2016).

❏ As previously mentioned, many Native American students feel uncomfortable in competitive situations—they believe they should not stand out from the group.

Table 7.1

Narrative Discourse Style Patterns in Native Americans

1. In contrast to Mainstream American English (MAE) speakers, who tell narratives with explicit details, Native American children may seem "minimalist" in their storytelling.

2. Plot structure differs in Native American stories. For example, story tellers may give more attention to information regarding background and setting than to initiating events and consequences.

3. Stories among Native Americans, especially the Navajo, may focus less on details relating to plot development than on descriptions of the landscape, places passed, etc.

4. Native Americans make fewer story elements explicit, relying upon the listener to "fill in" details in their own minds.

5. Native Americans may not fill in background details but, rather, "dive right in" to the story, expecting listeners to infer background information.

6. Native American stories often have purposes relating to how others should behave (e.g., warning others to change their ways).

7. Rather than telling stories in a structured, linear manner, many Native Americans tell stories in a circular manner. Story components are described as they occur in the speaker's mind.

8. In many mainstream stories, a happy ending relates to achievements and accomplishments made by an individual. In Native American stories, a happy ending results in positive outcomes for the whole group (e.g., the tribe).

Adapted from Costa-Guerra & Rhein, 2011; Paradis et al., 2011; Sue & Sue, 2016; Tsethlikai & Rogoff, 2013; Westby & Inglebret, 2012.

❑ Because Native American students often do not wish to be singled out from the group, they should be praised for special accomplishments in situations where others are not present. In some traditional cultures, it is taught that children should not attempt to outshine their peers.

❑ Some Native American children give less feedback than Anglo children during interactions (e.g., nodding, smiling, looking at the speaker). It is important not to judge these children as having clinically significant pragmatic language problems.

❑ Because many Native American families do not send their children to preschool, they should be informed about the advantages of participation in these programs. Care must be taken not to imply that families are "wrong" for keeping their children at home. Caregivers should be welcome to stay at the preschool and carry out volunteer activities; this permits them to remain near their children.

❏ In the Anglo European-American culture, children are encouraged to use the trial-and-error method of learning; for some Native American children, however, the cultural norm is that competence should truly precede performance. Many Native American students will observe an activity repeatedly before attempting to engage in it themselves Thus, professionals should allow Native American students to watch activities several times before participating; they should not be required to engage in trial-and-error behavior.

❏ In addition, Native American students may respond more often if they are allowed longer "wait times." Because of the cultural emphasis on silence, these students often do not answer a question immediately—but they will respond eventually if professionals are willing to wait.

❏ Because of the cultural emphasis on cooperation rather than competition, Native American students may feel uncomfortable defending themselves verbally or openly disagreeing with others. Thus, Native American students may need extra support in these kinds of situations.

❏ Because of cultural differences in the importance of time and punctuality, some Native American students have difficulty understanding why homework assignments are due on a specific date. This should not be interpreted as laziness or irresponsible behavior.

❏ Professionals should use materials in assessment and intervention that are culturally relevant (Harrington & Pavel, 2013; Inglebret et al., 2016; Lopez, Heilig, & Schram, 2013). Native American children and children from other cultural backgrounds may enjoy learning about local Indian history and traditions.

❏ Using Native American folktales for intervention activities is recommended. However, Reese (2007), a Pueblo Indian expert, stressed that these folktales not just represent Indians as "a vanquished people of the past" (p. 247). Current, modern-day Indians should also be pictured. Reese also recommended that stories depicting families should include extended families, not just nuclear ones.

❏ Inglebret, Bear Eagle, and Pavel (2007), reflecting a view that all things in life are interconnected, stated that many stories are told through the elements of the natural environment—plants, animals, and the forces of fire, wind, water, and earth. These stories frequently carry a message about the importance of caring for Mother Earth.

❏ Stories and intervention activities can emphasize the Native American concept of the Medicine Wheel, symbolizing the cyclical nature of the self and of the world.

❏ The Medicine Wheel depicts four directions, each of which represents an aspect of life that is necessary for harmony: mind, body, natural environment, and spirit. These directions or inner dimensions are connected dimensions flowing from one another. This interrelatedness of all living beings is symbolized by the Circle of Life, which is expressed in Native American art and tradition.

❏ Relevant activities that utilize these principles can involve the use of nature and pets in therapy. For example, children may plant gardens or care for animals.

❏ When evaluating Native American children for the possible presence of a communication disorder, professionals must be careful not to view culturally appropriate narrative differences as signs of a language impairment. For example, as stated, Native American children may tell stories in a manner that is circular, they may omit information that the listener is supposed to infer, and they may use a "minimalist" style that does not have the plot markers expected by mainstream clinicians and teachers.

❏ The celebration of holidays such as Thanksgiving and Columbus Day may be perceived as culturally insensitive by Native Americans. For many of them, Columbus Day is a day of mourning. The arrival of Columbus in North America is viewed as the beginning of cultural genocide among many Native American communities.

❏ Feathers are sacred to Native Americans and, therefore, their use in instructional activities may be viewed as offensive and disrespectful.

❏ Professionals should avoid using materials and terms that portray Native Americans in ways that promote negative stereotypes (e.g., using terms such as *injun, squaw, savage,* or *papoose;* singing songs such as "Ten Little Indians," or making a whooping war cry).

❏ To support Native American students with expressive language delays, professionals can utilize the Talking Circle, a group activity that emphasizes respect for self and others (Hunter & Sawyer, 2006; Rybak et al., 2004; Szlemko et al., 2006). The purpose of the Talking Circle is to bring people together and have them share. Everyone learns to speak and also to listen respectfully using the following activity:

  1. In the Talking Circle, an instrument is introduced. It can be an item such as a totem or decorated stick that is called the Talking Stick. After an individual speaks, she hands the Talking Stick to another group member.
  2. Individuals in the group who are handed the Talking Stick are not required to speak; they may hand the Talking Stick to someone else. The Talking Circle, again, can be used to encourage verbal expression, improve listening comprehension, and develop conversational turn-taking skills in students.

❏ Some Native Americans rename a child with an animal name to denote the values of strength and courage as well as to demonstrate respect for the child. In Native American folklore, certain animals stand for specific virtues. For example, dogs stand for loyalty, turtles for perseverance, hawks for watchfulness, ants or bees for cooperation, and squirrels for thriftiness.

❏ Children can be asked which animal they admire most and why. They can assign the name trait to themselves, design a mask, and write an essay or poem that describes the animal's qualities and how they relate to this animal. They can then wear the mask while sharing the essay or poem with the group.

❏ An activity called "Earth's gift" is also relevant for building self esteem and encouraging the development of receptive and expressive language skills. The professional should get a large stick and take a group of children on a nature walk. Each child makes an effort to find something special to contribute to the decoration of the stick. When each child finds a special object, he brings it to the group, talks about it, tells why it has special qualities, and then attaches it to the stick. All children are reminded to thank Mother Earth for sharing this special gift with them and to remember the importance of protecting the gifts that nature freely provides. The stick can then be presented to a special adult in the children's lives (Hunter & Sawyer, 2006).

❏ Story-telling is important within Native American families and can be used as a tool for teaching vocabulary. Stories should be accompanied by clear, nonbiased, realistic illustrations. Some students prefer to hear a story in its entirety before discussing it or answering questions about it.

❑ As previously mentioned, White-Kaulaity (2007) and Westby and Inglebret (2012) emphasized that oral traditions are far more important to many Native Americans than written traditions, and that for Native American people, reading has not traditionally been a way to attain knowledge. White-Kaulaity, Westby and Inglebret, and Inglebret et al. (2016) suggested specific strategies that professionals can use to help Native American children increase their literacy skills:

1. Use wordless books so that children can turn the pages and make up stories about pictures as they go.
2. Encourage children, especially young ones, to learn tribal songs.
3. Remember that many Native Americans especially value stories that include animals and that feature content of a sacred or spiritual nature.
4. Choose books that contain a considerable amount of dialogue. Rather than reading long descriptions of events, Native American students often prefer to "listen to people talking" in the pages of a book.
5. Remember that some students struggle with reading. Provide extra support for them, especially in the form of one-on-one assistance. This support can also be provided by older peer tutors or even adult volunteers.
6. Older Native American students may especially enjoy stories with Indian protagonists with whom they can relate.
7. It is helpful to read stories aloud and talk with the students before, during, and after presenting the stories. This helps students connect oral words to printed words.
8. Use differentiated instruction (DI) that promotes a high quality, flexible learning environment, individually-tailored learning, and activities that align with students' unique strengths. Be sure to interconnect the curricular elements of content, process, and product.
9. Use activities that connect students to the local community and allow students to "give back." For example, Inglebret et al. (2016) recommended that students create works of art that can be displayed in the community, teach what they have learned to younger children (mentoring), etc.
10. Remember that historical events commonly discussed within the school curriculum may be interpreted very differently by Native Americans. For example, Inglebret et al. (2016) discussed the fact that the "adventures of Lewis and Clark" may have been viewed very differently by the Native Americans who Lewis and Clark encountered on their journey across the U.S. Professionals should be aware and sensitive to how Native Americans may perceive "traditional" historical events that are told from a mainstream U.S. point of view.

Profile

Luis, a five-year-old Native American child from the Shoshone tribe, was referred to the special education team by his kindergarten teacher for assessment. She stated that Luis was "non-participatory, extremely shy, and lacking in social skills." In addition, he seemed to "catch on very slowly to new information" and was "slow to process directions."

The special education team contacted a member of the Shoshone tribe for a consultation. Joy Buffalo Earthwoman, the tribal member, observed Luis in class on several different occasions. When she reported back to the team, she indicated that Luis was behaving in a manner consistent with what he had learned growing up on the reservation. She cautioned that his parents had told him that he shouldn't talk too much or he will "sound like a White person." Thus, the team concluded that it was unnecessary to carry out an evaluation of Luis' cognitive and linguistic skills.

A Shoshone tutor was hired to work with Luis for 30 minutes each day in the classroom. At the end of the year, Luis was performing at grade level and had learned to be "bicultural" by speaking more frequently in the classroom, although he still remained quiet, as was culturally appropriate, when in the presence of adults on the reservation. Luis said, "At school, I talk like White people. At home, I'm an Indian."

Insights and Memories from a Special Native American
Remembering Alethea Chamberlain, member of the Linan Apache Indian tribe

This chapter is dedicated to the memory of Alethea Chamberlain, a dear friend and former graduate student from the Linan Apache Indian tribe. After a courageous fight with brain cancer, Alethea passed away in September, 2011. She personally taught me so much about her people, and I am indebted to her for her insights, wisdom, and friendship. She will always be remembered with love and gratitude. The following information is based upon a lecture she gave in my university senior class, Communication Disorders in Multicultural Populations.

Among my people, if you pursue a higher education, you are viewed as "acting White." You are crossing enemy lines, and you may get flack from members of your tribe. My mother was an Apache Indian, and my father was Hispanic. He always told me "Indians are dirty—tell people you're Mexican." Among my people, it is not frowned upon to get pregnant around 14 or 15 years of age. Birth control is not a priority. There are many single moms among my people, and as families, we try to live close to one another. As Indians, we value silence and learn by observation. We don't like to draw attention to ourselves. If you speak up too much, this is boastful; our actions should speak for us, not our words. It is not appropriate for children to verbally display themselves in front of adults. If a child misbehaves, it is dealt with privately and quietly, not publicly in front of others. When you reinforce a Native child for good behavior, don't be too bubbly—a simple nod and smile are enough.

As Indians, we value harmony and balance with nature. Water is spirit, wind is mind, earth is body, and fire is strength and power. All these elements must be in balance. Our medicine wheel has these four elements, and they must be in balance with one another. We do not believe in owning land—all of us share Mother Earth. Trees are our protectors. To us, the bear claw symbolizes strength.

When Alethea was first diagnosed with brain cancer, she went and got several tattoos to help her courageously deal with her illness. On her right forearm was a beautiful tattoo of a Medicine Wheel. On her left shoulder was a large tattoo of a tree. These tattoos helped Alethea to face her illness with courage and dignity. I was so privileged to be part of her journey, to support her, and hear her stories. She taught me a great deal, and her memory will always be with me.

I wish to offer my thanks and grateful acknowledgements to Dr. Sandra Gaskell, a speech-language pathologist, archaeologist, and member of the Southern New Jersey Lenape People, for her comments, edits, and suggestions relating to the content of this chapter.

STUDY QUESTIONS

1. Describe health issues that tend to impact members of the Native American community. What impact might these issues have on communication skills?

2. Summarize important points that you will keep in mind when working with Native American families.

3. You are giving an in-service to some student interns who are going to begin working in a Head Start program attended by many Native American children. List and describe five recommendations to help them provide services in a culturally sensitive and appropriate manner.

MULTIPLE CHOICE

4. Which one of the following is NOT considered characteristic of Native American communication styles?

   A. There is a great deal of nodding, smiling, and interjecting during conversations.
   B. Children look down or away to show respect for elders.
   C. In many families, adults do not carry out verbal exchanges with infants.
   D. It is polite to hesitate for a period of time before answering a question.
   E. Children may be rebuked for talking too much.

5. With regard to health care and longevity, which of the following statements are true?

   A. Native Americans have a high incidence of otitis media.
   B. Diseases common among Native Americans include diabetes, gastrointestinal disease, malignant neoplasms, and tuberculosis.
   C. The average life span within the Native American population is 82 years.
   D. Alcohol consumption is viewed as sinful and occurs rarely in Native American populations.

6. Native American students often experience challenges in the education system for the following reasons:

    A. There are many differences between Native American languages and mainstream English.
    B. Impulsivity is a common characteristic of their behavior.
    C. Confusion may result from a rigid classroom schedule packed with activities.
    D. Their competitive nature often results in disruptions within the classroom.
    E. They may not respond to a question if they are confident that the adult already knows the answer.

7 Culturally sensitive service delivery to Native American students and their families would include keeping the following facts in mind:

    A. Story-telling is not important and should be avoided because it is not culturally congruent for students.
    B. It is important to engage students in non-competitive, cooperative learning activities.
    C. Teachers should single out children so that they can be praised in front of their peers.
    D. The professional should ask a wide range of personal questions to demonstrate a sincere interest in what family members know.

8. Which one of the following is NOT commonly observed among Native Americans?

    A. They may be reluctant to discuss personal affairs.
    B. They try to avoid interfering in the affairs of others.
    C. Some believe that a child's disability is a gift.
    D. Happiness and harmony are valued highly.
    E. They greatly value the accumulation of material possessions.

9. You are working with Ahote, a Native American 5-year-old child who just started kindergarten. Ahote is a sweet, shy girl who has not been to preschool. She is reportedly very close to her family, and has been cared for primarily by her grandparents and extended family. You find out through appropriately sensitive assessment that Ahote does not have a language impairment; she is a typically-developing language learner. However, Ahote's teacher tells you that she is at risk for being retained in kindergarten if she does not make more progress in her English language and academic skills. Though you will not be seeing Ahote for speech-language therapy, you want to help the team make recommendations that will support Ahote's success in school. Which of the following would NOT be appropriate recommendations?

    A. Encourage Ahote to make direct eye contact during interactions with adults and to be verbally assertive both at school and at home.
    B. Meet with Ahote's extended family and have a respected member of the tribe present; at this meeting, ask the family if they would be willing to "read" wordless books with Ahote at home in their native language.
    C. When Ahote raises her hand in class and speaks, bring her to the front of the classroom and praise her for initiating in the classroom setting.
    D. Take advantage of the after-school "Homework Club," so that Ahote can meet privately with an adult tutor when help is needed with homework assignments.
    E. If Ahote does not know answers to questions, do not make her "guess" and do not use a trial-and-error method to arrive at conclusions.

10. Kwahu is a 10-year-old Native American boy who speaks Hopi and may have a language impairment. His mother, grandfather, and an aunt tell you that Kwahu is "different" from the other boys in his tribe. They have requested an evaluation. You do not speak Hopi, but a member of the tribe who is a teacher's aide in a local school has volunteered to assist you. What is important to remember as you prepare to evaluate Kwahu's language skills?

   A. Dynamic assessment may yield more valid results than standardized tests because standardized tests are likely to be biased.
   B. Kwahu may avoid eye contact with you and be silent in your presence; if so, these are signs of a language impairment and indicate that in therapy, you will need to work on his pragmatics skills.
   C. Narrative assessment may reveal that Kwahu's uses a "minimalist" communication style when telling stories. He gives little background information, but this is not a sign of a disorder.
   D. Kwahu may respond well if you are warm and caring.
   E. If you ask Kwahu questions and he takes a long time to answer, this is probably indicative of a clinically significant processing problem that will need to be addressed in therapy.

ANSWERS TO STUDY QUESTIONS

   4. A
   5. A and B
   6. A, C, and E
   7. B
   8. E
   9. A, C
   10. A, C, D

Chapter 8

Families from Pacific Island Backgrounds

Outline
- General Background information
- Pacific Island Family Life
- Pacific Island Education
- Cultural Customs and Courtesies
- Health Care and Disabling Conditions
- Pacific Island Communication Styles
- Pacific Island Language Considerations
- Implications for Professionals

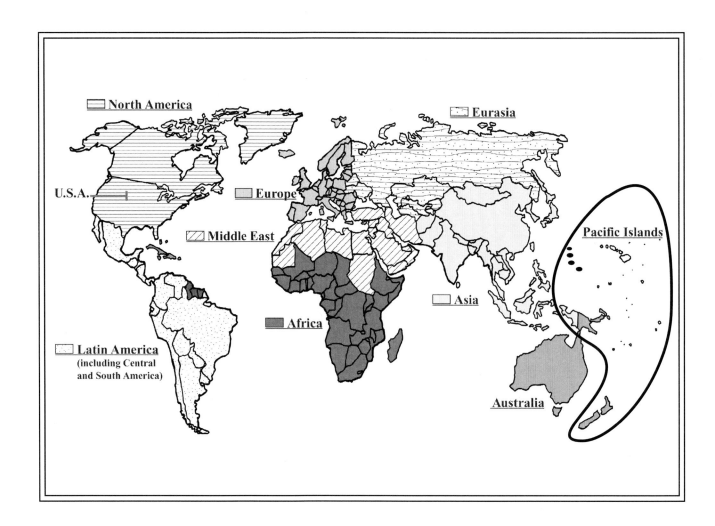

The three major regions of the Pacific Islands are Melanesia, Micronesia, and Polynesia, as shown in Figure 8.1. Within each of these areas are several island groups. Each island nation has a unique history that has influenced the customs and way of life of its inhabitants.

Figure 8.1

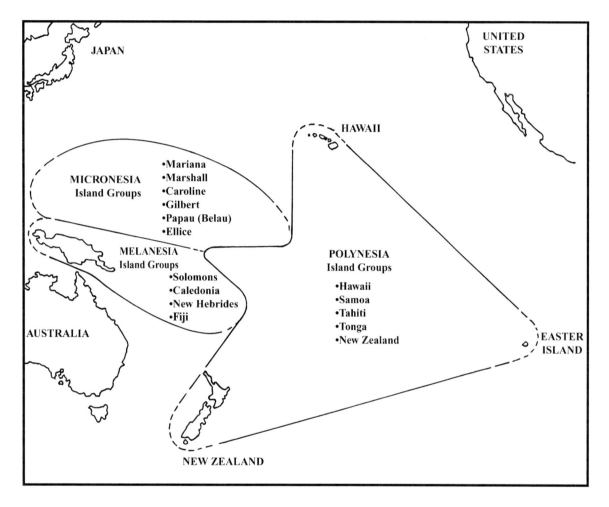

Melanesia

1. The island groups included in Melanesia are New Guinea, the Bismarck and Louisiade archipelagos, the Admiralty Islands, Bougainville Island, Solomon Islands, New Caledonia and Loyalty Islands, Vanuatu, Fiji, and Norfolk Island.

2. Most of the languages of Melanesia are members of the Papuan and Austronesian language families. Over 1300 languages are spoken in Melanesia. This country has the most dense concentration of languages in relation to land mass on earth.

Micronesia

1. The island groups included in Micronesia are Kiribati, Nauru, the Republic of the Marshall Islands, Palau (Belau), and the Federated States of Micronesia.

2. Guam of the Marianas is the most populous island in all of Micronesia and has over 95,000 inhabitants. Archeological evidence has identified civilizations dating back 5,000 years.

3. Micronesia has considerable diversity, especially between the societies of the low coral atolls and those of the high islands.

Polynesia

1. The island groups included in Polynesia are Hawaii, New Zealand, Easter Island, Samoa, Cook, Tonga, French Polynesia, Nuie Island, Tokelau and Tuvalu, Wallis and Futuna, and Pitcairn Island.

2. Polynesia encompasses the Hawaiian Islands, areas that have been influenced in a variety of ways by Filipino, Chinese, Korean, and Japanese cultures.

A variety of resources were reviewed to compile statistical data and background information relevant to the education of families from Pacific Island backgrounds (Asian and Pacific Islander American Health Forum, 2017; Buenconsejo-Lum, 2011; Centers for Disease Control and Prevention, 2017; Cheng, 2012; Faamanatu-Eteuati, 2011; Hishinuma, Chang, McArdle, & Hamagami, 2012; Medical News Today, 2017; Misatauveve, 2012; Mokuau & Tauilil'ili, 2011; Petaia, 2010; Pew Social Trends, 2015; Pew Research Center, 2016, 2017; Sue & Sue, 2016; Taimanglo, 2010; Tauili'ili, 2009; U.S. Census Bureau, 2017).

GENERAL BACKGROUND INFORMATION

❏ The largest populations in the Pacific Islands are the Hawaiians, followed by the Samoans and the Chamorros of Guam.

❏ The Pacific Islands have been influenced by cultural groups from many countries, including France, the United States, Spain, Portugal, Germany, and Japan. Many areas in the Pacific Islands have a history of colonialism and missionary influence.

❏ There has been a decline in the number of pure blood Native Hawaiians because of high mortality rates, poor health status, and interracial marriage. Many residents of Hawaii can trace their roots to four or more different backgrounds (e.g., Filipino, Japanese, Chinese, etc.).

❏ The median income for Native Hawaiian and Other Pacific Islanders is $60,133 and 17.3% live at the poverty level.

❏ Numerous religions are practiced in the Pacific Islands. Christianity is widespread, and many Pacific Islanders consider the Bible to be a major source of inspiration.

❏ Forms of Christianity (e.g., Catholicism, Protestantism) are often combined with folk medicine, which may include faith healing, herbs, etc. Magic and sorcery are practiced in some places, particularly in Melanesia.

❏ Most Samoans have strong religious beliefs; Samoa's motto is "Samoa is founded upon God."

❏ In Hawaii, there has been a resurgence of belief in spirituality. This spirituality includes values such as *pono* (perfect order), *malama'aina* (caring for the land), and *ho'oponopono* (holding family healing session).

❏ Most Pacific Islanders have expertise in fishing and farming. They prize resource management and conservation of land.

Profile

Joe, one of my graduate students, permitted me to share his story. He is the son of an Indian Fijian mother and Italian father. Joe spent part of his childhood in Fiji. Many residents of Fiji believe that disabilities are caused by black magic or the sins of the parents. Individuals with disabilities are often abandoned on the streets of Fiji and placed in orphanages. Joe had an uncle with autism spectrum disorder who was kept in a room like a prisoner—he was not allowed to go out. Joe remembers that a relative with Down syndrome was often ridiculed.

Joe recalls occasions in Fijian schools where the teacher would take off his belt and whip a child in front of the class. Joe's mother thinks that the U.S. schools are much too liberal, and that teachers should be given more authority. In Fiji, children are expected to obey their elders and individuals in positions of authority.

Joe is already 22 years of age but he is still not married. Within his culture, males his age are expected to be married. Also, Joe shared that males "do whatever they want but females must stay home and cook and clean." If Joe, a young acculturated male, tries to help with the dishes after a meal, he is told, "You should relax and let a girl do it."

To this day, Joe tries his best to avoid parking under trees. He was raised to believe that trees are inhabited by witches. These witches come into your dreams and then a family member dies.

PACIFIC ISLAND FAMILY LIFE

Immigrant Insight   Taylor S., married to a Chamorro man from Guam

My husband's brother has Autism Spectrum Disorder. The family views him as a gift from God and believes that he is super special. All his siblings argue over who has the privilege of having him live with them when his mom dies.

❏ Children are often viewed as gifts of God, and are cherished by extended families and villages. Extended families of several generations are quite common. Families may be quite large, with 12 or more children.

❏ Child care is frequently provided by multiple caretakers, including siblings. Children may be raised by members of the extended family or even friends.

❏ The Chamorro and Carolinian societies are matriarchal, with clearly defined roles for members of the nuclear family. Fathers make financial decisions, while mothers are responsible for housekeeping and the raising of children.

❑ In some Chamorro families, daughters live at home until they are married. Living alone can have negative moral connotations for a single woman.

❑ When a couple is married in the Northern Marianas, they will usually live with the groom's parents and conceive their first child within the first few years of the marriage.

❑ Villagers often have close ties and help one another in many situations. Reciprocity, interdependence, and cooperation are inherent values of many groups.

❑ Islanders place a strong emphasis on authority and respect. Children and subordinates must comply with the wishes of elders.

❑ Islanders are more concerned about the well-being of the family than about the rights of individuals. In Samoa, for example, a person is expected to help other members of the family, regardless of the cost.

❑ Although Samoans may appear to be poor in the eyes of outsiders, there is no "homelessness" in Samoa. Extended families and family networks freely share food, material goods, and shelter.

❑ The welfare of the family is considered a much higher priority than the welfare of individual children; children are often preoccupied with pleasing their parents. Everyone is expected to work together for the benefit of the community.

❑ Islanders generally value elders, who are viewed as having special wisdom and the ability to transmit culture to the younger generation.

❑ Many Hawaiian families are quite physically affectionate with their children. In some places such as Bali, a baby may be carried so much that he does not have contact with the floor for the first several months of his life.

❑ Mothers may not leave the home for at least one week after a child is born; in some groups, babies do not leave the house for the first month of life.

❑ In some homes, women may be physically abused by their husbands; violence against women is a concern in some Islander cultures.

Immigrant Insight   Sarawahan, woman from Fiji

In Fiji it is not a big deal if a female, let alone a married woman, is beaten by her husband. It is not that physical abuse is accepted; it is the fact that women feel they cannot confide in anyone because they are devoted to their family. It is shameful to call the cops and claim, "I am getting beaten up." I was sexually abused by my stepfather…when I stood up to him, my mother forced me to keep the family secret and say that I had fallen down the stairs. I had to stay home from school several times a month due to my stepfather's abuse, including a month-long stay in the hospital.

❑ Physical punishment is quite common among some groups in the Pacific Islands. Rulers, belts, and other implements may be used regularly to discipline children. In many of these families, physical discipline begins at about 3 years of age and continues through mid-adolescence.

❏ Among Samoans, loving and expressive parenting typically coexists with wide acceptance of physical punishment. Physical discipline ensures proper behavior from children (Pelczarski & Kemp, 2006). Many Samoans use corporal punishment to ingrain respect into their children so that, as adults, the children will fit into society's hierarchical structure. Many Samoans believe that Western parents tend to be socially irresponsible because they give children too much freedom.

PACIFIC ISLAND EDUCATION

❏ In the U.S., 87.1% of Americans age 25 and older have at least a high school diploma or its equivalency. Among Native Hawaiian and Other Pacific Islanders, 88.8% have a high school diploma or its equivalent.

❏ In the U.S., 21.5% of Native Hawaiian and Other Pacific Islanders 25 years of age and older have a Bachelor's degree or higher compared with 30.6% of the overall American population. In the overall American population age 25 or older, 11.6% have graduate or professional degrees, compared to 6.5% of Native Hawaiian and Other Pacific Islanders.

❏ In general, statistics show that Native Hawaiian and Other Pacific Islanders have a slightly higher high school equivalency achievement rate than Americans in general. However, their attainment of college/advanced degrees remains lower than the U.S. average.

❏ The educational style in the Islands is generally relaxed; absenteeism among both teachers and students is common in Guam, for example.

❏ Some classes, especially in Guam, are quite unstructured and informal; teachers may come to school without lesson plans.

Immigrant Insight   Guafi, male immigrant from Guam

A difference I have noticed between the U.S. and Guam is how education is valued here compared to Guam. The teachers and education system in Guam are not as strict as here and it is common to see that the highest level of education is a high school diploma. If someone wanted to go to college, they would have to come to America.

❏ Books and other educational resources are often in short supply because many areas are geographically remote.

❏ The educational tradition emphasizes oral learning. Rote memorization is a common learning strategy in many Island schools.

❏ Hawaiian public school students generally perform below their counterparts on the U.S. mainland on many measures of academic achievement. School readiness and academic achievement are negatively impacted by higher rates of depression, high rates of teen pregnancy, low income, and high rates of child neglect and abuse (Mokuau & Tauili'ili, 2011).

❑ Western Samoa, however, has a 98% literacy rate. In traditional villages, education is provided at a minister's school, where children learn to read. Later they attend both elementary and secondary schools (Cox, 2006). Some schools provide bilingual education in the native language and English.

❑ For many students, it is a major adjustment to go from Island schools to mainland schools in the United States; Island students often experience persistent disproportionate school failure.

❑ It is quite difficult for Pacific Islander students to go from relaxed schools in which orally-based learning and rote memorization are stressed to U.S. schools in which literacy, individual excellence, and creativity are emphasized.

❑ Educators in the United States have been concerned about the high percentage of Islander students who fail in school and/or drop out.

❑ A concern for American educators is that some Islander parents do not feel that it is important for children to attend school on a regular basis.

❑ Some Islander families want their children to go to work as soon as possible, feeling that children who continue in school selfishly drain the family's resources instead of contributing to the family's well-being. Many families encourage their children to enter the job market before completing high school.

❑ Samoans in the United States want very much for their children to be educated; however, values emphasized in school often conflict with those of the home.

❑ Research shows that Hawaiian, Tahitian, and Samoan children are often unaccustomed to interacting with adults because most of their interactions are with other children (Cheng, 2012). In school, children are generally not expected to speak in class; the teacher is the ultimate authority figure.

❑ In Samoan culture, obedience and deference to adults are high priorities. American schools, which emphasize verbal assertiveness and student-initiated classroom interactions, may be teaching Samoan students patterns of interaction that are unacceptable—and punishable—at home.

❑ An increasing number of Samoan youth are coming to U.S. colleges to play football. American Samoa produces more National Football League players, proportionate to its population, than anywhere else in the world.

Tech Tie-In

Samoa and American Football (60 Minutes)
This informative YouTube video provides information about Samoans in the U.S. playing football; it also includes interesting information about Samoan culture and practices, with beautiful footage of the islands.
https://www.youtube.com/watch?v=A69Z8fCpuAI

CULTURAL CUSTOMS AND COURTESIES

❏ Many Islanders have a "collective rights" attitude in which generosity and sharing are valued. Collectivism or group well-being and cooperation are important, whereas individualism and privacy are usually not priorities.

❏ In Guam, *inafa'maolek* (interdependence) is a key value which depends upon a spirit of cooperation and mutuality rather than individual rights. The essence of inafa'maolek is compassion, and working together for the good of all is a fundamental priority in Guam.

❏ Hospitality is important among many groups; festive occasions and celebrations with plenteous food are very common.

❏ In Samoa, the concept of *fa'asamoa* consists of five basic values: *aiga* (family), *gafa* (genealogies), *matai* (chiefly system), *lotu* (church), and *fa'alvelave* (ceremonial and family obligations). Love, service, respect, and discipline are also emphasized.

❏ In Samoa, many live in houses that consist of a single, large communal room. Adjusting to American homes with many rooms can be difficult for and very divisive to Samoan families that are accustomed to physical closeness among family members.

❏ Some Samoans consider it inappropriate to drink or eat while walking or standing.

❏ Compared to U.S. standards, the pace in the Pacific Islands is slow and relaxed. Many residents believe that "you get there when you get there," and human relationships are considered more important than the "clock." Many Islanders who immigrate to the U.S. experience substantial challenges adjusting to the fast pace of life and the emphasis on time.

❏ A concern of many Samoans who have immigrated to the U.S. is the loss of large kinship and social networks when they arrive in this country. Accustomed to extended church, family, and social obligations and occasions, many Samoans in the U.S. feel disenfranchised and alone. This may contribute to increasing crime and substance abuse among Samoan immigrants to the U.S.

HEALTH CARE AND DISABLING CONDITIONS

❏ When people are sick, families may call upon faith healers or practitioners of folk medicine. In countries such as Samoa, prayer for those with disabilities is common.

❏ Traditional Hawaiian philosophy does not separate non-physical and physical aspects of the world; all aspects of a person (physical, mental, emotional, and spiritual) must be healed.

❏ *Ho'oponopono*, a cultural practice of forgiveness and reconciliation to heal the whole person, is often guided by a priest, minister, healer, or family elder.

Immigrant Insight   Tausa'afia, woman from Samoa

My son Bati has been stuttering since he was 3 years old. The family would pray for Bati in an effort to cure him of his stuttering. My country believes strongly in "practice makes perfect," so when an individual has a weakness, they are encouraged to keep practicing. Individuals with disabilities are kept very close to the family so that the family can watch over them and make sure nothing happens to them.

❏ Among some groups, massage and the use of fruits, roots, and leaves in treatment are common.

❏ In some groups there is a belief that the more one weighs, the higher his status. When I was being raised in the Philippines, married women tried to be 20 or more pounds overweight because this was a sign of being married to a prosperous and successful man who could afford to feed you. If you were a slender married woman, you were quietly pitied because your husband was clearly an unsuccessful provider who could not afford to feed his wife.

❏ Cancer, coronary heart disease, and diabetes tend to be common health problems for Native Hawaiian and Other Pacific Islanders. Obesity is a common problem, and is increasing among children.

❏ As an example of obesity being a common problem, 52% of the men in the Polynesian kingdom of Tonga are estimated to be obese. Of the seven countries worldwide with female obesity rates of at least 50%, four were Pacific Island nations: Samoa, Tonga, Kiribati, and the Federated States of Micronesia.

❏ Obesity is common in the Samoan culture. In Tonga, type II diabetes is very common, even in children; it is primarily due to obesity.

❏ Unfortunately, as in many regions of the world, Pacific Island residents are contracting AIDS in greater numbers.

❏ Hearing problems due to factors such as impacted wax and otitis media are common among some groups. High rates of otitis media are common among Samoan and Hawaiian children.

❏ Islanders are at increased risk for ingesting high levels of mercury because of the amount of seafood in their diets. Children who are prenatally exposed to mercury are at risk for problems such as developmental delays, lowered IQs, and impaired hearing and vision.

❏ In many regions of the Pacific Islands, special education programs are scarce. Efforts are being made to provide programs for children with special needs and to integrate them into general education programs.

❏ Some families protect children with disabilities and do not expect them to be independent. Families believe that it is their responsibility to take care of children with disabilities, not the responsibility of outside agencies.

❏ Some Hawaiian families attribute physical disabilities to spiritual causes; the disabilities may be viewed as beyond the control of human beings.

❏ Some members of the Carolinian and Chamarro cultures believe that spirits can cause disabilities in children.

❏ Some cultures (e.g., the Chamorro culture) view a disability as God's gift, and believe that the individual should be cared for and protected.

❏ Among Samoans and some other groups, there is a tendency toward intolerance for persons with disabilities.

❏ Some Samoans believe that the birth of a child with a disability is a sign of God's displeasure with the family. The child's disability is viewed as punishment for parents' sins, and many children with disabilities are hidden from public view and do not attend school. A child with a disability "is a tangible representation of and constant reminder of sin" ((Faamanatu-Eteuati, 2011, p. 66).

❏ Currently in Samoa, efforts are being made to include children with disabilities in general education classes. There are many barriers, including negative attitudes on the part of teachers and parents; lack of access to appropriate supplies and equipment is also an issue. Despite these and other challenges, Samoan schools are beginning to successfully include and mainstream children with disabilities into general education settings. This suggests that Samoans are becoming more sensitive to the needs of special learners.

Immigrant Insight   Payaal, woman from Fiji

People with disabilities may be considered weak and viewed as outcasts. For this reason, people in Fiji often hide their disabilities and do not reach out for help. Families of those affected will be embarrassed to take a disabled child to parties and other family outings, but will also not send them to special facilities for proper treatment and care.

Profile

Lee T., a 16-year-old Chamorro, was diving off a cliff into the ocean with his friends. He struck his head on the rocks below and experienced a profound head injury. He was flown by helicopter to Hawaii, where doctors were able to save his life. However, after awakening from a coma two months later, Lee experienced major cognitive and linguistic deficits and had difficulty walking and dressing himself. The hospital staff offered the family both in- and out-patient rehabilitative services that included occupational, physical, and speech therapy. The family thanked the staff for their offer but declined to accept any services, saying that they would take care of Lee from that point on. The family did not feel that it was appropriate to try to "force" Lee to become independent again. They felt that he had suffered enough already, and they believed it was their job to protect him from now on.

PACIFIC ISLAND COMMUNICATION STYLES

❏ To avoid offending others, some Islanders will say what they think the listener wants to hear.

❏ Some groups (e.g., Hawaiians and Chamorros) tend to favor interpersonal communication styles that emphasize cooperation rather than competition.

❏ Children may be unaccustomed to interacting with adults on a one-to-one basis because their primary communication experiences are with other children, not adults.

❏ It may be considered inappropriate to touch a child on the top of the head because this area is considered sacred.

❏ Oral language proficiency and story-telling are often highly prized.

❏ Some Islanders view prolonged eye contact as a sign of disrespect.

❏ Persons from the Carolinian and Chamorro cultures use their eyebrows extensively to communicate meaning.

❏ Among many Samoans, it is inappropriate to walk past a person of status or authority without a display of deference such as downcast eyes.

❏ In some Samoan families, children, as a sign of respect, are expected to sit down when addressing an older person.

❏ In the Samoan culture, movement of the shoulders often indicates ambivalence or confusion.

❏ In the Samoan household, the mother has power and authority as chief caregiver. Since Samoan children are expected to accommodate adults, most Samoan mothers don't simplify their vocabulary or sentence structure when interacting with their children. If a child says something unintelligible, the Samoan mother may call attention to the problem and might even ignore the utterance.

❏ Many Samoan mothers play with their infants and cuddle them but do not respond to their vocalizations as intentional or social. Thus, in some homes there may be little emphasis on early language development.

Immigrant Insight   Aolani, female, senior university student from Hawaii

When I was growing up in Hawaii, I spoke Pidgin English. Among my friends, this was much cooler than regular English. There was a lot of peer pressure to speak Pidgin. Also, news traveled fast in my neighborhood—everybody knew everything about you. We had the "coconut wireless." People really cared for each other, and I miss that. Everyone in the mainland U.S. is so impersonal.

PACIFIC ISLAND LANGUAGE CONSIDERATIONS

❏ The Pacific Island languages fall within the Austronesian language family.

❏ More than 1300 indigenous languages are spoken in the Pacific Islands. Major languages include Fijian, Hawaiian, Samoan, Tahitian, Chamorro, Carolinian, Korean, Palauan, Marshallese, Papua New Guinean, Yapese, Trukese, and Pompean. Most Pacific Island languages are mutually unintelligible.

❏ The three major languages spoken in many areas of Micronesia are English, Chamorro, and Carolinian.

❏ Languages spoken in Hawaii include Mandarin, Tagalog, Samoan, Ilocano, Korean, Cantonese, Japanese, and Hawaiian. English is spoken by almost all Hawaiians.

❏ Some Hawaiians speak a fluent dominant language (e.g., English, Japanese) as well as Pidgin English.

❏ Many children of Hawaiian descent speak Pidgin English, also known as Hawaiian Creole. These children often need assistance in acquiring formal written and oral English skills.

❏ Today, the Hawaiian language is the only indigenous language in the U.S. that has shown growth. There has been a resurgence of interest in the Hawaiian language since the 1980s, and today there are more language immersion schools which focus on the Hawaiian language and culture.

❏ Language use and vocabulary are influenced by culture. In the Carolinian language, for example, there are more than 10 words that depict the various stages of a coconut's growth.

❏ Samoa's schools are bilingual (Samoan and English).

❏ Some cultures (e.g., Samoan and Hawaiian) place a strong emphasis on oral traditions.

❏ Many Pacific Islanders understand English but speak a pidgin form of the language.

❏ In the writing systems of languages spoken in the Pacific Islands, letters for vowels represent one sound only.

❏ The apostrophe within a word (e.g., *ali'i*) is pronounced as a glottal stop (momentary stopping of the breath in the throat).

❏ In general, consonants are identical or close approximations to their English equivalents. The "g" in English is usually hard; however, in Samoan, this consonant is always pronounced as "ng" (e.g., *Pago Pago* is pronounced *Pango Pango*).

❏ Characteristics of several languages spoken in the Pacific Islands are described below.

Hawaiian language

1. The language is alphabetical and polysyllabic, with stress being placed on the next to last syllable.
2. Five vowels are used: *a, e, i, o, u.*
3. Eight consonants are used: *w, p, n, m, h, l, k* and the glottal stop.
4. The language has no consonant clusters.
5. The language is characterized by words that always end in vowels.
6. *w* is pronounced as *v* when it follows an *e* or *i*.

Tahitian language

1. The alphabet has only 13 letters.
2. Five vowels are used:

   a (as in *father*)

   e (as in *May*; may also be pronounced as in *egg*)

   i (pronounced "ee" as in *tree*)

   o (pronounced "o" as in *goat*)

   u (pronounced "u" as in *flute*)
3. Eight consonants are used: *f, h, m, n, p, r, t, v*; these are pronounced like their English equivalents, but they are never used at the end of syllables.
4. Syllables end in vowels.
5. Vowels are often grouped together; each should be pronounced separately (e.g., *Faaa* is pronounced "Fa-ah-ah").
6. Most words are accented on the next to last syllable, except when an apostrophe separates the final vowel from the vowel preceding it; in this case, both vowels are given equal emphasis (e.g., *mataura'a* [custom] is pronounced "mah-tah-oo-ra-ah").

Fijian language

1. *b* is pronounced as if it is preceded by *m* (e.g., "ba" is pronounced as "mba").
2. *c* is pronounced as "th" (e.g., "Yanuca" becomes "Yanu tha").
3. *d* is pronounced as "nd" (e.g., "Nadee" becomes "Nan dee").
4. *g* is pronounced as "ng" (e.g., "Sigatoka" becomes "Singatokaî").
5. *q* is pronounced as "ngg" (e.g., "Beqa" becomes "Mbeng-ga").

Chamorro language

1. The language has six vowels and 11 allophonic variations of these vowels. Vowel sounds in Chamorro include *i, e, ae, a, o,* and *u.*
2. The language has 18 consonants and the glide *w.*
3. Most consonants are pronounced as they are in English with some exceptions.
4. *ch* is pronounced "ts" as in *tsar.*
5. *y* is pronounced "ds" as in *goods.*
6. *ñ* is pronounced "ny" as in *Bunyan.*
7. *w* is pronounced "gw" as in *Gwendolyn.*

Samoan language

1. This is an Austronesian language spoken in Western and American Samoa.
2. Vowels can be long or short. There are five vowels: "*a, e, i, o, u*"
3. Syllables consist of a vowel or a consonant plus a vowel.
4. The language uses the glottal stop frequently.
5. Consonants never appear together or in syllable-final position. Every consonant is followed by one, two, or three vowels (e.g., *paaa,* or *bone-dried; fa'afetai,* or *thank you*).
6. There are 12 consonants: "*f, g, l, m, n, p, s, t, v, h, k, r*"

Profile

I received a request to assess the language and articulation skills of Fa'aola T., a friendly fifth-grade Samoan girl who had transferred into the school. According to Fa'aola's school records, she was being raised by her mother; however, another set of records indicated that her aunt and uncle were her primary caregivers.

Fa'aola had developmental delays and had received special education services since kindergarten (in the previous school district). There were notations that Fa'aola had continuous allergies and appeared sleepy in class much of the time. According to her records, school personnel had asked her caregivers to take her to a doctor; there was no indication that this had occurred. Apparently, school personnel also had concerns about Fa'aola's hearing and vision; there was no home follow-through in these areas either.

When I assessed Fa'aola, I found her language skills to be commensurate with those of a kindergartner. When I evaluated her articulation, it became apparent that major dental and orthodontic deviations were having a strong impact on her intelligibility. I wrote a lengthy diagnostic report, with very specific recommendations for supporting Fa'aola in all areas tested. When I checked on Fa'aola a few months later, I discovered that she and her family had moved and had left no forwarding address.

IMPLICATIONS FOR PROFESSIONALS

❏ Professionals should remember that families may be late for meetings or may not come at all if a family matter arises; family needs are generally a higher priority than meetings.

❏ Professionals should not automatically assume that the biological parents are in charge of a student because care-taking may rotate among relatives (e.g., aunts, uncles, grandparents, older siblings). Thus, when contacting the home, professionals may need to find out who is currently in charge of the student.

❏ It is imperative to involve the entire family in any processes and decisions, not just the student. Some parents want elders to be present during decision-making.

❏ Professionals should be formal when addressing authority figures within the family.

❏ In the matriarchal Carolinian and Chamorro societies, an elder female such as the paternal grandmother may have the final say in some family matters. Professionals should relate positively with this person because her opinions may determine whether or not a child receives services.

❏ Professionals may observe bruises on students or hear reports of physical punishment. It is critical for parents to be informed about American laws regarding child abuse. In addition, professionals should be aware that physical punishment may occur at home if the parents learn that the child was disciplined at school. In cases such as these, professionals will want to work with the local community and local churches in order to intervene in culturally appropriate ways in matters relating to discipline.

❏ During interactions with parents, professionals may need to emphasize the importance of keeping students in school until at least high school graduation. Professionals can emphasize that by remaining in school, students will be better equipped to find jobs in the work force and support their families.

❏ Some students (e.g., Carolinian) come from an environment in which several languages are spoken. Thus the identification of a "primary" language may prove to be a challenge. When assessing these students, professionals must rely heavily on information from parents and teachers and on natural, ecologic, assessment methods.

❏ It is considered culturally appropriate for professionals to show their concern and interest in the welfare of the entire family. However, professionals should not venture immediately into frank discussions about personal problems or difficulties.

❏ Among some groups, it is considered rude for people to converse when they are standing. It is best to converse from a sitting position.

❏ Professionals must remember that although families may say "yes" to indicate that they acknowledge receiving information, a "yes" response does not necessarily indicate agreement with what has been said. For this reason it is better to ask open-ended questions than *yes-no* questions.

❏ Professionals should respect the family's spiritual values and beliefs about healing. Western professionals can work in collaboration with traditional folk healers, as they continue to enjoy status even in contemporary times.

❏ Islanders tend to take a holistic approach to problems. Professionals can utilize the services and support of the family, community, and church to support families.

❏ Professionals must fully explain forms that require signatures. Many parents are accustomed to signing only documents relating to major life events such as births and deaths. They may not understand why signatures are needed on school forms.

❏ When parents are asked to come to school for a meeting, they may feel that their child is being criticized. The purpose of the meeting should be explained clearly.

Important considerations for professionals working with Islander students include the following:

1. Remember that students who are proficient in basic conversational English do not necessarily have the language skills necessary to perform effectively in classroom reading and writing activities.
2. Remember that students may come from low socioeconomic backgrounds in which there have been few opportunities for language stimulation.
3. Encourage a "buddy system" in which students are paired with peers from the same background.
4. Increase knowledge of the home language (e.g., learning basic vocabulary).
5. Become familiar with the sociolinguistic/pragmatic rules of discourse within the child's language (e.g., leave-taking, greeting, complimenting, etc.).
6. Remember that at home, students are often taught to be quiet, observant, and not to challenge authority. The classroom learning environment, however, may require the child to criticize, evaluate, speculate, and render judgments. Such behaviors conflict with behavioral expectations in the home environment.
7. Teach students how to interact with adults at school if they are not accustomed to such interactions at home. Help students learn to codeswitch, or use "school talk" at school and "home talk" at home. For example, professionals can affirm that it is appropriate for students to lower their eyes and to refrain from initiating conversation with adults at home. Adults at school, however, expect direct eye contact and verbal assertiveness.

Immigrant Insight   Alkire, male immigrant from Yap, speaker of Yapese

At home, there is a chain of command we have to follow. Fathers provide for and support the household. They are the authority figure in the family. In Yap, the communication is also very formal....we bow down and say "Excuse me" if we have to walk by someone. We believe that "when parents talk, kids don't talk." Kids are not present in adult conversations to avoid interruptions. Kids have to come and sit by the parent and wait until the parent asks what they need.

---

8. Teach students story-telling skills. Professionals can build listening and story-telling skills with folktales that are congruent with children's cultural background. Talk-story, a give-and-take conversational structure in Hawaii, can be used with children who are familiar with this method of communication.
9. Provide opportunities for culturally responsive learning. Use literature and symbols from students' cultures. For example, a recent book, *The Rat and the Bat: And Other Short Stories*, passes on Samoan cultural knowledge, encourages reading, and promotes the building of relationships. Native Hawaiian culture can be incorporated into the curriculum through field trips, Hawaiian songs and stories, and study of Hawaiian nature and geology (Coyne, 2012).

10. Provide summer orientation programs for students who are unfamiliar with conventional school routines. These programs familiarize the student with the structure of the classroom and the school so that they will be better prepared for academic success. (On a personal note: growing up in barrios in the island nation of the Philippines, we frequently went barefoot and walked freely on beaches, in rivers, and on fields and dirt roads. I was shocked when my son's kindergarten principal told me not to walk on the school grass.)

11. Remember that the traditional American educational system, which relies on competition and individualized learning, encourages students to interact in ways that students may not have experienced within their culture. These students may learn more efficiently if opportunities for cooperative learning are provided.

Profile

Alisi, a Samoan 7-year-old, recently moved to the U.S. with her family. She was quiet in class, and struggled academically, so the speech-language pathologist collaborated with the teacher to help Alisi increase linguistic and cognitive skills in English. Alisi was learning to raise her hand, give opinions, ask questions of the teacher, and engage in verbal problem-solving.

One day Alisi came to school with bruises on her face, arms, and back. The teacher noticed the bruises immediately, and the case was referred to Child Protective Services (CPS). When the CPS worker came to the school and spoke with Alisi, she told him that her parents had beaten her for asking too many questions and challenging their authority.

Alisi's parents were called to court for breaking U.S. child abuse laws. They defended their actions, saying that Alisi has been showing a lack of respect for her elders. They stated that she was becoming too "mouthy" and Americanized.

After this incident, the teacher and speech-language pathologist arranged a meeting with the pastor of the local Samoan church that Alisi's family attended. The pastor explained U.S. child abuse laws in further detail to Alisi's parents. The need for the child to be verbally assertive in the classroom was also stressed. The parents did not agree with this recommendation but indicated that they would find other ways to discipline the child. They also indicated that they would make an effort to be more understanding of differences in how the school expected children to interact with others.

STUDY QUESTIONS

1. Describe common communication patterns during interactions between adults and children in the Islands. How might these patterns impact interaction between speech-language pathologists and children?

2. Discuss health concerns that are common among Pacific Islanders. How might these concerns impact communication skills, if at all?

3. Describe educational practices of schools in the Pacific Islands. How do these practices impact the adjustment of students who move to the U.S. and enroll in school?

MULTIPLE CHOICE

4. The following may be observed in the Pacific Islands:

   A. Some Hawaiian families attribute physical disabilities to spiritual causes; the disabilities may be viewed as beyond the control of human beings.
   B. Some Samoans feel that the birth of a child with a disability is a sign of God's displeasure with the family.
   C. Some cultures (e.g., the Chamorro culture) view a disability as a gift from God, and hence the individual is to be protected and sheltered.
   D. Most Pacific Islanders believe that an individual with disabilities should be given as many rehabilitative services as possible.
   E. Healers or folk medicine practitioners may be called upon by some groups.

5. When professionals work with Pacific Islander students, they can be most helpful by thinking about and doing the following:

   A. Professionals should remember that students who are proficient in basic conversation do not necessarily have the language skills necessary to perform effectively in classroom reading and writing activities.
   B. Professionals should understand that many of these students come from middle class socioeconomic backgrounds that have supported learning experiences in schools.
   C. Professionals should focus on critical thinking and evaluation tasks because students are encouraged to give opinions and render judgments at home.
   D. Professionals should use collective story-telling methods.
   E. Professionals should teach problem-solving skills.

6. Which of the following are TRUE?

   A. The Pacific Island languages fall within the Austronesian language family.
   B. Hawaiian is alphabetical and polysyllabic, with stress being placed on the next to last syllable.
   C. Vowels are often grouped together in the Tahitian language, but each should be pronounced separately.
   D. Samoan is the most widely used language in the Philippines.

7. Aspects of communication that are important to remember when working with families from the Pacific Islands include the following:

   A. Oral language proficiency and story-telling are often highly prized.
   B. It may be considered inappropriate to touch the top of a child's head.
   C. Samoan mothers often cuddle and physically care for their babies but do not respond to the infants' vocalizations as meaningful attempts to communicate.
   D. The frequent asking of questions is encouraged in the classroom in all cultural groups within the Pacific Islands.

8. A Chamorro child has been found to have a communication disorder, and you need to discuss the assessment results with his family. What should you be aware of in planning your meeting?

   A. The family will arrive promptly to avoid experiencing feelings of shame that are often associated with tardiness.
   B. The grandmother may be the primary decision maker.
   C. The biological parents are in charge of the child, so questions should be directed to them first.
   D. It is best to ask *yes-no* questions (rather than open-ended questions) to reduce feelings of anxiety that family members might experience.
   E. If family members agree to have the child placed in a special education program, it is highly likely that they will make sure that all homework assignments are completed.

9. Petelo is a 6-year-old child from Samoa who recently moved to the U.S with his family. He has never been to school because he has a cleft palate and the family feels disgraced. Petelo has had surgery to repair his cleft palate, but his overall speech and language skills are delayed. It is felt that Petelo would benefit from speech and language therapy. Which one of the following would NOT be advisable when discussing the need for speech and language services with his parents?

   A. Suggest to the family that if Petelo receives speech and language therapy, he has a better chance of growing up to be a productive employee who can help support his family through his job.
   B. Sensitively share with Petelo's parents scientifically-based information about potential causes of cleft palate.
   C. To ensure that confidentiality is maintained, school professionals should be the only ones permitted to give parents information about how the school's special education services benefit students.
   D. Share with parents that if Petelo receives therapy, his oral language and story-telling skills will improve.
   E. If possible, arrange for a peer buddy to help Petelo make friends and increase his social language skills.

10. You are providing fluency therapy to Lokelani, a 16-year-old Hawaiian girl in a high school setting. One day in therapy, she confides to you that she is pregnant. You help Lokelani book an appointment with the school counselor, who promises to follow through with appropriate actions. Which of the following are important for you and the school counselor to remember?

   A. Pacific Islander women usually obtain prenatal care early in the pregnancy, so personnel probably don't need to worry that Lokelani will receive appropriate care.
   B. If Lokelani and her family have relied on a folk health care practitioner in the community, it would be advisable to work with this person to help Lokelani and her family deal constructively with her situation.
   C. If you are asked to be part of the group that meets with Lokelani's family to discuss her pregnancy issues, demonstrate warmth and a sincere concern for the whole family before expressing specific concerns about Lokelani's pregnancy.
   D. A, B
   E. B, C

ANSWERS TO STUDY QUESTIONS

4. A, B, C, E
5. A, D, E
6. A, B, C
7. A, B, C
8. B
9. C
10. E

Chapter 9

Families from Middle Eastern Backgrounds

Outline
- General Background Information
- Middle Eastern Family Life
- Education and Literacy
- Cultural Customs, Courtesies, and Beliefs
- Health Care and Disabling Conditions
- Middle Eastern Communication Styles
- Middle Eastern Language Considerations
- Implications for Professionals

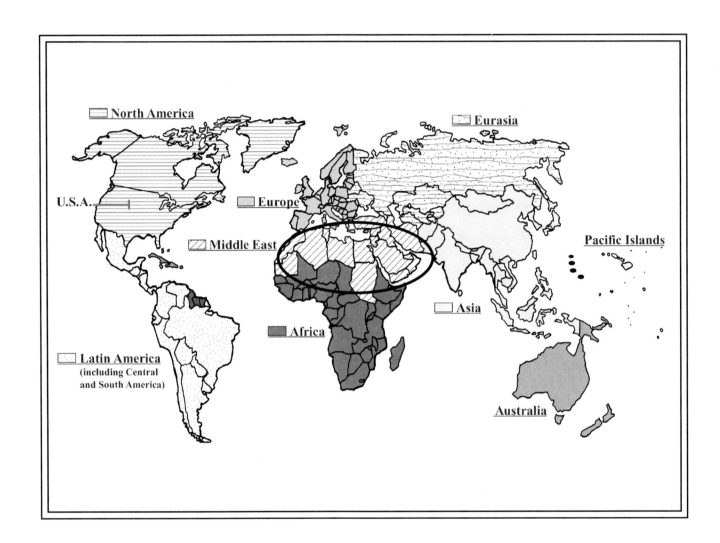

The Middle East is often called the cradle of civilization. Countries included in this area are Israel, Syria, Lebanon, the Occupied Territories, Iraq, Iran, Jordan, Saudi Arabia, Bahrain, Kuwait, Qatar, Oman, Yemen, the United Arab Emirates, Egypt, Turkey, and Sudan, as shown in Figure 9.1.

Figure 9.1

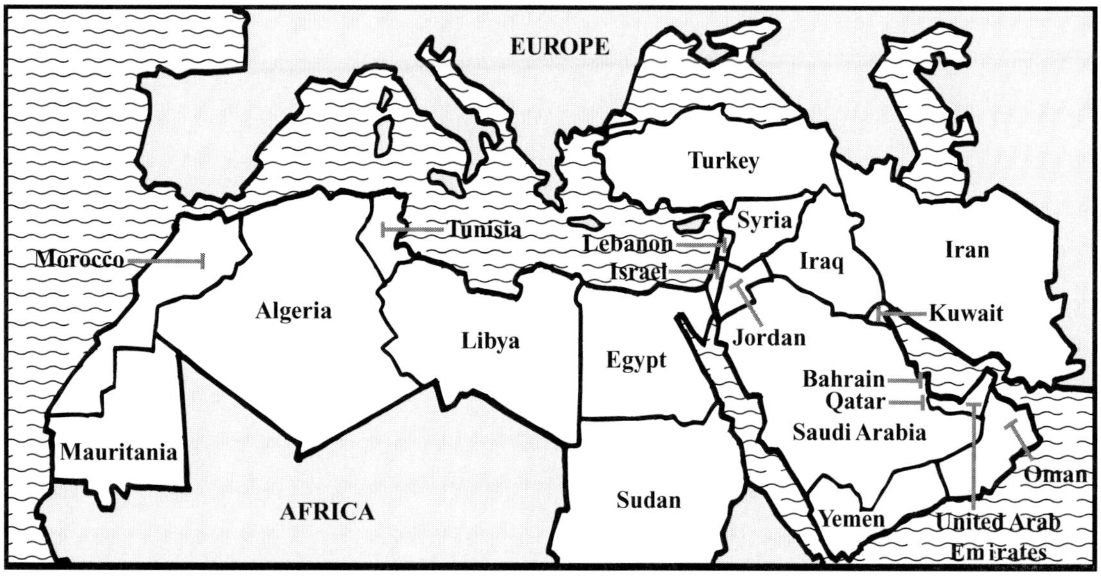

The Middle East stretches over a large area, approximately the size of the United States, where the continents of Africa, Asia, and Europe come together. The largest country in the Middle East is Saudi Arabia. It is one million square miles in size, roughly one-third the size of the United States. Saudi Arabia is often considered a bridge between Asia and the Western world. The Middle East is comprised mostly of deserts.

GENERAL BACKGROUND INFORMATION

❏ The Muslim holy cities of Mecca and Medina are located in Saudi Arabia. Thousands of Muslims journey to these cities annually (especially Mecca) to pray and worship.

❏ The Arab population in the Middle East is larger than that of any other group. Thus, the majority (but not all) of Middle Easterners are Arabs. More than 75% of the people in the Middle East identify themselves as Arabs. Ninety percent of Arabs are Muslim (IOR Global Services, 2017). According to Campbell-Wilson (2012, p. 63):

   …[the term] Arab is best used within a cultural context…Arab countries are those in which the primary language is Arabic and the primary religion is Islam. Consequently, the Middle East makes up the greatest portion of the Arab world, a world that reflects one of Islam from an embryonic phenomenon into a vast sphere of influence and civilization.

❑ The Arab countries include Morocco, Mauritania, Algeria, Tunisia, Libya, Chad, Sudan, Egypt, Syria, Iraq, Jordan, Lebanon, Kuwait, Saudi Arabia, Bahrain, Qatar, United Arab Emirates, Yemen, and Oman.

❑ The Arabic language provides a linguistic bond among the Arab countries. Anyone who speaks Arabic as a native is considered to be an Arab, no matter what country he or she is from. The term "Arab" is not based on race; Arabs have widely varied physical features. (*Note: In this chapter, the terms "Arab" and "Middle Easterner" are used interchangeably although readers need to be aware of the distinctions between the two groups.)

❑ The Arab population is a distinct ancestry group and is highly heterogeneous, composed of groups with different ethnic origins originally from North Africa and the Middle East.

❑ Key values for many Arabs include family and religion. Religion is an integral part of everyday life and activity.

❑ For Arabs, religious affiliation is essential; it is not acceptable to be an agnostic or atheist. Because Arabs respect religious people, they may lose respect for people who have no religious affiliation or who do not believe in God (Nydell, 2012).

❑ Approximately 92% of Arabs in the Middle East are Muslim (Ahmad, 2004). Most belong to the Sunni branch of Islam. In Lebanon, however, approximately half of the population is Christian. Most residents of Israel are Jewish.

❑ Other religious groups include the Bahais, Zoroastrians, and Armenian Christians.

❑ The Bahai faith is derived from Islam, but Bahais take Bahaullah as their prophet and they emphasize modernization and equality. Bahais in Iran have been persecuted by Shi'ite Muslims, and many Iranian Bahais have fled to other countries.

Immigrant Insight   Habib, male, speaker of Farsi from Iran

> I am of the Bahai faith, and was not able to find a job or attend university in Iran because of my religion. I fled to Turkey where I learned to speak Turkish. In Turkey, I was accepted as a believer of the Bahai faith, but could not find work because I was a refugee. Thus, I immigrated to the U.S. for increased opportunities.

❑ Many Middle Easterners live in small villages. There are small numbers of semi-nomadic or nomadic people who live in sparsely populated areas.

❑ Some nomads in Saudi Arabia are called "Bedouins" (the Arabic word for "people who live in the open country"); many of them are shepherds who live in clans and tribes.

❑ Middle Easterners in the U.S. are often stereotyped in negative ways (Al Zidjaly, 2012). These stereotypes are caused by several phenomena, which include actions in the U.S. and in Middle Eastern countries by extremist Muslim groups.

❑ The increase in terrorism world-wide has led to greater support for efforts to ban immigration to the U.S from "Muslim countries" and the frequent expression of negative feelings relating to their religious beliefs.

❑ Since the attacks of 9/11/01, Arabs in the U.S. have experienced discriminatory practices in a variety of settings. In addition, the current political climate in the U.S. has fostered increased hate crimes and attacks upon American Arabs.

Immigrant Insight   Nastaran K., university senior, speaker of Farsi, immigrant from Iran

We came to the U.S. from Iran when I was 9 years old. Iran is a very Islamic country—you do what your parents tell you to do. There is no middle class—you are either very rich or are subsisting. As a woman, you must wear a hijab. People are very touch-oriented. For example, if you are talking to my mom, she will tap you repeatedly during the conversation.

I spoke only Farsi until we moved here. In Iran, we wore uniforms and there were separate schools for boys and girls. Our colleges are co-ed, but boys and girls sit on opposite sides of the room. When we arrived in the U.S., I was put into all-English classrooms in school. I spoke no English and used gestures to communicate. I had no friends and felt very isolated. Kids bullied me and called me a terrorist and camel-rider. There was so much name-calling! It went on for a very long time. Things became better for a while, but these days, with the current political climate, I feel the familiar fear rushing back. I feel like today, I am re-living the fears experienced by my 9-year-old self. I'm so scared every time I fly. It's really, really hard.

❑ The civil war in Syria has been one of the largest drivers of the global refugee crisis, which has left 65 million people displaced. With neighboring countries no longer able to absorb uprooted Syrians after more than five years of fighting, hundreds of thousands of refugees have fled to other countr\ies to seek safety and better lives (Rescue.org, 2017).

❑ The majority of Arab Americans were born in the U.S., and nearly 82% of Arabs in the U.S. are citizens (Arab American Institute, 2017).

❑ The Arab American population in the U.S. grew by more than 72% between 2000 and 2010. The states with the highest numbers of Arab Americans are California, Michigan, and New York (Arab American Institute, 2017).

MIDDLE EASTERN FAMILY LIFE

❑ In traditional Arab families where Islam is the spiritual tradition, family members live out their roles as prescribed in the Koran. For example, the Koran values wealth and preeminence of male children and subordination of women to men.

❑ The family is the primary focus of loyalty for many Middle Easterners; families are usually considered the pillars of society. Children are loved and cherished. Families live near one another and spend a considerable amount of time together. If they come to the U.S. and experience a nuclear family situation, they may feel quite lonely and isolated (Al Khatib, 2017).

❏ Extended, multigenerational families are quite common. The achievements of any individual in the family affect how the family is perceived by others in the community. Loyalty to the family takes precedence over personal desires and needs (IOR Global Services, 2017).

❏ For many Middle Eastern parents, seeing that their children get married is a major life goal. Children's marriages mark the success and self-actualization of the parents.

❏ In many marriages, procreation is a higher priority than marital love and intimacy. Children are greatly valued, and not having children may be a cause for unhappiness (Sharifzadeh, 2011).

❏ If a daughter in a traditional family does not get married, she may be negatively judged by society and, as a result, her family will probably feel personally hurt. Thus, traditional families often make their daughters available for marriage at young ages.

❏ Traditionally, girls stay at home until they are married. In some groups, women may not be allowed to speak to strangers until after marriage.

❏ Divorce is rare and, in some groups, brings shame upon the woman and her family. A divorced woman may not be permitted to marry again.

❏ Parents may continue to provide for children even after the children have married. Parents expect to remain part of and involved in their children's lives for as long as possible (Sue & Sue, 2016).

❏ In Saudi Arabia and some other areas, marriages are often arranged by the parents of the bride and groom. Sometimes the bride and groom meet one another before the wedding, but not always.

❏ In America, girls are free to date at very young ages and do not usually seek the approval of their families. Most of the time, in Iran, the father of the daughter picks the husband and does not always consult with his daughter. Women are not allowed to commit adultery and, in previous years, they could be stoned to death if caught cheating on their husbands. The government has changed in the last few years, so stoning is no longer a common practice, although it still exists under Islamic government rule.

❏ Though this may be shocking to mainstream Americans, many families view arranged marriages as something that parents do to help their adult children find happiness.

❏ Polygamy is practiced in some areas. In Iran, for example, men are often allowed to have up to four wives as long as they can provide for them. Each wife is supposed to be treated equally in all respects.

Tech Tie-In

http://www.adc.org is the website for the American-Arab Anti-Discrimination Committee. This website offers information and legal resources for Arab Americans experiencing discrimination.

❏ Among Muslim Arabs, especially in nomadic and rural communities, people prefer to marry first or second cousins. In 1996, 58% of Iraqis married their cousins, followed by 55% of Saudi Arabians, 54% of Kuwaitis, and 50% of Jordanians. Intermarriage ensures that the spouse is a "known quantity" and that money and possessions stay within the family (Nydell, 2012).

❏ Marriage among blood relatives may increase the incidence of genetic disorders such as Down syndrome, sickle cell anemia, and severe sensorineural hearing loss.

❏ Generally, the father is the head of the household; most Middle Eastern societies are patriarchal. Women are treated with honor and respect, and are expected to manage the home and children (Campbell-Wilson, 2012; Ibrahim & Dykeman, 2011).

❏ Husbands often take little responsibility for the care of very young children and infants. However, when boys reach the age of 4 or 5, fathers often assume a more active role in their care (Sharifzadeh, 2011).

❏ There is a direct relationship between the number of children in a family (especially boys) and the amount of prestige experienced by the father and his family. A large family is a sign of prestige.

❏ Male children are often preferred over female children, in part, because boys carry on the family tradition and name. In agricultural societies, the male's potential for economic contribution is greater than that of the female.

❏ Arab boys may be expected to be decisive and aggressive, and girls may be expected to play a passive role.

❏ Arab adults generally do not reason with young children. They tell them to do things because "that is how it is done" or teach their children to avoid certain actions because of the fear of what others might think or say. Children are taught that it is important to conform to an expected social image (Nydell, 2012).

❏ Children are not to interrupt when adults are talking and may not question rules relating to obedience and authority.

❏ Among Arabs, the most important aspect of acceptable conduct among children is respectful behavior in front of adults.

Immigrant Insight   Roaa M., university senior, speaker of Arabic, immigrant from Syria

In our culture, we focus on boys' education because boys are the family providers. Girls become moms. Arranged marriages are common. In my Muslim community, we don't date. My boyfriend (who I married) asked my parents' permission to get to know me, and we became engaged and then got married. You would never live together outside of marriage. I don't shake men's hands. I choose to wear a hijab because I want to.

❏ Younger members of the family respect and care for the elderly. Many children support their parents in old age.

❏ Many mothers in the Middle East emphasize attachment and parent-child bonding rather than individualism and independence (Sharifzadeh, 2011).

❏ Children are encouraged at early ages to take on family and household responsibilities. Girls are expected to take on household chores at about 5 years of age, but boys are generally exempt from these chores (Sharifzadeh, 2011).

❏ Many young Arabs admire and prefer Western entertainment, dress, and liberal thought. This can be distressing to older, traditional Arabs, and has created an increasing generation gap in the Arab world (Nydell, 2012).

❏ Historically, family relationships and gender roles in Middle Eastern cultures have been based on Islam and have been influenced little by changes in other parts of the world. Middle Eastern countries, however, are becoming more Westernized, resulting in changed attitudes toward marriage and family life.

Profile

Omar Y., a 4-year-old Middle Eastern boy, was brought to the local preschool by his mother. She wanted him to learn English (his primary language was Yemeni) and socialize with other children. Her husband traveled much of the time for business, and she was concerned that Omar was exposed primarily to her at home and was not receiving enough outside stimulation. The American preschool teachers noticed that Omar expected them to help him complete tasks such as putting on his sweater and throwing out leftovers from his snacks. They also noticed that Omar was so extremely respectful that he never asked questions or interacted with the teachers at all, even after learning some English.

One of the teachers, who had lived in the Middle East for several years as a Peace Corps volunteer, asked Omar's mother to meet with her after preschool for tea and snacks while Omar played nearby. The teacher related her challenging experience of raising American children in the Middle East, with its different cultural mores, and discussed the changes that had to be made in her parenting while the family lived in Saudi Arabia. The teacher also discussed U.S. expectations for children's independence as well as the American school system's expectation that children initiate interactions with teachers.

Omar's mother was open and receptive to the teacher's suggestions, so the teacher invited her to observe classroom instruction. Mrs. Y. observed for 20 minutes each day, and the teachers began to see an increase in Omar's social interaction skills and independent activity in the classroom.

Immigrant Insight   Neeka G., university senior, speaker of Farsi,
                                       daughter of Iranian immigrants

In Iran, boys are put on pedestals and grow up spoiled and careless. My brother refused to speak out in class or converse with authority figures because he just didn't want to—they thought he had a disability of some sort. Girls typically get married at 18 or 19 and start having babies. They don't move out of the house until they get married. Dowries are a big deal. My family would never allow me to marry outside my race. In Iran, people don't believe in invisible disabilities. You almost must be in a wheelchair in order for people to view you as disabled. My family is very strict with me about my education. If I get a 95% on an exam, my dad will say "What happened to the other 5%?" When I told him I wanted to be a speech-language pathologist, he said "That's silly—it's just about books and toys."

EDUCATION AND LITERACY

❏ In terms of educational attainment, 89% of Arab Americans have at least a high school diploma. Compared with 27% of the general population, 45% of Arab Americans have a Bachelor's degree or higher. While 10% of the U.S. general population has a post-graduate degree, 18% of Arab Americans hold such a degree (Arab American Institute, 2017).

❏ Arab nations as a whole have more than 70 million illiterate persons. Sixty eight percent of illiterate persons in the Middle East are from Egypt, Yemen, Sudan, Morocco, and Algeria.

❏ Women are vulnerable to illiteracy. For example, in Iraq, 74.8% of women are illiterate; in Yemen, 61.4% of women are illiterate. Female illiteracy rates are in the double digits in all Arab nations except Palestine, Qatar, and Kuwait (Kawach, 2010).

❏ In many countries, classes are often quite large and may have as many as 60 students (elementary level). Formal Arabic is taught in many schools.

❏ The education of children is a high priority in many families. Parents see education as a means of professional and financial advancement.

❏ Some girls do not continue their education beyond elementary school because of the fear that they will be exposed to and left unprotected in inappropriate social situations within the school environment (Sharifzadeh, 2011).

❏ Traditionally, females were not encouraged to attend college. Higher education for women, however, is viewed more positively than in previous years and is becoming more common (Sharifzadeh, 2011).

❏ Co-educational schools are not an option for children in many Middle Eastern countries. Compulsory education usually begins at around 6 or 7 years of age.

❏ In Iran, some schools are segregated based on gender. There is one school for boys and another for girls. Children of the opposite sex are not allowed to play together or sit together.

❏ Story-telling is very common in schools in the Middle East. Children from middle-class, educated families often learn poems and share storybook reading activities with their parents.

Immigrant Insight   Amal Al Yousef, female immigrant from Jordan, speaker of Arabic

I just got back from Jordan and wanted to report the results of my conversations and observations. In Jordan, speech-language pathology is a new profession that got started around 2003. In the Jordanian public school system, there is no such thing as special education. In lower-priced private schools, all the children with any kind of disability are kept in one classroom with no intervention provided. In more expensive private schools, there is a special education teacher for the classroom. No public or private school accepts children with autism. There are specialized centers (private and extremely expensive) for children with autism. Therapy for these children is not provided in hospitals or public clinics.

CULTURAL CUSTOMS, COURTESIES, AND BELIEFS

❏ Some of the character traits most important to Middle Easterners are generosity, bravery, friendship, and hospitality.

❏ Guests generally are treated with kindness; food is available in abundance.

❏ Some groups (e.g., Saudi Arabians) generally do not talk much during meals; these groups prefer to talk after meals.

❏ Women in some cultures may be expected to eat in separate rooms from men.

❏ Some groups (e.g., Saudi Arabians) consider the left hand to be unclean. It is to be used for lavatory purposes only. Some people will be offended if the left hand is used when greeting others.

❏ Among many Arabs, there is no concept of privacy. When translated, the Arabic word that most closely resembles the concept of privacy is "loneliness" (Nydell, 2012).

❏ Arabs tend to have a relaxed attitude about time and are not expected to apologize when they arrive late for meetings or events.

❏ Arab society is conservative and demands conformity from its members. Arabs have a high regard for tradition, and they are not as mobile as Westerners (Nydell, 2012).

❏ It is acceptable in most places for friends of the same sex to show public affection (e.g., holding hands). Members of the opposite sex, however, generally do not show affection in public.

❏ In some areas, women are not to talk to strangers and may not leave the home without permission from the husband. In some parts of the Middle East, males are not supposed to approach women.

❏ There is a strong emphasis on premarital chastity, especially for girls. Some immigrant Middle Eastern families leave the United States because of a fear that their daughters will engage in premarital sexual activity (Sharifzadeh, 2011).

❏ Some Arab men wear robes; these allow for maximum circulation of air around the body, which keeps the body cool in hot climates. The head dress, which varies from tribe to tribe, helps protect the head from the hot sun.

❏ In some areas, women cover themselves in clothing from head to toe before going out in public. Many women wear modest clothes and do not show their faces. Dress varies from country to country.

❏ Traditional Arabs view clothing restrictions for women as a means of providing protection from the competition, stress, temptations, and indignities found in outside society. Many Arab women themselves feel that the present social system gives them protection, security, and respect (Nydell, 2012).

❏ Many Middle Easterners do not wear bright colors.

❏ In the Arabian Gulf states, Yemen, and Saudi Arabia, few women work outside the home. The few with employment outside the home work in all-female environments or in the medical professions.

❏ Some Middle Eastern women in the United States work outside the home. This has led to a reversal of roles for many women who did not work outside the home in their countries of origin. Some Middle Eastern men have difficulty accepting the greater freedom that women are afforded in the U.S. (Sharifzadeh, 2011; Sue & Sue, 2016).

Immigrant Insight   Thoraia A., university senior, speaker of Yemeni

Arabs put a lot of emphasis on lineage and tribal background. If a family is of lower lineage, no matter how much money they have, they may not marry someone from a higher lineage. In Yemen we have arranged marriages. We are the poorest nation in the Arab world. Yemenis will often ask personal questions of you as a professional. They may ask "How old are you?" and "Are you married?" They are just trying to get to know you as a person.

HEALTH CARE AND DISABLING CONDITIONS

❏ Health conditions and the availability of health care vary from country to country. Wars and armed conflicts have directly affected some countries more than others. These affected countries include Palestine, Iraq, Lebanon, and Sudan. It is estimated that as a result of war, for every person killed, three are left with a permanent disability (Al Thani, 2009).

❏ In some war-torn countries, thousands of children have died because of inadequate health care, embargoes on food, and other war-related problems. Lack of care for pregnant women is a serious problem in war-torn areas; some of these women never see a doctor until the day the baby is born.

❏ Some Middle Eastern countries have focused on prevention in the form of public awareness campaigns about land mines and the dangers of driving too fast (the latter often results in spinal cord injury).

❏ Hearing loss is common in the Middle East; the prevalence of deafness in children at birth in the Middle East is twice that of children in the U.S. (Campbell-Wilson, 2012).

❏ In some countries, there is inter-familial marriage. These marriages play a major role in perpetuating disability through several generations (Al Thani, 2009).

❏ Awareness of disabilities may be lower in Arab communities than in others. For example, Europeans place the percentage of persons with disabilities in the double digits, while the Arab countries report that less than 5% of their citizens have disabilities (Al Thani, 2009).

❏ The diagnosis of a disability in a child can be devastating for families because disabilities carry a stigma. Families may be reluctant to seek out help because of the stigma (Al Khatib, 2017).

According to Al Thani (2009):

> The general condition of persons with disabilities in Arab societies is invisibility. In particular, persons with intellectual, developmental, or psychosocial disabilities are considered a source of shame and a burden...but none more so than women with disabilities... as women, they are segregated from male society, but as women with disabilities they are also isolated from the lives of other women...they are invisible...In a social structure that is male dominated in the best of cases, women with disabilities do not stand a chance for rehabilitation, education, accessibility, and any number of services available to men with disabilities....Children with disabilities are not integrated into the mainstream educational system...schools have not been made accessible...Persons with disabilities are a source of shame, a financial burden, even seen as a curse on their families. (p. 4)

❏ In many traditional Muslim families, it is considered unacceptable for women to be examined by male doctors. Experienced older women often provide health care to female patients. Many Middle Easterners prefer to be treated by a professional of the same gender.

❏ Minor health problems experienced by children may be treated using nutritional remedies. For example, pediatricians in Iran often put children with chicken pox or small pox on a strict watermelon diet.

❏ If a child is born with a disability, it is common for the mother to feel shame and guilt; the father may view the child's disability as a personal defeat and a blemish on the family's pride.

❏ Reactions to a child with disabilities may include denial, isolation, overprotection, or in some cases total abandonment.

❏ Many Middle Eastern families have strong beliefs about the causes of serious mental disabilities. Families with children who have these disabilities may become isolated from everyone except other family members (Sharifzadeh, 2011).

❏ Fortunately, in the Arab world, there has been increased awareness about the necessity of services for those with communication disorders. The Arab world has imported speech-language pathologists and audiologists from the U.S., Canada, the United Kingdom, Jordan, Egypt, Sweden, and other countries (Campbell-Wilson, 2012).

MIDDLE EASTERN COMMUNICATION STYLES

Middle Eastern communication styles have been described by a number of authors (Al Khatib, 2017; Campbell-Wilson, 2012; Nydell, 2012; Sharifzadeh, 2011; Sue & Sue, 2016).

❑ It is generally acceptable to speak loudly in conversation. Loudness in the Arab culture connotes sincerity and strength; speaking softly implies that one is frail. Observers, however, may think that conversational partners are angry because of the loudness of the communication.

❑ Arabs tend to speak rapidly. Americans may view their speaking rate as "too fast."

❑ Gestures, intonation, and facial expressions are important factors in communication, with intense and interactive dialogues being common.

❑ In the Arab world, a good personal relationship is the most important factor in successfully conducting business. A few minutes at the beginning of a meeting may be devoted to developing such a relationship by discussing recent activities and matters relating to the well-being of others.

❑ Arabs look directly into the eyes of the person with whom they are communicating and may do so for an extended period of time. Eye contact is an indication that one is using words truthfully and also conveys an interest in what is being said. In many Arab cultures, however, it is taboo for a woman to look a man in the eye.

❑ Among Arabs, verbal eloquence is highly prized. Common rhetorical patterns include repetition, overassertion, and exaggeration. Emphatic assertions are common.

❑ The love of talk has its roots in the rich nomadic oral tradition of greeting travelers and exchanging information. Poetry, creative speech, and flowery blessings are common and prized.

❑ Poets are held in high esteem in Arabic societies; many educated Arabs attempt to write poetry at some point in their careers.

❑ In communication, Arabs highly value displays of emotion that Westerners may regard as immature. Westerners may label Arabs as too emotional while Arabs may find Westerners inscrutable and cold.

❑ Arab writers look to the Koran as the ultimate book of grammar and style, in much the same way that writers in English once relied on the King James version of the Bible.

❑ It may be difficult to obtain a direct answer from an Arab; a common answer is *inshalla* (God willing).

❑ Usually it is considered discourteous to say "no." Words such as "perhaps" or "maybe" are often used in place of the word "no."

❑ Communication is often indirect and, therefore, listeners must be sensitive to the underlying meaning of the speaker's message.

❑ It may be unacceptable, in some groups, to cross one's legs or stretch one's legs in a group setting.

❑ Among some groups, it is acceptable during conversations to retreat into silence and internal reflection. "Tuning out" is accepted and valued.

❑ During conversations, many Middle Easterners stand or sit close to other persons. Americans tend to maintain a distance of approximately five feet between themselves and their conversational partners, but for Middle Easterners a distance of two feet is typical. Touching during conversations is common.

❑ It is generally expected that people will show proper respect to others. Titles and last names are used in greetings.

❑ Lack of eye contact between men and women during conversation is common to maintain respect and proper distance between genders.

MIDDLE EASTERN LANGUAGE CONSIDERATIONS

❑ Middle Eastern languages are divided into three different language families: Altic, Hamito-Semitic, and Indo-European.

❑ Arabic, the language spoken most widely in the Middle East, is the world's fourth most common language after Mandarin, English, and Spanish. It is spoken by over 220 million people worldwide. Characteristics of the Arabic speaker's articulation and language are presented in Table 9.2.

❑ Arabic falls under the Semitic subdivision of the Hamito-Semitic language family.

❑ Other common Middle Eastern languages are Kurdish, Farsi (Persian), and Turkish. Hebrew is the official language of Israel. Amharic (Ethiopian) is another Semitic language.

❑ Farsi is the official language of Iran. Farsi shares 28 of its 32 letters with Arabic and is written from right to left.

❑ Arabic, as it is used during conversation, differs in important ways from the written form of the language. Written, classic, formal Arabic is unchangeable and is used everywhere. Written Arabic is more grammatically complex and includes a richer vocabulary than spoken Arabic. There are many spoken dialects of Arabic, some of which are mutually unintelligible.

❑ Most educated Arabs are bilingual. They speak Modern Standard Arabic as well as their local Arabic dialect.

❑ There are 29 letters in the Arabic alphabet. All but one of the letters is a consonant. The Arabic language is written from right to left.

❑ The most common word order in Arabic is verb + subject + object.

❑ The Arabic language has some consonants that are not used in English. Among these consonants are glottal stops, voiceless and voiced uvular fricatives, and voiced and voiceless pharyngeal fricatives.

❑ Several features of Arabic impact English production: a "staccato" effect stemming from fewer clearly articulated vowels; exaggerated articulation with equal stress on all syllables; the use of glottal stops before initial vowels (Campbell-Wilson, 2012).

❑ Young Arabs in other countries are shifting toward English-dominant bilingualism despite strong affiliations to the Arabic language and community. For example, in one study in the United Kingdom, young Yemenis were found to be openly shifting to English as their dominant language despite their affiliation with their communities and cultures of origin (Ferguson, 2013).

Table 9.2
Articulation and Language Differences Commonly Observed Among Arabic Speakers

Articulation Characteristics	Possible English Errors
n/ng substitution	son/song, nothin'/nothing
sh/ch substitution	mush/much, shoe/chew
w/v substitution or f/v substitution	west/vest, Walerie/Valerie fife/five, abofe/above
t/voiceless "th" substitution or s/voiceless "th" substitution	bat/bath, noting/nothing sing/thing, somesing/something
z/voiced "th" substitution	brozer/brother, zese/these zhoke/joke, fuzh/fudge
retroflex /r/ doesn't exist;	speakers of Arabic will use a tap or trilled /r/
There are no triple consonant clusters in Arabic, so epenthesis may occur	kinduhly/kindly, harduhly/hardly
o/a substitutions	hole/hall, bowl/ball
o/oi substitutions	bowl/boil, foble/foible
uh/a substitutions	snuck/snack, ruck/rack
ee/i substitutions	cheep/chip, sheep/ship

Language Characteristics	Possible English Errors
Omission of possessives 's and "of"	That Kathy book. The title the story is...
Omission of plurals	She has 5 horse in her stable. He has 3 pen in his pocket.
Omission of prepositions	Put your shoes.
Omission of form "to be"	She ___ my friend.
Inversion of noun constructs	Let's go to the station gas.

Immigrant Insight   Asmahan M., university senior, speaker of Arabic,
                                       daughter of immigrants from Palestine

I was originally going to be a doctor. When I decided to become a speech-language pathologist, my mom was angry and very devastated. I showed her my Anatomy and Physiology
textbook, and said that nurses study this information too! That made her feel a lot better. In the
Eastern Orthodox Arabic community, we don't talk about disabilities. People with disabilities are
looked down upon. If there is an invisible disability such as autism or a language impairment,
give people information and pamphlets to help them understand. Don't bring up the fact that
a child needs an IEP during the first meeting. Take several meetings to have the family get to
know you and build trust before talking about the child's special needs. Emphasize children's
strengths as well.

IMPLICATIONS FOR PROFESSIONALS

❏ As stated in a previous chapter, it is ideal if professionals can cultivate relationships with
Islamic clergy. These relationships can provide professionals with a deeper understanding of
Arab values, cultural customs, and world views. Many clergy are very happy to share their
expertise with professionals, as they are usually strong pillars of support for immigrant families especially.

❏ Be accepting of families who are Muslim and who want to use prayer and fasting as means
of reducing distress (Sue & Sue, 2016). If families are experiencing distress over a child's
communication disorder, prayer and fasting may help them cope better.

❏ Because of the many negative stereotypes that Americans hold of Arabs, professionals should
make sure that families feel comfortable and understood.

❏ Professionals should begin meetings with inquiries about the family and informal, light conversation. Most Arabs regard people who discuss business immediately as being brusque.
Arabs mistrust people who do not appear to take an interest in them personally. If Arabs do
not like or trust someone, they will often not listen to that person.

Immigrant Insight   Absaar, female college student, daughter of immigrants
                                       from Palestine, speaker of Palestinian and Arabic

I am Muslim and wear a hijab. I have been called a "terrorist" by Americans, and have
been told "Go back to where you came from." When I was in elementary school, kids would
follow me home. I was terrified to go to lunch (for fear of being bullied and harassed), and
my mother had to come and pick me up and bring me home to eat. My family and I have an
extremely hard time in airports. My 18-year-old brother has been harassed and detained for
hours, and we all have been subjected to extra screenings. My parents are much more protective of me than they are of my brothers, although we have a very loving family. They would not
let me leave them to attend graduate school in another city.

❏ Professionals may be more successful in communicating with families if they are informal and perceived as "family friends" rather than authority figures. It may be difficult for some families to trust those outside the extended family circle. Many Arabs do not feel comfortable going to strangers for help with problems.

❏ Some families will be offended if professionals offer their left hand in greeting, as the left hand is often considered unclean.

❏ It may not be considered appropriate for female professionals to shake hands with male family members.

❏ Most Arabs accept Western female professionals and especially admire those who are well educated. Thus, female professionals may want to find a comfortable, non-threatening way to reveal their professional education and credentials to families. Sharing a professional business card at the beginning of the first meeting can be helpful in establishing credibility.

❏ Professionals should sit with good posture and dress formally to indicate respect for the family. It is considered disrespectful to talk when slouching, leaning against a wall, or holding one's hands in one's pockets.

❏ Families may be late for appointments or may not keep appointments at all. Professionals should emphasize the need for promptness so that families can receive the time and support that they need within the professional's schedule.

❏ Many professionals speak to the student's mother first. In some Middle Eastern families, the father is the official liaison between the family and any "strangers." Thus, professionals may need to consult with the father first.

❏ It is important to find out family members' titles and use them—omission of a title may be considered an insult, especially to older, more traditional Arabs.

❏ Arab families may communicate emotionally during interactions with professionals, a pattern of behavior that is viewed as acceptable within their culture.

❏ Arabs are quite aware of social class, and upper-class Arabs may not socialize with those from lower socio-economic backgrounds. If an interpreter is from a social class different from that of the family, feelings of alienation may affect their interactions.

❏ Arabs are often uncomfortable during discussions that focus directly on death, illness, or disasters; they may use euphemisms or avoid these topics altogether.

❏ Disabilities are often associated with feelings of denial, shame, and guilt that impede communication in a formal interview situation. Seeking therapy may be a last resort (Al Khatib, 2017). Thus, professionals should approach discussions of disabilities with tact and diplomacy.

❏ Honor (sharaf) is highly valued in Arab families. Arabs may deny the existence of conditions that threaten their personal dignity (e.g., a child's disability) because honor is more important than facts.

❏ Professionals should not be shocked if Arabs ask such personal questions as "What is your salary?" or "Why do you have no children?" These clients are trying to establish rapport and get to know professionals as people.

❑ Professionals who are used to keeping physical distance when interacting with others may feel uncomfortable when Arabs stand close to them or touch them during conversations. It is important not to move away or appear to be disturbed by these communication patterns.

❑ The limited knowledge that many Arabs have about speech, language, and hearing services can affect their willingness to accept and participate in service delivery. They may feel uncomfortable utilizing services provided by a non-Arab.

❑ Many Arab countries provide free universal health care; private care costs much less than it does in the U.S. Thus, new Arab immigrants may have difficulty understanding aspects of the complex U.S. health care system (e.g., third-party insurance), and professionals may need to help them negotiate the system.

❑ Many American professionals emphasize that both parents need to work together to help their children. Some Arab men resist child-rearing activities because they do not see child-rearing as their responsibility. Child care is generally the province of women, especially in the early years (Sharifzadeh, 2011).

❑ Arab fathers in traditional religious families frequently want their sons to have excellent communication skills due to theological debates and long conversations that occur with other males. Professionals should point out how the participation of fathers in intervention can facilitate the achievement of these goals.

❑ The mastery of self-help skills at an early age is often not considered critical in Middle Eastern families. Professionals should not label children as "delayed" or "immature" based on developmental expectations for mainstream, U.S.-born children.

❑ The emphasis on interdependence within the family may conflict with the professional's goal of independence for a student with a disability. Remember that mothers may overprotect children with disabilities and foster dependence (Al Khatib, 2017). These mothers should be encouraged to gradually allow their children to do more for themselves so that they can become more independent.

❑ Some families indicate agreement with the recommendations of professionals because the expression of disagreement is considered rude. A "yes" response may be an expression of good will rather than an indication that recommendations will be followed.

❑ Rather than saying "no" directly, most Arabs will give a noncommittal answer. Arabs may not directly state what they want you to know, and will communicate with subtle cues (e.g., body language). It is important to obtain the trust of family members and to encourage them to express any concerns that they may have (Al Khatib, 2017).

❑ Conveying bad news is very sensitive in the Arab world. Many Arabs will "sugar coat" bad news, and thus professionals must be cautious about being too blunt when presenting assessment results and diagnosing disabilities. It is best to begin by talking about a child's strengths, and then gradually initiate a frank discussion about the problems that are being observed in the classroom.

❑ Professionals need to have frequent contacts with families to make sure that appropriate action is being taken to meet the needs of children.

❏ Because families are expected to take care of the needs of family members, problems may be encountered when outside agencies intervene to provide assistance. Professionals need to help families understand how these agencies can help them.

❏ In Arab countries, special education practices emphasize training and counseling with families but rarely involve establishing family-professional partnerships. Parents may view special education personnel as authority figures to whom they should defer; if they question these authority figures, it is disrespectful (Al Khatib, 2017). Thus, professionals can reassure families by emphasizing their importance in intervention.

❏ Because of the frequent use of exaggeration, assertion, and repetition among Arabs, professionals should use repetition and emphasis to convey to families that what is said is truly meant to be taken seriously. If professionals speak softly and only make a statement one time, Arabs may wonder if they really mean what they are saying (Nydell, 2012).

❏ Some Middle Easterners view the term "Middle East" as ethnocentric. Thus, professionals may wish to avoid this term when communicating with families. It is best to base any statements on the family's actual country of origin (e.g., "Pakistani American").

❏ Arabs who are Muslim often rely on religiously-based rather than medically-based explanations about the cause of a disability.

Profile

Mahbohbah K., a 9-year-old girl, came to the U.S. from Kuwait with her parents. In Kuwait, Mahbohbah had been diagnosed with cerebral palsy. She had been kept at home and was cared for by her mother. Mahbohbah had never attended school, and her family ensured that her needs were met.

In the Colorado city where the family settled, school personnel became aware of Mahbohbah and told her parents that school attendance was mandatory in the U.S. The parents objected strongly. School professionals met with the parents, discussed all the special education options that were available to Mahbohbah, and recommended placement in a special education program. The family refused to sign the program enrollment forms.

Finally the speech-language pathologist was able to obtain assistance from Abdullah S., a respected member of the local Muslim mosque. After much discussion in Arabic between the family and Abdullah, the family agreed to allow Mahbohbah to attend school and to receive special education services. Abdullah later told the speech-language pathologist privately that Mahbohbah's father felt that it was the duty of the family to care for this child's needs. The father didn't view education as being important for girls. Abdullah had worked hard to convince the family of the importance in America of educating both boys and girls. The family was informed that Mahbohbah would be at a severe disadvantage without the services offered by the school district.

STUDY QUESTIONS

1. Describe the traditional roles of men and women in the Middle East. How might these roles impact the relationship and communication between a female professional and a Middle Eastern man?

2. Discuss views of disabilities that are common in the Middle East.

3. List three practical suggestions that will help professionals communicate more effectively with Middle Eastern families.

MULTIPLE CHOICE

4. Which country is not referred to as either a Middle Eastern or Arab country?

   A. Jordan
   B. Iran
   C. Bahrain
   D. Kuwait
   E. China

5. A five-year-old Middle Eastern child, Farrah, has been referred to you. Her teacher suspects a developmental delay. You realize that you will need to meet with the special education team and the child's family to discuss the importance of a full psychoeducational assessment. What are some important things to keep in mind before and during this meeting?

   A. Most Middle Eastern parents strongly encourage early independence for their children.
   B. It will be best to direct the questions to Farrah's father during the meeting.
   C. To help family members relax so that they will not feel intimidated, you should dress informally and slouch slightly during the meeting.
   D. The family may deny the existence of any disability because it is a discredit to their honor.
   E. You need to repeat yourself and emphasize important points several times.

6. Which of the following is/are true about Farsi?

   A. Farsi is the official language of Iraq.
   B. Farsi shares 28 of its 32 letters with Arabic.
   C. Farsi is written from right to left.
   D. Farsi is the smallest country in the Middle East.
   E. Farsi is a city that separates two very different cultures.

7. Consonants that occur in Arabic but not in English include:

   A. Voiceless and voiced uvular fricatives
   B. Glottal stops
   C. Alveolar laterals
   D. Voiced and voiceless pharyngeal fricatives
   E. Voiced bilabial fricatives

8. Which of the following are TRUE statements about education in the Middle East?

   A. Schools are often co-educational.
   B. Formal Arabic is taught in many schools.
   C. Traditionally, most females were not encouraged to attend college.
   D. The education of boys is a high priority in many families.
   E. Compulsory education usually begins at around 5 years of age.

9. You are working with Abdul, a high school student from Qatar who stutters. Abdul's family has been the target of discrimination, and the resulting stress causes him to become more disfluent, especially in situations where he is confronted by authority figures. Which of the following might you assume that Abdul and his family have experienced?

   A. Being detained and questioned in airports
   B. Being conveyed, by popular and mass media, as intellectuals who look down upon those whom they feel are inferior
   C. Strengthened identity as Arab Americans
   D. Vulnerability to hate crimes and violent incidences
   E. Temptation to stop attending mosque prayer services to avoid harassment

10. Afeefa M. is a fourth grade Yemeni student whose family came to the U.S. eight months ago when her father got a job with a technology company in your area. Afeefa's teacher reports that although Afeefa is sweet and well behaved, she is much less verbally assertive than other children. Afeefa has few friends and seems to be uncomfortable during literacy and English Language Arts instruction. As you prepare to assess Afeefa for a possible language impairment, which of the following should you consider as factors that may be relevant to her performance in the classroom.

    A. Afeefa's mother does not read books at home.
    B. Afeefa may have been taught to believe that woman are supposed to stay home, bear children, and run the household. Therefore, performing well in school is not a high priority,
    C. Afeefa may have been told not to trust you because you always start meetings with informal conversation.
    D. Afeefa won't respect you if you are highly educated.
    E. Afeefa may be offended if you are holding papers with your right hand and offer your left hand when greeting her.

ANSWERS TO STUDY QUESTIONS

   4. E
   5. B, D, and E
   6. B and C
   7. A, B, and D
   8. B, C, and D
   9. A, C, D, E
 10. A, B, E

Part 2

Assessment of Culturally and Linguistically Diverse Students

Chapter 10

Bilingualism and Second Language Learning

Outline
- **Typical Processes of Second Language Acquisition**
- **Affective Variables in Second Language Acquisition**
- **Second Language Learning Styles and Strategies**
- **Types of Language Proficiency**
- **Issues in Bilingualism and Bilingual Education**
- **Conclusion**

When a child is referred for assessment because of possible language impairment (LI), it is necessary to determine how the observed behavior differs from that of children who acquire communication skills without difficulties. A major challenge confronting professionals is that "typical behavior" varies widely even among monolingual children. When working with English Language Learner (ELL) student populations, the picture becomes far more complex.

In spite of the complexity of the situation confronting professionals who work with ELL students, there are certain general facts about second language acquisition and bilingualism that can be outlined and then used as a foundation for distinguishing language differences from LIs (Brice, 2015). In this chapter, these facts and recent research findings are reviewed.

As discussed elsewhere in this book, it is extremely important to understand aspects of second language acquisition and bilingualism because of the greatly increasing numbers of ELL students in American schools who are learning English as a second or third language (Moore & Montgomery, 2018). Nearly 75% of American classrooms now include at least one ELL, and approximately 10% of students in the U.S. are ELLs (Sparks, 2016). Clearly, the rising number of ELLs in our schools makes it imperative to understand typical phenomena involved in second language acquisition and bilingualism as a foundation for distinguishing language difference from problems that are indicative of LI.

As mentioned in a previous chapter, professionals have used a variety of terms to refer to ELLs. Some professionals refer to individuals learning English as ESL (English as a Second Language) students. EAL (English as an Additional Language) is a term commonly used in the United Kingdom and South Africa where students routinely speak three or more languages. At this time, in North America, the term ELL is most commonly used by both state and federal agencies in referring to students who are learning English as an additional language (Paradis, 2016). The term EL (English Learner) is also being used.

TYPICAL PROCESSES OF SECOND LANGUAGE ACQUISITION

❏ The processes of second language acquisition in typically-developing students must be understood if one is to differentiate between language difference and LI. Typical second language acquisition processes often result in differences that can impact communication (Brice, 2015). These differences need to be recognized as normal, typical behaviors for students who are in the process of gaining English proficiency.

❏ Students who are learning English often demonstrate specific difficulties that are similar to those commonly observed among students with LI. Moreover, they are likely to perform significantly below the mean if norm-referenced English language tests are used in assessment. These students will appear to have language impairment if their language background and environmental experiences are not considered.

Familiarity with the processes commonly observed when children learn a second language will reduce the likelihood that children are inappropriately diagnosed as having LI (Paradis, 2016). Some of the most commonly observed behaviors are described below:

1. Transfer

Transfer refers to a process in which a communicative behavior from the first language is carried over into the second language. Also referred to as *cross-linguistic influence*, transfer can occur in all areas: syntax, morphology, phonology, pragmatics, and semantics (Brice, 2015).

❑ Some speech and language characteristics from the first language may be carried over into the second language. For example, ELL students often experience challenges acquiring grammatical morphemes when learning English (e.g. past tense –ed, plural –s, and present progressive –ing), resulting in omission of these morphemes. In another example of transfer, a little girl named Araceli (speaker of Spanish) once said to me, "Miss Roseberry, I like berry berry much espeech!" Araceli was showing transfer of Spanish syntax and phonology.

❑ Language patterns from the first language may influence how one phrases a particular message in the second language. In Visayan (a dialect spoken in the Philippines), "Ambot sa iya" literally translates to "I don't know to you." A Filipino would use this expression to mean "I don't know—it's completely up to you." A Filipino student who says, "I don't know to you" could easily be diagnosed as having LI if assessment personnel do not consider the influences of the first language on English production.

❑ When the second language is not the language of the student's social milieu, transfer is greater. Thus, when ELLs produce errors in English, it is important to consider the possibility that these errors result from language transfer or from the student's limited experience in using English.

❑ Bilingual paraprofessionals can be of great assistance in helping the professional determine the presence of first language transfer. One must be certain, however, that the paraprofessional is familiar with the dialect spoken by the student.

2. Fossilization

Fossilization occurs when specific second language "errors" remain firmly entrenched despite good proficiency in the second language.

❑ These errors are often observed among individuals who have been speaking a second language for many years. For example, a fluent English-speaking individual from Cuba was heard to habitually say, "the news are that...." This same individual, however, had flawless grammar most of the time. In another example, a speaker from Spain with excellent English frequently said "clothies" rather than "clothes" when talking about clothing.

❑ Fossilized items can be idiosyncratic to a child, or can be common within a linguistic community. Fossilized items may occur because of the inconsistencies of the English language. For example, irregular past tense and plural forms may be fossilized (e.g., "My foots are sore") because they are inconsistent. Fossilized items should not be viewed as signs of LI. It is more important to focus on the child's ability to communicate meaning appropriately than on the ability to use flawless English grammar and vocabulary.

Immigrant Insight   Fely, female speaker of Tagalog, Philippines

We arrived in the U.S. when I was 13. The only difficulty I have to this day (now 37 years old) is correct use of subject pronouns "he" and "she." In Tagalog, we only use "siya" as the pronoun for both genders. This is actually a Filipino error that we all make, no matter how long we have been in the U.S.

3. Silent Period

Some students, when learning a second language, go through a *silent period* in which there is much listening/comprehension and little output. These students are learning the rules of the language during this silent period; they may be covertly rehearsing what they are hearing.

❏ The silent period can last anywhere from three to six months, although estimates vary.

❏ Practitioners might be led to believe that a student has an expressive language delay, when in reality the student's attention is focused on learning the language. Generally, the younger the child is when exposure to the second language occurs, the longer the silent period lasts. Children exposed to a second language during their preschool years may have a silent period that stretches into a year or longer. It is my experience that teachers and caregivers often become afraid that the child has an expressive language delay when in reality, the child is merely in a normal silent period.

Profile

Arisbel R., a 3-year-old Spanish-speaking girl, was brought to a local preschool where only English was spoken. According to Arisbel's mother, Arisbel had no problems acquiring Spanish, and her Spanish language skills were commensurate with those of her siblings. However, the preschool teachers contacted the local speech-language pathologist after two months because Arisbel "isn't talking and we think she might have a language delay."

Arisbel was assessed in Spanish in both the home and preschool settings. An extensive case history was collected from Arisbel's parents. Based on the information obtained, the speech-language pathologist concluded that Arisbel was a typically-developing language learner who was going through the "silent period" that is often observed when young children are beginning to learn a new language. Ten months later, Arisbel was making functional use of the second language and interacting effectively with the other children in the preschool setting.

4. Interlanguage

Paradis et al. (2011) defined *interlanguage* as the period in second language development that extends from the time when the learner starts to use language productively until the time when that individual reaches a competence level similar to that of a native speaker. Paradis (2007, p. 2) described interlanguage as "...a dynamic system balancing first language transfer processes with target language developmental processes that gradually moves closer to the target language system."

❏ When learning a second language, the learner tests hypotheses about how language works and forms a personal set of rules for using language. The individual's production changes over time as language is experienced in different contexts.

❏ ELL students in the interlanguage stage frequently make inconsistent errors. Inconsistent errors reflect the progress that the student is making in learning a new language and should not be viewed as evidence of LI. In the example below, a 5-year-old child makes inconsistent language errors when talking about toy farm animals that she is playing with:

First the cows going to walk over there. There are three pig eating, and they standing by the cats. I don't know why those cat aren't hungry, but they not hungry. Oh, the horses are run now—I think they scared of the dog that are chasing. The horse run into the barn to hide from the dogs.

5. Language Loss

❏ If use of the first language decreases, it is common for the learner to lose skills in that language as proficiency is acquired in the second language (Brice, Brice, & Kester, 2010; Brice, 2015; Pham & Kohnert, 2014; Riquelme & Rosas, 2014). This process is referred to as *language loss*.

❏ Many ELL children hear and speak only English in the school environment; bilingual education is often nonexistent, especially for students who speak languages that are not spoken by any of the teachers. Since English is the dominant language of society in the U.S., children often experience language loss in the first language and a gradual replacement of that language by English.

❏ As discussed later in the chapter, this is particularly true for children who speak languages that are either of minority status (e.g., those of working class immigrants) or are spoken by people who have limited access to the political and economic institutions of the dominant group (Anderson, 2012).

❏ If a student has experienced language loss and is still acquiring English, the student may appear to be low-functioning in both languages (see Figure 10.1). Based on language test scores, one might incorrectly conclude that the student has LI. Differentiating between language difference and LI in a situation where language loss has occurred is challenging indeed.

6. Code-switching

Code-switching is the alternation between two languages within a single constituent, sentence, or discourse. Language alternation within a sentence is also called *code-mixing*. Code-switching/mixing behavior is used by typical, proficient bilingual speakers throughout the world (Brice, 2015; Dixon & Zhao, 2017).

❏ Children who live in homes where codeswitching occurs do not appear to be "confused" in their usage of language. Alternating between two languages in discourse is commonly observed among bilingual speakers and is not necessarily an indicator of a problem.

❏ During the early stages of second language learning, the learner may substitute structures, forms, or lexical items from the first language for forms in the second language that have not yet been learned. Bilingual children commonly use code-switching as a strategy, and it seems to help bridge the two languages that a child is learning.

❏ Children may code-switch in some situations more than others; the context of the interaction is a variable. Although code-switching is a typical communicative behavior, it may occur excessively in situations in which an individual lacks competence in one language.

AFFECTIVE VARIABLES IN SECOND LANGUAGE ACQUISITION

Many researchers have documented the influence of affective variables in second language acquisition (Brice, 2015; Edwards, 2010; Paradis et al., 2011; Rosa-Lugo et al., 2012). In this section, these variables are described in terms of their effect on the academic and linguistic performance of ELLs.

Figure 10.1
English-Language Learners at Risk

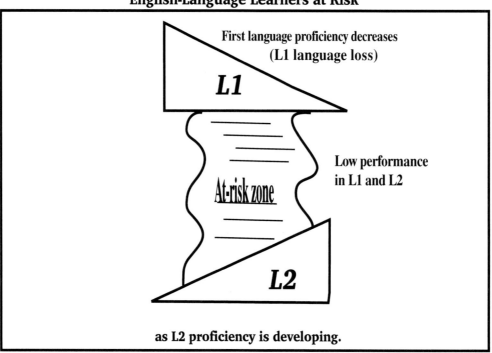

First language proficiency decreases
(L1 language loss)

L1

At-risk zone

Low performance
in L1 and L2

L2

as L2 proficiency is developing.

Immigrant Insight   Tan, female speaker of Mien from Laos

We came to the States when I was 10 and starting third grade. I just knew "Hi, my name is Tan," my ABCs, and how to write my name. Kids used to tease me because I couldn't speak English, but luckily I was able to speak Hmong and Laotian with some of the other kids. I was getting a "D" in English and a "C" in Math. I went to the library and checked out picture books because that was the only way I was going to learn. I also checked out library books with CDs so I could listen and follow along. I told myself I'm not going to be this dumb kid. I know I'm smart; I just need time to learn. Now I am a nurse.

1. Motivation

Motivation impacts a student's success in acquiring a second language. When attempting to determine a student's level of motivation, the following questions can be asked:

A. *Is the student becoming acculturated into the English language environment?*
   Acculturation refers to psychological integration with speakers of the second language. Often second language learners acquire the second language to the degree that they acculturate. Thus, if a student is not integrated into situations with English-speaking peers, he or she may not be highly motivated to learn English.

B. *How much enclosure exists between the student's culture and the American culture?*
   Enclosure refers to the degree to which ethnic groups share the same things in life: schools, churches, recreational facilities, professions, leisure activities, etc. If a student

comes from an ethnic-linguistic community that has little enclosure, or little in common with the dominant English-speaking community, he may not acquire English rapidly.

C. *Is there congruence between the student's cultural group and the dominant group?*
The more congruent, or similar two cultures are, the greater the likelihood that members of the culture will experience the social contact necessary for success in learning the second language.

D. *What are the attitudes of the ELL student group and the dominant group toward one another?*
A student from a cultural group that has positive feelings toward Americans will probably learn English more quickly than will a student from a cultural group that expresses frequent negative feelings.

E. *How long does the ELL student's family intend to stay in the United States?*
Will the family be going back to the home country? In families that plan to remain in the United States, motivation to learn English is often higher than in families that plan to return to their homeland and live there permanently.

F. *Does the student feel that learning a second language will threaten his or her identity?*
If a student is rejected by family and/or peers for speaking English, motivation will be affected. I have observed this in some teen-age ELLs I've worked with, especially those who are members of gangs that discourage use of English.

G. *Have the student and her family experienced trauma in the home country?*
Immigrant and refugee students who have experienced trauma in their home countries may have challenges that affect their willingness to adapt to a new culture and learn a second language. If they suffer from post traumatic stress disorder, the learning of English may be a challenge.

Profile

I have a full-time position as a university professor and also work part-time as an itinerant SLP in the public schools. My school district is the third largest receiver of immigrant and refugee families in the U.S., and many of these families are from war-torn Middle Eastern countries. The fastest-growing languages in my district are Farsi and Arabic. We work hard to help our families in all aspects of their lives, including making professionals available to provide counseling and other psychological services to individuals with post traumatic stress disorder. If treatment is not provided, many of these immigrants will struggle to learn English and to succeed in mainstream society.

2. Personality

Personality characteristics may also affect second language acquisition (Brice, 2015; Paradis, 2007). It is important for professionals to keep these characteristics in mind, as they can impact a student's developing English skills.

A. **Self-esteem**. The student's feelings and judgments relating to his/her own abilities and worthiness have an effect on second language acquisition. To maximize learning, students need to have a positive self-concept and a positive attitude. Students whose first language and culture are rejected may have low self-esteem and consequently learn English more slowly than children whose backgrounds are accepted. In today's political climate, ELLs from some backgrounds experience fear, rejection, and bullying. Professionals must make every attempt to prevent this and help students feel safe.

B. **Extroversion.** There is some evidence that extroverted students learn English conversational skills faster than introverted students (Wong Fillmore, 1976). Shy students may take longer to develop conversational competence than outgoing students.

C. **Assertiveness.** Being assertive can be helpful in facilitating second language learning, as assertive learners avail themselves of increased opportunities for second language practice. If a student is non-assertive, there may be fewer opportunities to practice English skills with native speakers.

3. Anxiety Level

Motivated individuals with a low anxiety level are more readily able to benefit from language input in the second language. These students are better able to learn because they are in an environment that is relatively stress-free and accepting. If students have a high level of anxiety, there can be a resulting "mental block" that prevents optimal learning.

SECOND LANGUAGE LEARNING STYLES AND STRATEGIES

Students bring a variety of language learning styles and strategies to the second language learning situation. This section delineates learning styles and strategies that might influence students' communication.

1. Modeling

❑ A student may exhibit language patterns similar to those used by parents and other family members. When conducting assessments, it is important for professionals to familiarize themselves with the student's daily speech and language models. Many professionals have had the experience of assessing a student and subsequently talking with a parent about the child's performance. It is often discovered that the parents' speech and language patterns sound very similar to those of the child!

❑ In addition to considering the impact of parents as language models, it is important to consider the influence of siblings, peers, grandparents, day care providers, and others in the student's environment. Some students come from extended families in which they spend much time with grandparents or care providers who are not native speakers of English.

Profile

L. M. was referred to me for speech-language screening by his first-grade teacher. I assessed L. M. informally in the classroom setting. He conversed readily and confided that he wanted to be a pediatrician in the future. Language comprehension appeared to be good. Some morphosyntactic errors were noted during conversation. In addition, L. M. was slightly difficult to understand due to misarticulated speech sounds. I reviewed the Home Language Survey in the student's school file. The survey, filled out by his mother, indicated that English was the language used most often by the student and other family members. Because this was the case, I felt that L. M. should be formally tested to determine if he was eligible for speech and language intervention.

After receiving information about the proposed assessment, the student's father came to the school and informed me that the child's mother spoke several Filipino dialects in the home, although use of these languages was not indicated on the Home Language Survey. The mother was not a proficient English speaker, but she tutored her child in English on a daily basis. The father was from Cuba, spoke rapidly, was difficult to understand, and made frequent grammatical errors in English.

It appeared that L. M.'s speech and language patterns were influenced by the language models available to him in the home. L. M.'s parents did not feel that the child was having difficulty learning language. The student did not appear to be self-conscious about his speech, and his classmates did not make fun of him. Although the student made some expressive errors in English, the teacher stated that these errors were not negatively impacting his access to the curriculum. Clearly, L.M.'s speech and language patterns were modeled after those of his parents; there was no indication of an underlying LI.

2. Avoidance

A student may avoid communicating in the second language to avoid ridicule from others. This strategy could result in the student's language performance appearing to be inadequate even though he is learning the language appropriately. Students don't want to be laughed at when they speak. This may be particularly true of older students who speak English with a pronounced accent.

3. Practice Opportunities

Much of a student's progress in second language acquisition depends on the availability of functional opportunities for second language practice. Some students speak English in the classroom but not in any other contexts. The learning of a second language is likely to be slow if the student makes little use of that language with family and friends outside of the classroom.

Profile

P. B. was a Laotian kindergarten student who came to school speaking only Laotian. The Home Language Survey in her school file indicated that only Laotian was spoken in the home. P. B.'s refugee family came to the United States when P. B. was one year old. When P. B. came to school, she was evaluated with an oral language proficiency test and classified as "non-English speaking." A language dominance test, administered one month later, showed the student to be "Limited Bilingual," with limited skills in English and Laotian. Laotian was found to be her dominant language.

P. B. was retained in kindergarten. At the end of her second year in kindergarten, she showed little progress in acquiring English skills although she apparently got along quite well in class. Her teachers were not concerned at this point because P. B. was a cooperative child who followed the daily curriculum and was good at art. The teachers did not feel that P. B. was a child with special education needs. Nevertheless, I was concerned because P. B.'s basic English conversational skills continued to be quite limited. Pre- and post-testing during the second year of kindergarten revealed little progress in learning even informal spoken English.

Upon gathering information about P. B.'s background, I learned that she interacted almost exclusively with Laotian-speaking students at school and in her neighborhood. She received no extra support in either English or Laotian. Her parents, monolingual speakers of Laotian, were nonliterate, and unable to help her with homework.

Did P. B. have LI? Should she undergo special education testing because of her limited progress in acquiring English? This would be an easy conclusion to reach; however, P. B.'s limited opportunities for practice in English had to be considered. Since she rarely spoke English inside or outside of the classroom, her opportunities for acquiring English were limited indeed. Should special education testing occur anyway?

I decided that P. B.'s limited progress in acquiring English may have resulted from limited experiences in using the English language. I recommended tutoring to develop Laotian language skills and skills in using English. I also recommended that her oral language proficiency be tested again, following a period of instruction, to assess progress in learning English. Finally, I spoke with the site English as a second language specialist and asked him to monitor P. B. for problems that might be indicative of LI.

4. Use of Formulaic Language

❏ The English learner who uses phrases such as "Have a good day" that are learned as a whole is using formulaic language. Formulaic language involves memorized phrases that children rely on heavily when they are in the early stages of learning English (Paradis et al., 2011). Second language learners may use these phrases appropriately, although they may not know the meaning or grammatical function of individual words within the phrases.

❏ Students who use these memorized phrases are often able to initiate and sustain simple conversation and, therefore, give the false impression that they are fluent speakers of the language. Ironically, although the use of formulaic language is a helpful strategy in the early stages of learning a second language, busy classroom teachers may over-extrapolate this "fluent English" to mean that students are capable of carrying out complex academic English tasks.

TYPES OF LANGUAGE PROFICIENCY

Language proficiency is a complex phenomenon that has been defined in a variety of ways (Dixon & Zhao, 2017). In this section, several models of language proficiency are described. Knowledge of these types of proficiency is critical in the process of differentiating language difference from difficulties that are indicative of LI.

Separate Underlying Proficiency versus Common Underlying Proficiency

Cummins (2017) described two models of language proficiency: (1) Separate Underlying Proficiency Model and (2) Common Underlying Proficiency Model. In the Separate Underlying Proficiency (SUP) model, language proficiency in the first language is viewed as entirely separate from proficiency in the second language and, therefore, skills learned in the first language will not transfer to the second language. Supporters of the SUP model believe that language development activities in the first language will not enhance learning of a second language. Thus, in order to "help" a child learn English faster, they will try to eradicate or discourage use of the child's first language.

❏ Unfortunately, many professionals who believe in the SUP model tell parents of ELL children to discontinue use of the first language at home and "just speak English." However, many of these parents speak very little English; if they do speak English, it is not fluent. Children who learn English from models who lack proficiency in the language will speak the language as they hear it used in their environment.

❑ Supporters of the SUP model believe that exposure to nonstandard, nonfluent language models in English will be more beneficial in facilitating English language skills than exposure to fluent speakers of the child's first language.

❑ In addition, supporters of the SUP model do not account for the fact that family relationships may become strained if use of the first language is not continued with children in the home.

There is no evidence to support the SUP model (Cummins, 2017; Shoebottom, 2013). The first language is a foundation for learning a second language. This foundation needs to be solid and strong. High quality language exposure enhances the learning of concepts that are important for cognitive and linguistic development. As children hear and use their native language in a variety of contexts, they develop the conceptual knowledge and cognitive strategies necessary for success in acquiring new information and linguistic skills.

In the Common Underlying Proficiency (CUP) model of language proficiency (see Figure 10.2), the development of skills in the first language is viewed as a process that will facilitate the learning of additional languages. According to Cummins (2017), experience with either language can promote development of the proficiency underlying both languages, given adequate motivation and exposure to both either in school or in the wider environment. In the CUP model, the literacy-related aspects of a bilingual's proficiency in the first language and second language are seen as common or interdependent across languages.

❑ Research shows that promoting early literacy skills in a child's first language promotes development of skills in the second language (Brice, 2015; Goodrich, Lonigan, & Farver, 2013; Schwinge, 2017). Conversely, the student who does not read in the first language at all is likely to have a more difficult time reading in English than the student who reads fluently in the first language.

❑ The CUP model has major implications for professionals working with ELL children. If a student has had limited exposure and experience in the first language, the conceptual foundation necessary for success in the classroom will be underdeveloped.

❑ It is ideal to strengthen the foundation in the first language before instruction is attempted in the second language. Negative cognitive consequences may result if efforts are made to switch the child to English before the first language is fully developed.

❑ Using the second language for instruction when the first language has not yet been fully developed is like building a house on an unstable foundation (see Figure 10.3). By building a solid foundation in the first language, the child acquires concepts and strategies that will facilitate learning another language.

❑ Rather than trying to eradicate the first language, efforts should be made to help students become fluent bilingual speakers. By helping students to develop high levels of proficiency in the first and second languages, students may experience growth in various cognitive skills that have been associated with success in school. Being a fluent bilingual individual has many advantages that are described later in this book.

❑ The ramifications for ELL students are clear. If a student is struggling academically or not learning English as rapidly as would be expected, professionals may incorrectly assume that special education services are needed. Limited progress in school is often due, at least in part, to limited skills in the first language and lack of opportunities for continued development of skills in that language.

Figure 10.2

Two Models of Language Proficiency

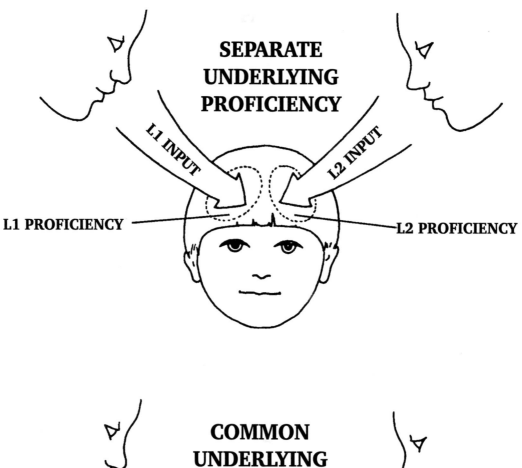

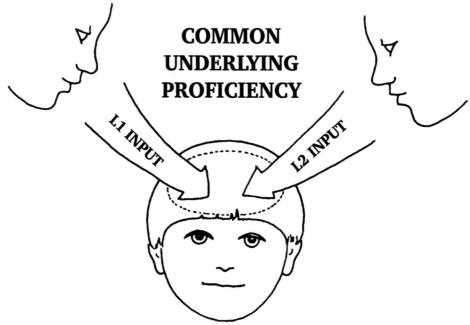

Source: Adapted from Cummins, J. (2017). Teaching for transfer in multilingual school contexts. In O. Garcia, A. Lin and S. May (Eds.), *Bilingual and multilingual education* (pp. 103-115). New York: Springer International Publishing.

Figure 10.3
Thresholds of Bilingual Development

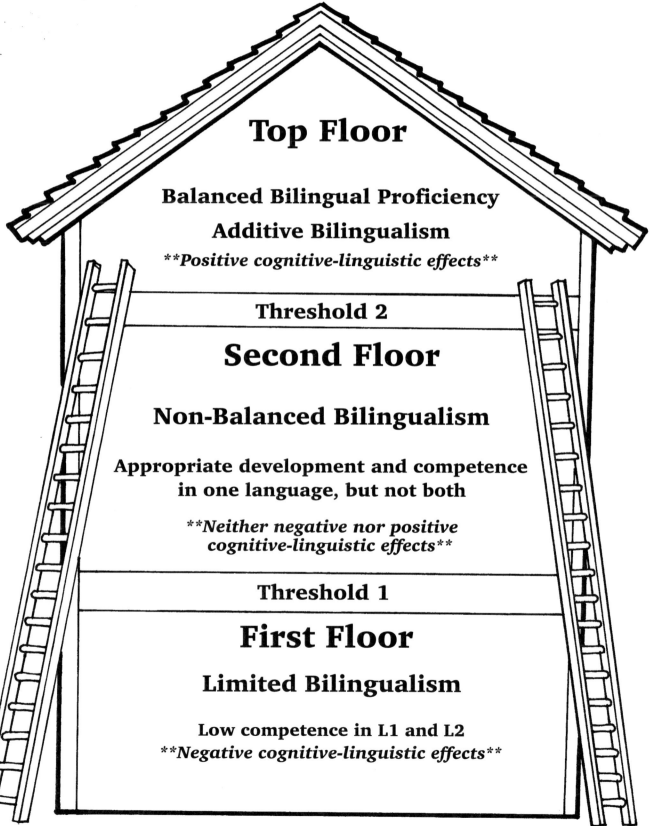

In sum, if a student's first language foundation is weak, the student is likely to have difficulty developing strong second language (English) skills. Promoting the development of skills in the first language helps children to develop cognitive strategies that will facilitate growth in English and success in the language curriculum. Children who have weak language skills in both their first language and English do not necessarily have disabilities.

Basic Interpersonal Communication Skills and Cognitive Academic Language Proficiency

When assessing language proficiency, it is important to distinguish between Basic Interpersonal Communication Skills (BICS) and Cognitive Academic Language Proficiency (CALP) (Cummins, 2017). The pioneering work of Cummins created this helpful distinction, which served for many years to alert professionals to the fact that when children are learning a second language, there are different types of language proficiency and time frames for acquiring each type of proficiency (Cummins, 1992a, 2000). Originally, Cummins stated that under ideal conditions, it takes second language learners 2-3 years to acquire BICS and 5-7 years to acquire CALP that is commensurate with the skills of native speakers.

❏ BICS refers to the context-embedded communication that children develop for social interaction in daily life. It is learned naturally in daily environments and is supported by paralinguistic cues such as intonation, facial expressions, and gestures. In BICS, formulaic language is sometimes used. For example, a student demonstrating BICS might say to a friend at the bus stop after school, "Have a great weekend!" In another example, a student using BICS might say "Hey—what's up?"

❏ In BICS, there is a shared reality between the speakers; they are generally discussing things that are present in the here and now. For example, BICS might involve a discussion about a field trip; there is a shared reality and participants can negotiate meaning with one another. Gestures and facial expressions facilitate the communication of meaning in this context-embedded situation.

❏ BICS is also demonstrated in a situation where some students express a desire to play tether ball and others express their preference for volleyball. A discussion of these choices has a shared reality, a concrete and visible situation, and nonverbal cues to support the interaction.

CALP refers to context-reduced forms of communication, or expertise in understanding and using more formal, expository (informational) forms of oral and written language (see Table 10.1). Context-reduced communication does not assume a shared reality. It may rely exclusively on oral or written linguistic cues for meaning.

❏ CALP is usually taught explicitly in academic settings, and there is usually limited or no context to support what is being discussed. Context-reduced communication is typical in many U.S. classroom settings today, even beginning in kindergarten. The adoption of the Common Core State Standards has sharply increased the use of CALP in the early grades.

❏ Proficiency in context-reduced communication involves the ability to make complex meanings clear by means of language itself rather than by use of contextual support or paralinguistic cues.

Table 10.1
Interpersonal and Academic Language Proficiency

Basic Interpersonal Communication Skills (BICS) (Conversational Informal Language Fluency)	**Cognitive Academic Language Proficiency (CALP)** (Formal Academic Language Fluency)
• Oral language only	• Oral and written language
• Used for social interaction in daily life	• Gained primarily through schooling
• Learned naturally in daily environments	• Mostly taught explicitly in academic settings
• Context-embedded	• Context-reduced
• Shared reality between speakers	• Assumes listener knowledge; usually minimal shared reality
• Supported by paralinguistic cues (e.g., gestures, intonation)	• Not usually supported by paralinguistic cues such as facial expression and intonation
• Used in casual, informal communication	• Usually used in reading, writing, formal oral communication
• Formulaic language sometimes used	• Formulaic language rarely used; characterized by specialized vocabulary, grammar, and discourse patterns
• Characterized by short, simple sentences	• Characterized by longer, more complex sentences

❏ CALP assumes that the listener brings certain background knowledge to the situation. Formulaic language is almost never used in CALP; CALP is characterized by specialized vocabulary, grammar, and discourse patterns.

❏ Even in oral CALP, longer sentences and less common vocabulary are usually used. For example, a teacher might say to the class, "The original experiment involving electric current flow was conducted by the scientists at a university that specialized in this particular area."

Over the years, whether or not it was Cummins' original intent, professionals often described BICS as consisting of oral language skills and CALP as consisting of non-oral reading and writing skills. CALP, however, also includes the formal oral language skills used within the academic curriculum.

When professionals are assessing a student because of a suspected LI, it is important to examine the school environment. Is the student in a classroom situation where CALP tasks are presented regularly with little support and explanation? How much contextual information is available to facilitate comprehension? Students will struggle if they have not yet acquired the cognitive academic skills necessary to complete classroom assignments.

With the advent of the Common Core State Standards, students are particularly pressured to master complex skills at earlier ages. For example, the increasing use of expository or informational text in the early grades requires students to have a broader understanding of vocabulary and the cognitive strategies necessary to understand abstract language.

❏ While the creators of the Common Core State Standards state that ELL students must master the standards in all areas, including language arts, no specific methods are prescribed for helping young children acquire complex skills in the early grades (Silverman & Doyle, 2013). Even listening and speaking standards (oral language) clearly involve CALP (See Table 10.2). Many children with language impairment lack the vocabulary and cognitive strategies necessary to benefit from the instructional materials commonly used in classrooms to teach these skills.

❏ ELL students in public schools are often placed into submersion or sink-or-swim classrooms in which only English is spoken. Moreover, often no special provisions are made to help these students learn the English CALP that they need to succeed academically and to meet the requirements of the Common Core State Standards.

❏ Because the initial exposure to English in our schools often targets language skills in context-reduced situations, many students fail to acquire a solid conceptual foundation and end up struggling academically. Helping students to develop a basic conceptual foundation is critical if students are to acquire the strategies necessary for academic success.

Many ELL students are in the Zone of Vulnerability (see Figure 10.4) where they have some mastery of BICS but have not yet acquired CALP. When students are in this zone, they are frequently behind their classmates academically and vulnerable to being referred for special education testing.

❏ Often, students' development of a basic conceptual foundation is measured by English language proficiency tests. Many of these tests evaluate only English BICS. The student may be asked to respond to simple questions such as, "What do you like to watch on TV?" or "What is your favorite food?" A problem occurs when professionals use these English language proficiency test results to determine whether or not the student has the language skills necessary to function appropriately in an English-only program of academic instruction.

❏ Another related problem is that teachers often assume that students identified as "Fully English Proficient" on BICS-type proficiency measures are fully capable of functioning effectively within the English language curriculum. These students, however, do not necessarily have the academic language skills necessary to succeed within the classroom. They may also lack the language competencies required to perform adequately on tests standardized on monolingual, English-speaking children.

❏ Students with LI may appear to be "Fully English Proficient" if only BICS-type language proficiency measures are used. When assessing language proficiency, it is important to assess performance on the types of language tasks that are used in the classroom setting. Both BICS and CALP should be assessed.

Table 10.2

Common Core State Standards:
Examples of Cognitive Academic Language Proficiency Requirements

Listening and Speaking Standards (Oral Language)

Grade 1 - Standard 3: Ask and answer questions about what a speaker says in order to gather additional information or clarify something that is not understood.

Grade 2 - Standard 2: Recount or describe key ideas or details from a text read aloud or information presented orally or through other media.

Grade 3 - Standard 2: Determine the main ideas and supporting details of a text read aloud or information presented in diverse media and formats, including visually, quantitatively, and orally.

Grade 4 - Standard 4: Report on a topic or text, tell a story, or recount an experience in an organized manner, using appropriate facts and relevant, descriptive details to support main ideas or themes; speak clearly at an understandable pace.

Grade 5 - Standard 3: Summarize the points a speaker makes and explain how each claim is supported by reasons and evidence.

Grade 9 - Standard 3: Evaluate a speaker's point of view, reasoning, and use of evidence and rhetoric, identifying any fallacious reasoning or exaggerated or distorted evidence.

Reading Informational Text (Written Language)

Kindergarten - Standard 9: With prompting and support, identify basic similarities and differences between two texts on the same topic (e.g., illustrations, descriptions, or procedures).

Grade 1 - Standard 5: Know and use various text features (e.g., headings, tables of contents, glossaries, electronic menus, icons) to locate key facts or information in a text.

Grade 3 - Standard 8: Describe the logical connection between particular sentences and paragraphs in a text (e.g., comparison, cause/effect, first/second/third in a sequence).

Grade 6 - Standard 5: Analyze how a particular sentence, paragraph, chapter, or section fits into the overall structure of a text and contributes to the development of the ideas.

Grade 10 - Standard 9: Analyze seminal U.S. documents of historical and literary significance (e.g., The Gettysburg Address, Roosevelt's Four Freedoms Speech), including how they address related themes and concepts.

Figure 10.4
Zone of Vulnerability

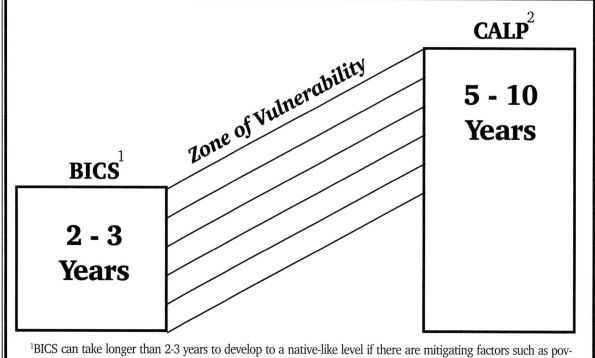

[1]BICS can take longer than 2-3 years to develop to a native-like level if there are mitigating factors such as poverty, homelessness, or truancy.
[2]CALP can develop in a shorter time period if the student has a solid oral and written base in the first language.

Profile

P. S., a male second grade student from India, was referred to our Student Study Team by his teacher because of problems in reading and math. The teacher reported that the child had good receptive and expressive oral language skills. P. S. was described as cooperative, courteous, and helpful, and he frequently asked questions when he did not understand classroom assignments. Areas of concern included sight word vocabulary, knowledge of phonics, basic word attack skills, sentence structure, written expression, spelling, and math concepts. P. S. was able to do well in math when manipulatives were used, and he was ahead of some of his classmates in several math skills.

When I asked about the student's language background, no one on the team was able to provide this information. I left the meeting briefly to check the student's school records. A review of the Home Language Survey revealed that Hindi was the primary language of the home and the language that P. S. most often used. He had been exposed to English for 2.5 years, but spoke only Hindi when he entered kindergarten. I brought this information back to the Student Study Team.

I told the classroom teacher about the CALP versus BICS distinction. She had never heard about this distinction and realized that the student's BICS were quite good. He would need more time to acquire the CALP necessary for success in academic subjects. Thus, rather than testing P. S. for special education, the team concluded that he should receive support in Hindi and English from a bilingual paraprofessional who was assigned to assist him in the classroom.

In looking at the student's profile, it was clear that he had mastered BICS. He was, however, having difficulty with CALP. This is very typical of children who enter kindergarten speaking only their first language. This case illustrates the importance of utilizing language proficiency models when attempting to determine the cause of a child's difficulties in the classroom. The case of P. S. also underscores the great importance of taking the time to gather information about children's language backgrounds. I was able to obtain this information in less than five minutes. If I had not looked up information about this student's language background, he might have been inappropriately placed into special education.

When professionals make judgments about overall proficiency in English based on a student's performance in conversational face-to-face communication situations, they risk the possibility of creating academic deficits in these students (Cummins, 2012, 2017; Paradis et al., 2011; Rosa-Lugo et al., 2012) (see Figure 10.5). Again, it is important to keep in mind that BICS is generally acquired more quickly and easily than CALP.

Timelines for Language Proficiency Development

As more information has become available over time, it has been suggested that Cummins' originally proposed timelines for BICS and CALP development be modified (Gindis, 2013; Paradis et al., 2011). There are a number of variables that impact the length of time it takes second language learners to acquire both BICS and CALP.

❑ Socioeconomic status plays a strong role in oral and literate language acquisition. Students from backgrounds of poverty may take longer to acquire BICS and CALP (Sparks, 2016). Gindis (2013) pointed out that some of Cummins' original research was conducted with low-income immigrants who did not have the benefit of a formal education. If parents have a high level of formal education, BICS and CALP may develop more quickly.

❑ The length of time that it takes ELL children to develop oral English language skills that are commensurate with those of native English speakers depends greatly upon how oral language skills are defined (Paradis, 2007). As stated by Paradis et al. (2011, p. 169):

> It is important to not equate conversational language with oral language in general—academic language is both oral and written...Nevertheless, it is still the case that children gain competence in academic language use primarily, and often only, through schooling...

❑ It can take much longer than 2-3 years for the oral language of ELL children to reach the same level as that of their monolingual peers. There are different timelines for the development of informal conversational oral skills as compared to the oral and literacy-related skills needed within the academic language curriculum.

❑ Hakuta, Butler, and Witt (2000) analyzed language test information from more than 1,800 ELL children in San Francisco. They concluded from their analysis that these students took 3-5 years of full-time English schooling to develop oral English abilities that were similar to those of native English speakers. Hakuta et al. also found that academic language proficiency took 4-7 years for ELLs to master.

Figure 10.5

LANGUAGE FLUENCY MISDIAGNOSIS MODEL

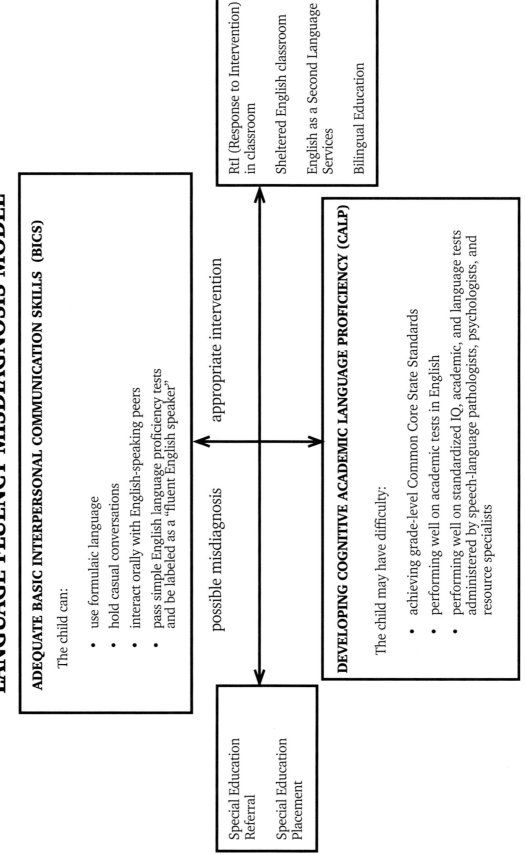

❏ Saunders and O'Brien (2006) reviewed many studies of the English abilities of children learning English as a second language and concluded that it was not until the later elementary years that these ELLs developed proficiency that was commensurate with that of native speakers.

❏ Shohamy (1999) found that students who immigrated to Israel took 7 to 9 years to arrive at the level of native Hebrew students in literacy, and slightly less time to reach the level of native Hebrew speakers in mathematics. Shohamy, Levine, Spolsky, Kere-Levy, Inbar, and Shemesh (2002) showed that children who immigrated to Israel from the former USSR and Ethiopia often took more than 7 years to develop CALP.

❏ Paradis (2016) emphasized that "the time frame for ELLs to approach age-expected monolingual abilities in English well exceeds 3 years for most linguistic subdomains" (p. 179). She stated that linguistic skills may develop asynchronously, and that the development of these skills depends on multiple variables such as age, first language, language learning aptitude, maternal education, richness of the English environment outside of school, and length of exposure to English in school.

It is very difficult to provide a specific timeline for how long it takes BICS and CALP to develop because, as stated, there are so many variables that impact rate of acquisition. Nevertheless, professionals need to be aware of the distinction between CALP and BICS to avoid misidentifying ELLs as having language impairment when these students are merely demonstrating expected differences in types of language proficiency.

ISSUES IN BILINGUALISM AND BILINGUAL EDUCATION

Immigrant Insight   Ujang, female from Malaysia, speaker of Malay and Chinese

When we started school in Malaysia, we were taught to speak both Malay and English. I speak multiple dialects of Cantonese and Mandarin. I am glad I still speak Malay so I can talk on the phone with my family back home.

Additive and Subtractive Bilingualism

Additive bilingualism occurs when both languages spoken by the student are reinforced, resulting in high levels of proficiency in the two languages. The student's first language continues to be nurtured and encouraged as the child learns the second language (Dixon & Zhao, 2017). The goal is to help the student become a fluent and balanced bilingual speaker. Biliteracy is ideal (Schwinge, 2017).

As stated previously, there are advantages to additive bilingualism. By becoming fully bilingual, individuals enhance their employability and increase their potential for making valuable contributions to society (Pham & Kohnert, 2014).

Today, more of the world's population is bilingual or multilingual than monolingual (Brice, Leung, & Gorman, 2014). In today's global economy, bilingualism is a great asset. In many parts of the world, multilingual individuals are considered educated and cosmopolitan.

❏ Research clearly demonstrates the advantages of fluent, additive bilingualism over monolingualism. The cognitive and neurological benefits of bilingualism extend from early childhood to old age.

❏ The bilingual brain more efficiently processes information, staves off cognitive decline, and has enriched cognitive control (Bialystok, Craik, & Luk, 2012; Marian & Shook, 2012). Bilingualism is associated with improved metalinguistic awareness, better novel word comprehension, better memory, enhanced creativity, morphological awareness, and visual-spatial skills (Kan, Sadagopan, Janich, & Andrade, 2014; Marian & Kaushanskaya, 2011; Roberts, 2013; Schwartz, Taha, Assad, Khamaisi, & Eviatar, 2016). The trilingual brain may have even more cognitive advantages than the bilingual brain (Schroeder & Marian, 2016).

❏ Children who experience additive bilingualism continue to be able to speak with their families in the first language. This is extremely important because many parents and especially grandparents communicate best (with the most possible intimacy and naturalness of expression) in the first language. For children, being bilingual provides a bridge across generations (Hampton, Rabagliati, Sorace, & Fletcher-Watson, 2017). When children can no longer speak the first language, relationships with immediate and extended family members suffer. Unfortunately, this situation is common in the U.S.

Subtractive bilingualism is a phenomenon in which the student's first language is replaced by the second language. Language loss occurs in the first language, and the student gradually becomes a monolingual speaker of English or the majority language. However, if English skills are considerably below those of their monolingual peers, the student's cognitive and linguistic growth is likely to be negatively affected.

❏ Children who are sequential language learners (described later) and belong to a minority ethnolinguistic community may be especially vulnerable to subtractive bilingualism (Paradis et al., 2011). A minority ethnolinguistic community is one in which the language has lower social status, is less widely valued and spoken, and receives little to no institutional support (Centeno, 2007).

❏ ELL students who struggle academically and linguistically from year to year are often those who have experienced subtractive bilingualism. Subtractive bilingualism often creates negative cognitive effects; children are left with a reduced conceptual foundation on which to build academic and linguistic skills. These students, however, do not have "disabilities" and, therefore, are not appropriate candidates for special education.

Children who belong to majority ethnolinguistic communities are much less vulnerable to experiencing subtractive bilingualism and often experience additive bilingualism when they are exposed to a second language. In this situation, their first language (English in this discussion) is widely used and has high social status. It is the language of business and enjoys widespread institutional support. These children's parents often place them into language programs where they learn a second language for enrichment purposes.

❏ The state of Utah has initiated total language immersion programs for their students in kindergarten through grade 12. In fall 2013, there were 20,000 children in 100 schools (20% of all elementary students in the state) who were participating in these programs. The programs offer total immersion (for English-speaking students) in such diverse languages as Mandarin, French, Spanish, Portuguese, and many others (Utah State Board of Education, 2017).

❏ In California's Silicon Valley, there is a private school called the French-American School of Silicon Valley. Parents are urged to give their children the benefit and gift of bilingual education.

❏ West Portal Elementary School in San Francisco offers elementary Cantonese immersion classes for English-speaking children whose parents want them to learn Cantonese. In some high schools, Chinese has been included in the Advanced Placement program. Parents want their children to partake of this opportunity to broaden their linguistic skills and enhance their desirability to future employers.

Simultaneous versus Sequential Bilingualism

❏ Researchers have broadly delineated two types of bilingualism: *simultaneous* and *sequential.* **Simultaneous acquisition** occurs when two languages are acquired simultaneously from infancy (Dixon & Zhao, 2017). Children who learn two languages from birth follow the same milestones for language acquisition as do monolingual children—for example, they speak their first words at the same time as monolingual children.

❏ Children who acquire two languages simultaneously in naturalistic situations seem to do so with minimal interference. If the situation is one of additive bilingualism, children experience cognitive-linguistic and social benefits. Simultaneous acquisition results in equivalent levels of language proficiency in both languages more often than does sequential acquisition.

❏ Students who experience **sequential acquisition** of the second language learn the first language and are exposed to the second language at a later point in time. For example, a child might be exposed to Spanish first in the home and then to English in preschool when she is 4 years old.

Some sequential learners show greater diversity in rates and stages of acquisition. Although some students acquire the second language with minimal interference, others may experience challenges.

❏ If a student is introduced to a second language before a basic first language foundation has been reached, the development of the first language may be arrested or may regress while the child is focused on the learning of a second language. Jacobsen and Walden (2013, p. 555) stated that "For children who are sequential learners, disruptions to the first language can result in linguistic profiles that would otherwise indicate delay or impairment, thus making diagnosis of LI more challenging."

❏ Since proficiency in the second language is partially a function of competence in the first language, sequential learners with limited skills in the first language and English may have greater difficulty developing CALP. Thus, when professionals are working with ELL students in the schools, it is necessary when a student appears "low functioning" to find out if language development occurred simultaneously or sequentially.

❏ If languages were acquired sequentially, what was the effect of second language acquisition on the development of proficiency in the first language? Did the student develop a high enough level of language proficiency in the first language to respond to the cognitive demands of the classroom?

❏ If the student was "switched" to English before acquiring strong first language skills, it is likely that many classroom tasks will be difficult. Moreover, students who have had limited exposure to decontextualized language in the home are often at risk for academic difficulties (Roseberry-McKibbin, 2015).

Table 10.3 shows typical behaviors of sequential bilingual learners as they go through the process of learning English. By using this information, professionals will be better able to distinguish typical second language learners from students who have "disabilities."

Table 10.3

Four Stages of Second Language Acquisition in Typically-Developing Sequential Bilingual Learners

Stage 1: Preproduction	Stage 2: Early Production	Stage 3: Speech Emergence	Stage 4: Intermediate Fluency
10 hours-6 months of English exposure	6 mos-1 year English exposure	1-3 years English exposure	3-4 years English exposure
300 English words (receptive)	1,000 English words (receptive)	7,000 English words (receptive)	12,000 English words (receptive)
Primarily listening; *yes-no* English responses	Primarily listening; formulaic language; 1-2 word responses	Speaks in short phrases and sentences; describes	Engages regularly in dialogue; explains summarizes, gives opinions, debates
Silent period	Participates using familiar words	Good comprehension	Stable BICS; CALP develops steadily emerging reading and writing competence
Responds to commands	Uses present tense verbs	Some grammatical errors	Few grammatical errors
Points and gives other nonverbal responses	Confidently follows basic classroom routines	Basic communication skills develop continuously	

Sources: Cummins, 2017; Edwards, 2010; Hearne, 2000; Paradis et al., 2011; Rosa-Lugo et al., 2012; Silverman & Doyle, 2013

Bilingual Education and Academic Success

Many people living in the United States have negative feelings about bilingualism and school programs that provide opportunities for instruction in more than one language. As a result of these attitudes, bilingual education programs have suffered (Wright & Baker, 2017). In the early 20th century, when there was a huge wave of non-English-speaking immigrants from Europe, families were advised to "assimilate" by giving up the languages of their home countries. Parents were told that being bilingual would confuse their children.

In the early 1920s, researchers concluded that bilingualism caused children to perform poorly in school. Even today, more than 100 years later, many U.S. citizens cling to the outmoded, inaccurate belief that being bilingual has negative cognitive, linguistic, and social effects on children.

Most educators hold one of three views regarding children who bring other languages to the school setting: (1) language-as-resource, (2) language-as-right, and (3) language-as-problem. Unfortunately, many U.S. educators subscribe to the language-as-problem view. This comes from long-held assumptions based on the traditional, negative beliefs about bilingualism that were explained earlier.

❏ Many educators believe that learning two languages has a negative effect on the child's ability to develop skills in English. The *limited capacity hypothesis*, as described by Paradis et al. (2011), is based on the belief that the child's cognitive system is designed to cope with only one language. According to this hypothesis, the child's underlying mental language-learning capacity is like a balloon that can only contain so much air; when the balloon inflates as a result of acquiring one language, there is limited space for acquisition of another language.

❏ The monolingual-norm assumption/limited capacity hypothesis gave rise to the negative myths surrounding bilingualism—bilingualism has been blamed for cognitive, social, and emotional damage to children.

❏ In the case of some language minority groups in the U.S., language diversity is seen by those in power as a problem to be solved rather than a right to be protected or resource to be conserved. But when majority White members of U.S. society learn a second language, their bilingual skills are held in high esteem and often rewarded economically.

❏ In contrast, the bilingual skills of immigrant or language minority groups tend to be undervalued or disparaged outright. Their bilingual skills are often perceived as a sign of divided loyalty between their home countries and the U.S., and as barriers to their full participation in U.S. society.

When I was being raised in the Philippines, my sisters and I spoke Standard English inside our home with each other and with our parents. We spoke Odionganon with our friends in the barrio of Odiongan, learned Tagalog in school, and were exposed to Hiligaynon in church. I am very aware of the difficulties encountered by students when they have limited proficiency in the language of instruction. Learning two languages, however, does not cause learning difficulties. Developing proficiency in more than one language is advantageous and is highly valued in countries throughout the world.

❏ Armenians believe that the more languages a person speaks, the more educated and well-rounded she is. Armenians take pride in speaking as many as six languages. Most Swiss are trilingual, speaking German, French, and Italian. In Luxembourg, citizens commonly switch back and forth between Flemish, English, Dutch, German, and French.

❏ May (2017) views additive bilingualism as the ideal for all students. To promote additive bilingualism, optimally, students should participate in bilingual education beginning in preschool and continuing throughout the schooling experience.

❏ Bilingual education programs provide students with culturally appropriate learning, opportunities for continued use of the first language, and experiences designed to promote the learning and effective use of a second language. Garcia and Lin (2017) maintained that effective bilingual education programs promote social justice for participants and increase their ability to contribute to a 21st century global economy.

Although it is important for U.S. students to develop English language skills, prohibiting the use of languages other than English is not the answer. Efforts to promote the learning of multiple languages should be encouraged in our schools. Fortunately, some progress is being made toward achieving this goal.

❏ In the U.S., the State Seal of Biliteracy (SSB) is being awarded to high school graduates who have attained a high level of proficiency in speaking, reading, and writing one or more languages in addition to English (sealofbiliteracy.org, 2017). These students are viewed as valuable assets in college programs and in the work place.

❏ In November 2016, California repealed Proposition 227 which outlawed bilingual education. Schools in California are also offering Mandarin and Spanish immersion programs for students who speak English as their first language.

Immigrant Insight   Esteban, male speaker of Spanish, Puerto Rico

I was a 17-year-old senior in high school when we moved to the U.S. I did not know anyone besides my sister in the whole school. I am shy as it is, but when I tried to ask teachers or the other students questions, they would laugh at my accent or they would not understand what I was saying at all. Because of my Spanish background, the counselors put me in all remedial classes. I was an "A" student back in Puerto Rico, so it frustrated me when school started because I already knew everything that was being taught. My mom did not know much about the school system here in the U.S., so I had to take placement tests to prove to the counselors that I was able to take on level, if not advanced, classes. I did not have one friend my senior year of high school. It wasn't until my accent went away (as a young adult) that I started gaining respect from my coworkers and even from other parents at my child's school. I am now a county parks manager.

CONCLUSION

When professionals evaluate ELL students' linguistic, intellectual, and academic performance, they must take into account factors relating to second language acquisition and bilingual development. In many cases, errors in judgment and the consequent inappropriate placement of students in special education programs can be avoided. The greater the understanding that professionals have of typical second-language learning and bilingualism, the more unbiased and appropriate will be the services provided to ELL students in the school.

STUDY QUESTIONS

1. Describe three affective variables that are critical in second language acquisition.

2. Define the terms *simultaneous acquisition* and *sequential acquisition*. Will the child who is a simultaneous language learner or the child who is a sequential language learner be more likely to experience difficulty in the classroom? Why?

3. Describe the negative myths about bilingualism in the U.S. How have these negative myths impacted actual practice in U.S. school systems?

MULTIPLE CHOICE

4. Which term refers to a process in which a communicative behavior or structure from the first language is carried over into the second language?

   A. Fossilization
   B. Interference/transfer
   C. Interlanguage
   D. Silent period
   E. Enclosure

5. Which of the following statements are TRUE?

   A. BICS involves conversational informal language fluency.
   B. CALP involves formal academic language fluency.
   C. Usually ELLs acquire BICS and CALP at about the same rate.
   D. Most tests of English fluency are accurate predictors of performance by ELLs in the classroom setting.
   E. When an ELL is designated as "Fully English Proficient" by measures that assess English BICS, professionals may confidently administer formal English tests that have been standardized on monolingual English speakers.

6. A student who said "Me gustaría manejar. I'll take the car. Muchas grácias! See you later!" would be manifesting:

   A. Transfer from Spanish to English
   B. Language loss of the first language
   C. Interlanguage
   D. Codeswitching
   E. Lack of congruence

7. For children who are learning two languages, which of the following are true?
   A. It is ideal to learn both languages from infancy.
   B. A strong first language base contributes positively to learning the second language adequately.
   C. Students who do not learn either the first language or second language adequately often experience a state of limited bilingualism that leads to negative cognitive effects.
   D. Bilingualism almost always has detrimental effects when two languages are learned simultaneously.

8. Francisco L., a 5-year-old monolingual Spanish-speaking boy, is attending an all-English kindergarten classroom. He has lived his whole life in a trailer with his parents, grandparents, and six siblings. Francisco has never been to preschool. His parents are migrant workers who lack literacy skills in both Spanish and English. Following three months of kindergarten, the teacher refers Francisco for an evaluation to determine if he has LI. The student speaks occasionally in class and has friends, but he performs poorly on writing, spelling, and math activities. What would be the best course of action for the special education team to take?

   A. Use English special education tests because Francisco is in an all-English-speaking school and he will eventually need to perform at the same level as his English-speaking peers.
   B. Test Francisco in both Spanish and English using BICS- and CALP-oriented special education tests.
   C. Assess Francisco's level of proficiency in both English and Spanish, provide him with English as a second language services to support English acquisition, assign a Spanish-speaking aide to the classroom to support his Spanish skills, and re-evaluate him in a year to assess progress.
   D. Do not assess Francisco in any way at this time because his limited language exposure will invalidate any tests that are given.
   E. Place Francisco in special education so that he can receive an individualized program of English language instruction that targets the conceptual skills necessary for success in the general education curriculum.

9. You are working with a group of Spanish-speaking parents in your school district. Unfortunately, they have been told by various professionals to speak only English when interacting with their children at home. You want the parents to understand that fluent bilingualism has many advantages. Among these advantages are the following:

   A. Enhanced employment opportunities
   B. More efficient information processing
   C. Better overall memory
   D. Increased metalinguistic awareness
   E. Better visual-spatial skills

10. Shoxrux is a 10-year-old boy whose family arrived in the U.S. from Uzbekistan two years ago speaking no English. He is friendly and gets along well with his classmates, but his teacher is concerned about Shoxrux' academic skills. She states that "He has good English comprehension and understands many words, but I am concerned because when he talks, he has some grammatical errors and also has difficulty summarizing reading passages—especially in language arts. I think he may have a language impairment." In this case, the best thing to do would be to:

    A. Refer Shoxrux immediately to the school Resource Specialist for academic testing, because he is clearly not meeting expectations for typically-developing bilingual sequential learners.
    B. Engage the services of an Uzbeki-speaking tutor to help support Shoxrux' Uzbeki skills.

C. Enroll Shoxrux in speech-language therapy and write treatment goals to specifically target written language.
D. Check to see if there are non-special education options (e.g., an after school Homework Club) where Shoxrux can get extra support in language arts.
E. Speak with the English as a Second Language (ESL) specialist to find out if Shoxrux has received any ESL services; if not, determine whether Shoxrux is eligible to participate in ESL services that target English grammar.

ANSWERS TO STUDY QUESTIONS

   4. B
   5. A, B
   6. D
   7. A, B, C
   8. C
   9. A, B, C, D, E
  10. B, D, E

Chapter 11

Introduction to Assessment: Foundational Principles

THE DIAGNOSTIC CHALLENGE

When professionals are confronted with English language learners (ELLs) who appear to be struggling in school, the cause of the "learning problem" is often difficult to determine. Does the student have a language difference or language impairment (LI)? Does the student need special education services? Language differences are behaviors that are commonly observed among second language learners. Transfer from the primary language to English results in differences in speech sound production, vocabulary, sentence structure, and other aspects of language. Unfortunately, children with language differences that result from transfer from the primary language are often misidentified as having LI (Pieretti & Roseberry-McKibbin, 2016). The "language-impairment" diagnosis is appropriate only for students with disabilities affecting their underlying ability to learn language. In this chapter and the one that follows, strategies are presented to help professionals accurately identify LI in students who are learning English. By using these strategies, professionals will be able to reduce the likelihood that students will be placed inappropriately into special education programs.

Language Difference vs. Language Impairment: Impact of the Environment

Bloom and Lahey (1978) defined language as a system of symbols used to represent concepts formed through exposure and experience. Exposure and experience are critical for success in acquiring a language. Children must hear language and must be provided with experience in using it. Language can be learned through oral or written communication.

Teachers typically assume that students entering school have had opportunities to listen to stories, to explore books, to cut with scissors, to color pictures with crayons, and to use language for a variety of purposes. It is assumed that children have been taken to stores, parks, zoos, libraries, and other places in the community.

Some students come from backgrounds in which they have had all of these experiences. Children who immigrate to the U.S. may have traveled to a variety of countries and may speak and write several languages. These students have much to share about their cultural backgrounds and their experiences when they interact with mainstream American students in the school setting.

Other students, however, have had limited experiences with books and other opportunities for language enrichment. These students and their families may be non-literate for one or more reasons. Perhaps family members have not had the opportunity to attend school or their experience in school was limited.

There are some students who come from backgrounds in which there is no written form of the language. In the Netherlands, for example, some students from isolated areas speak Berber languages that do not have a tradition of literacy. These students struggle in school. Some Native American groups and speakers of Haitian Creole have predominantly oral traditions with no formal written language.

I have stated throughout this book that, unfortunately, members of culturally and linguistically diverse groups experience poverty in much greater numbers than White, monolingual English speakers. It is imperative that professionals remember that poverty alone has a strong impact on children's school performance. Poverty coupled with lack of knowledge of English can have a major influence on students' performance in school, even in the absence of LI.

Educators are confronted with the challenge of disentangling the variables of poverty, ELL status, possible LI, cultural differences, and other factors that impact students' performance and cause difficulties in the classroom.

Another issue that impacts many ELL students is lack of preschool experience. When children come to kindergarten not speaking English, not having preschool experience, and experiencing poverty, the task of succeeding in school is daunting indeed.

In a study by Winsler et al. (2012), 13,191 ethnically diverse, at-risk children were examined to identify predictors of delayed entry into kindergarten and kindergarten retention. Delayed entry into kindergarten was not common. Students entered kindergarten at age 5, a typical expectation. These researchers, however, discovered that children who were poor, of ELL status, and who lacked preschool experience were more likely than other children to be retained in kindergarten because of problems experienced in school.

If a student's background experiences are different from those of most other children in the school system, he or she may exhibit language behaviors that stand out as being "problematic." For example, students from backgrounds of poverty and children who have had limited exposure to books may struggle because their backgrounds have not provided them with the foundation that the school expects.

When difficulties observed in school result from differences in the student's experiences, professionals might assume that there is something inherently wrong with the student. During assessment, emphasis is often placed on searching for a disability to explain the challenges that the student is experiencing. Disabilities and special education labels such as LI are often created for students who, in reality, need greater exposure, experience, and support to meet the demands of the classroom curriculum. Children will be inappropriately identified as having LI if school professionals do not consider their environmental experiences and language stimulation opportunities.

DIAGNOSTIC PIE

The "diagnostic pie" in Figure 11.1 is a simple conceptual framework that professionals can use to distinguish language differences from LI in students who are learning English as an additional language. Consideration of the child's background experiences is critical in any evaluation.

Quadrant 1

Students who fall into this quadrant of the pie are typical language learners who have no deficits in their underlying ability to learn language. They come from backgrounds that may be rich in stimulation and general experiences, but their experiences have not been consistent with expectations in mainstream U.S. schools.

These students generally have the conceptual foundation necessary for academic success. The needs of these students can usually be served best in bilingual classrooms that provide opportunities for language development both in English and in the primary language.

If bilingual education is not available, these students can benefit from Sheltered English (academic content taught in English that is comprehensible) or, barring this, a program that teaches English as a second language (ESL). Again, if these students are given time, attention, and support, they will generally succeed in school.

Quadrant 2

These students have no difficulties learning language skills. However, they come from backgrounds where they may have experienced some environmental limitations. They may be experiencing poverty and lack of oral and literate language stimulation opportunities.

Figure 11.1

Diagnostic Pie

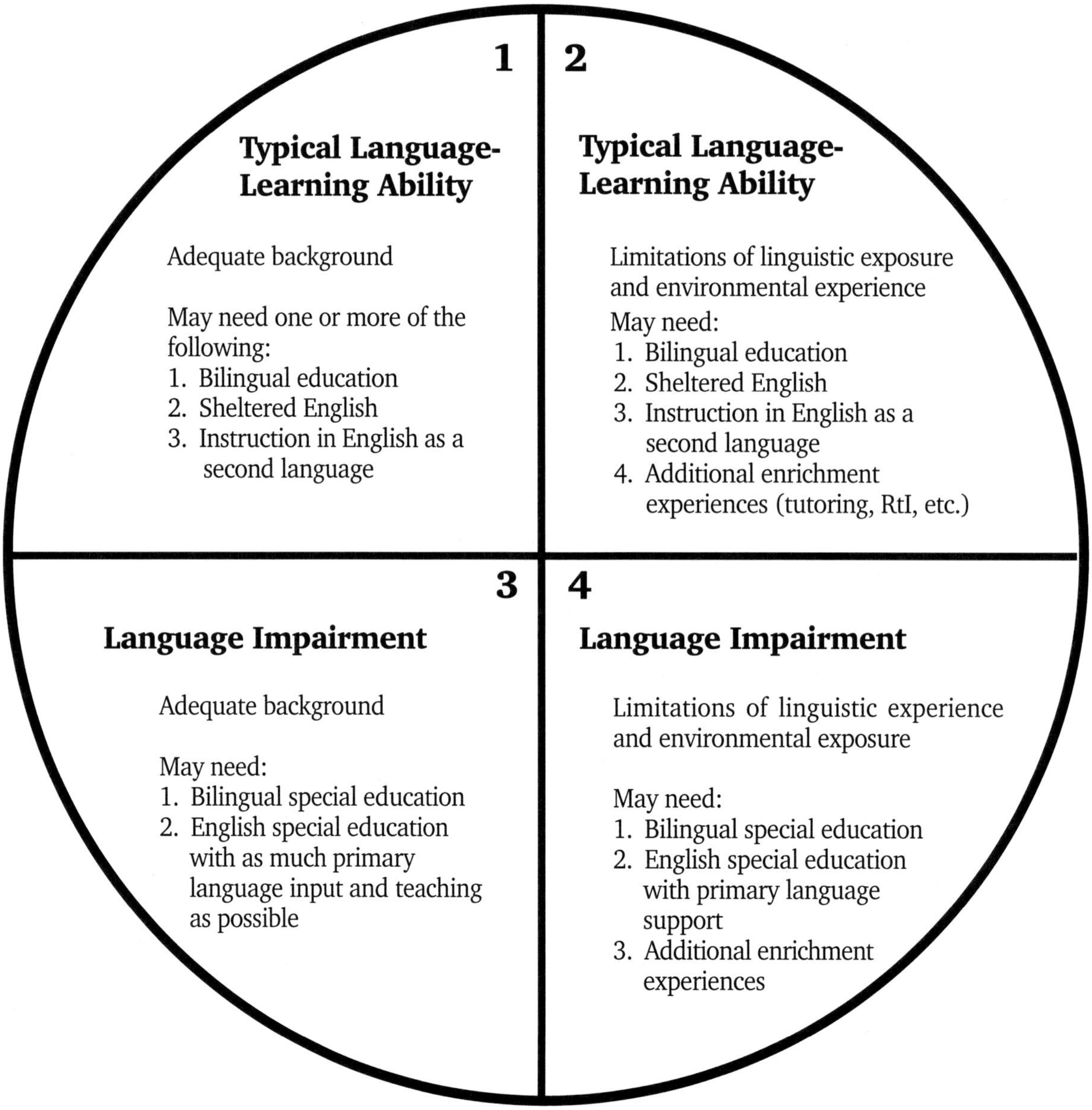

1

Typical Language-Learning Ability

Adequate background

May need one or more of the following:
1. Bilingual education
2. Sheltered English
3. Instruction in English as a second language

2

Typical Language-Learning Ability

Limitations of linguistic exposure and environmental experience

May need:
1. Bilingual education
2. Sheltered English
3. Instruction in English as a second language
4. Additional enrichment experiences (tutoring, RtI, etc.)

3

Language Impairment

Adequate background

May need:
1. Bilingual special education
2. English special education with as much primary language input and teaching as possible

4

Language Impairment

Limitations of linguistic experience and environmental exposure

May need:
1. Bilingual special education
2. English special education with primary language support
3. Additional enrichment experiences

Although these students have typical language learning abilities, life circumstances have curtailed their learning opportunities and experiences prior to entering school. As stated, if these students live in poverty, they are more vulnerable and at risk than students raised in literate, middle-class environments.

These students often perform poorly on standardized tests that are based on mainstream, middle-class expectations and that assume certain background knowledge, including literacy exposure. If these students have not had the experiences necessary to perform well on tests, they may appear to have LI.

Students in Quadrant 2 are likely to make adequate progress in school if they receive enough input, exposure, and stimulation. Bilingual education, ESL, and/or Sheltered English programs may be effective because they enhance skills in both the primary language and English. These students often benefit greatly from other non-special education supports such as Response to Intervention (RtI) programs, explained in more detail in later chapters.

For example, at the elementary school where I provide speech and language services, classroom teachers and aides use special reading enhancement programs with students who are struggling with written language skills. These students are not in special education programs but are, rather, in general education classrooms and are also receiving additional support. Those whose language-learning ability is intact generally respond well to this additional support and do not require special education services.

Quadrant 3

Students in Quadrant 3 come from backgrounds in which they have had adequate exposure and language stimulation. The life experiences of some of these students are consistent with those expected in mainstream schools. Often parents have given these students as much help as possible in the home, and the students still do not succeed in school.

Other students may not have had life experiences and opportunities that are commensurate with school expectations. However, the school has provided much additional help and support over time to assist these students in developing academic skills (e.g., tutoring, ESL programs).

Despite the fact that school personnel have provided supplemental activities within the general education curriculum in an effort to stimulate academic growth, the students continue to acquire new information more slowly than peers from similar cultural and linguistic backgrounds; they continue to manifest learning difficulties despite extra school support.

Students with these characteristics have an underlying LI that hinders their ability to learn and use any language adequately, despite home and/or school backgrounds that have provided opportunities for appropriate environmental and linguistic stimulation. These students need to receive special education services so that their unique disabilities can be appropriately addressed by personnel with specialized training. Opportunities for instruction in the primary language should be provided, if possible, so that these children can make use of their previously acquired knowledge to learn new information.

Profile

Tanveer D., a sixth-grade speaker of Urdu from a Pakistani family, was referred to me for special education assessment. His teacher was especially concerned about his written language skills. His parents, who did not speak English, were unable to assist Tanveer with his homework. Thus the school provided Tanveer with an Urdu tutor who worked with him weekly on an individual basis for two years. Tanveer had participated in the school's Homework Club, an after-school program for students who needed extra academic support. In addition, Tanveer had attended Reading Clinic (a non-special education program to provide reading support for struggling students) for the last year. Despite this extra support, Tanveer was unable to recite the alphabet and could not identify simple printed words such as "cat" and "the." The other Urdu-speaking students in the school had surpassed Tanveer academically, and the Urdu interpreter confided that Tanveer was "much lower than other Urdu students I have worked with in this district."

Extensive testing revealed evidence of LI affecting both Urdu and English, as well as a clinically significant reading disability. Tanveer was placed in special education so that he could receive the necessary services to address the disability that was negatively affecting learning in both languages.

Quadrant 4

Students in Quadrant 4 come from backgrounds in which there are known limitations in background experiences that may be contributing to problems identified in the school setting. These children, however, also have underlying language-learning deficits and thus can be considered to have LI.

Students in Quadrant 4 ideally need special education with additional enrichment activities to compensate for limited learning opportunities in their environments. Students should be provided with opportunities for support in the primary language to the maximum extent possible.

Diagnostic Decision Making

In order to determine which quadrant of the Diagnostic Pie is most appropriate for an individual student, professionals must consider the following variables:

1. Child's background, including socioeconomic status, school attendance, and literacy exposure
2. Impact of second language acquisition factors
3. Determination of student's levels of linguistic proficiency in the first language and English
4. Case history and classroom teacher's evaluation of student performance
5. Results of assessment for underlying language impairment

DEFINITION OF LANGUAGE IMPAIRMENT

Students should not be considered to have LI if difficulties are observed only in English. If the student has a true LI, problems in communication should be evident in BOTH ENGLISH AND THE PRIMARY LANGUAGE (Pieretti & Roseberry-McKibbin, 2016).

LI is a disability and, therefore, it will affect the child's acquisition of any language. Speech-language pathologists may not legally label a child as having LI unless deficits are observed in both the primary language and English.

Tech Tie-In

The American Speech and Hearing Association (ASHA) has developed a brochure in Spanish and English called How Does Your Child Hear and Talk? This helpful, easy-to-read brochure lists important language acquisition milestones from birth to 5 years of age. The information is also available for free on ASHA's website at this link:

http://www.asha.org/public/speech/development/01/

Students who speak a language other than English should never be diagnosed as LI based solely on results obtained from tests administered in English. Information about language functioning in both the primary language and English should be obtained before special education placement decisions are made.

Table 11.1 lists universal indicators of language impairment that have been found among children with LI from language groups that speak English, Cantonese, Spanish, Dutch, French, German, Hebrew, and various other languages.

LEGAL CONSIDERATIONS

It is well known that ELL students are overrepresented in special education programs. This has been a persistent problem in U.S. schools for decades; underrepresentation can also be an issue if appropriate assessment practices are not being implemented.

Professionals responsible for conducting special education evaluations need to be aware of legal mandates governing the assessment of ELL children. Federal legislation (IDEA, 2004) requires the use of culturally and linguistically appropriate assessment tools to prevent the inappropriate identification and mislabeling of ethnically and linguistically diverse students.

❑ *2004 Individuals with Disabilities Improvement Act* (IDEA, 2004; updated from IDEA, 1997)

1. There must be procedures to ensure that testing and evaluation materials and methods are provided and administered in the child's native language or mode of communication, unless it is clearly not feasible to do so.

2. Those who assess students must use a variety of data-gathering strategies and tools and may not rely upon any single procedure.

3. Evaluation materials should be used that yield valid and reliable information.

4. In order to qualify students for services under the category of "learning disability," professionals no longer are required to demonstrate a severe discrepancy between intellectual ability and achievement, although individual states may continue to require this if they choose to.

5. Alternative, research-based procedures may be used in evaluating students if standardized tests are not appropriate.

6. States must permit the use of a process based on the child's response to scientific, research-based intervention (also known as RtI, or Response to Intervention). A major goal of RtI is to minimize overidentification and prevent unnecessary referrals to special education.

7. States are required to keep track of how many ELL students are being identified for special education and are required to provide coordinated, comprehensive, early-intervention programs for children in groups that are determined to be overrepresented. Schools are now allowed to use up to 15% of their annual funds, in combination with other funds, to develop and implement coordinated early intervention services. These services are for students in all grades, with a special focus on students in kindergarten through third grade who have not been identified as needing special education and related services, but who need additional academic and behavioral support to succeed in an academic environment.

8. Additional support may include, but not be limited to the following:

   A. Offering professional development opportunities for teachers and other staff to train them to deliver scientifically-based behavioral and academic interventions

Table 11.1

Universal Indicators of Language Impairment

1. Slower acquisition of language milestones than siblings in primary language (parent report). Universal norms: *12 months*—first spoken word; *18 months*—50 spoken words and the child is putting two words together; *24 months*—200-300 spoken words and the child is speaking mostly in short phrases.

2. Difficulty communicating at home in the primary language

3. Reliance on gestures rather than speech to communicate

4. Family history of special education/learning difficulties

5. Deficits in vocabulary; word retrieval problems and use of general all-purpose (GAP) nouns and verbs instead of more precise vocabulary

6. Verbal and written definitions of words are vague and lack detail

7. Difficulty describing the function of objects (e.g., "what is this used for? What do you do with it?")

8. Short mean length of utterance; sentences that are too short and simple for the child's age, even in the primary language

9. Specific difficulty with morphology in both the first language and English, especially verb tense

10. Working memory deficits (e.g., repeating a sequence of digits or nonwords)

11. Lack of organization, structure, and sequence in spoken and written language; difficulty conveying thoughts; poor narrative skills

12. Inordinate slowness in responding to requests; long latencies or pauses before answering

13. General disorganization and confusion, including prolonged difficulty with basic routines

14. Difficulty paying attention

15. Need for frequent repetition and prompts during instruction

16. Need for a program of instruction that is more structured than that used with most similar peers

17. Inappropriate social use of language (e.g., interrupts frequently, digresses from topic, is insensitive to the needs or communication goals of conversational partners, cannot stay on the topic of discussion, cannot take turns in conversation)

18. Difficulty interacting with peers from a similar cultural and linguistic background

19. Overall communication skills that are substantially poorer than those of similar peers

Sources: Dixon & Zhao, 2017; Kan & Windsor, 2010; Karanth, Roseberry-McKibbin, & James, 2017a; Krok & Leonard, 2015; Langdon & Saenz, 2016; Mancilla-Martinez et al., 2016; Moore & Montgomery, 2018; Owens, 2016; Paradis et al., 2013; Paradis, 2016; Paul, Norbury, & Gosse, 2018; Pieretti & Roseberry-McKibbin, 2016; Ratner, 2017; Riquelme & Rosas, 2014; Rosa-Lugo et al., 2012; Roseberry-McKibbin & Hegde, 2016; Washington & Iglesias, 2015.

   B. Providing students with behavioral and educational evaluations, services, and supports, including scientifically-based literacy instruction

❏ *Every Student Succeeds Act (ESSA)*

   (Information gathered primarily from U.S. Department of Education [2017] and Editorial Projects in Education Research Center, 2016)

   1. Signed by President Obama on December 10, 2015, the ESSA is a bipartisan measure which is committed to equal opportunity for all students.

   2. Under ESSA, individual states can choose their own short- and long-term goals. These goals must address proficiency on tests, English language proficiency, and high school graduation rates.

   3. English language proficiency is considered an academic indicator of accountability under ESSA.

   4. States still have to test students in math and reading in grades 3 through 8 and once in high school. States must break out the data for English learners, special education students, racial minorities, and children in poverty.

   5. During their first year in the U.S., ELL immigrant/refugee students will need to take both math and reading assessments and have the results publicly reported. However, these first year scores won't count toward a school's rating.

   6. In ELLs' second year, the state has to incorporate their test results for both math and reading, using some measure of growth. During their third year in the U.S., ELLs' proficiency scores will be treated just like those of any other student.

   7. As stated in the previous chapter, it can take 5-10 years for an ELL to achieve cognitive-academic language proficiency (CALP) that is commensurate with that of native English speakers. The ESSA's emphasis on elevating the math and reading scores of ELLs so that they are roughly equivalent to those of native English speakers could result in an increase in referrals for special education testing.

   8. Speech-language pathologists and other professionals must be sure to educate teachers about typical timelines for ELLs to develop CALP so that special education caseloads do not become even more inflated with ELL students who do not have true disabilities.

THE PRE-EVALUATION PROCESS

   As stated, relying solely on the typical assessment process depicted in Figure 11.2 is inappropriate when ELL students are referred for testing. When professionals are planning to assess ELLs who are struggling and thus suspected of having LI, a team approach should be implemented, and a variety of strategies should be used to collect the assessment data. When a team approach to assessment is used, the possibilities of a misdiagnosis are greatly diminished.

   There are several steps that should be completed before a student undergoes a formal evaluation. The pre-evaluation process consists of the following components:

   1. Comprehensive teacher evaluation of the student's classroom performance

   2. The collection of a case history from parents

Figure 11.2

Typical Referral and Assessment Procedures

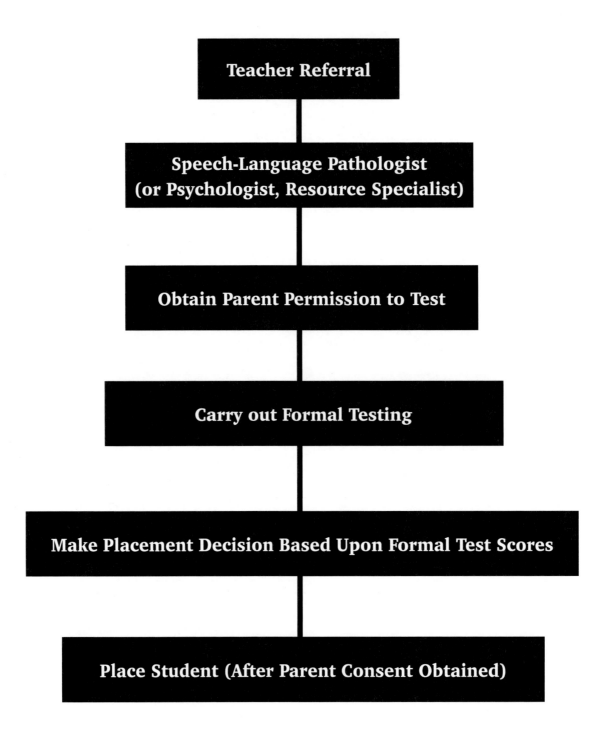

3. Language proficiency testing to determine levels of proficiency in the first language and English

Again, these components should be completed BEFORE a formal evaluation is conducted. When the pre-evaluation process is carried out by a team of professionals, the information gathered will facilitate decision making regarding the student's need for special education intervention. As Riquelme and Rosas (2014, p. 242) stated, "The most powerful weapon that SLPs have in their diagnostic repertoire is information. The more data one collects from colleagues, the community, family, and the child, the more likely one is to diagnose the child correctly."

The pre-referral model shown in Figure 11.3 can be used as a guide when collecting information about a student's performance.

Teacher Evaluation of Classroom Performance

Before conducting a formal assessment, the student's classroom teacher should be asked to describe concerns relating to the student's classroom performance. The opinions and observations of experienced teachers can provide valuable diagnostic information.

In a recent study in Singapore, researchers found that preschool teachers' subjective ratings of children's language skills constituted an effective method of screening bilingual children for language impairment (Pua, Lee, & Liow, 2017). Other research has found that teacher reports correlate with children's actual language performance (Bedore, Peña, Joyner, & Macken, 2011).

The English Language Learner Pre-Referral Screening (Reproducible Form 11.1), is a reproducible form that can be filled out by teachers and other individuals who are concerned about the student's performance in various areas. As a practicing public school clinician, I often interview the teacher, parent, and any tutors, bilingual associates, or other personnel who have worked with the student in question. I fill out their responses in different colors of ink, and triangulate the data to ascertain areas of concern that seem to be common among respondents. These results are shared with the Student Study Team before any formal request for assessment takes place.

Some SLPs require classroom teachers to fill out the screening form before the Student Study Team meeting and certainly before any formal request for special education evaluation takes place.

Filling out the form helps teachers think through their concerns and thoroughly investigate students' backgrounds before requesting formal testing; often, teachers find that their concerns are based on environmental differences and students' ELL status, not on an underlying LI.

The Linguistic and Conceptual Development Checklist (Reproducible Form 11.2) is an assessment tool that can be used to collect information related to the impact of the student's environment on her conceptual development. If a student's difficulties appear to be primarily based upon environmental and ELL concerns, this checklist can help personnel further investigate the source of these concerns and address them through non-special education enrichment programs.

The Case History

The collection of case history information is critical when students are being considered for special education assessment (see Appendix). Research over the years with families from a number of different cultures has shown that parent reports can be quite helpful to professionals in identifying LI in children (Dollaghan & Horner, 2011; Goldstein, Bunta, Lange, Rodriguez, & Burrows, 2010; Grech & McLeod, 2012; Guiberson et al., 2011; Paradis et al., 2013; Paradis, 2016; Riquelme & Rosas, 2014; Simon-Cereijido, 2013).

When gathering a case history, it is especially important to ascertain whether or not there are early vocabulary delays. Morgan et al. (2016) analyzed data from the Early Childhood Longitudinal Study—Birth Cohort, a nationally representative data set that is maintained by the U.S. Department

Figure 11.3

ASSESSMENT PRE-REFERRAL PARADIGM

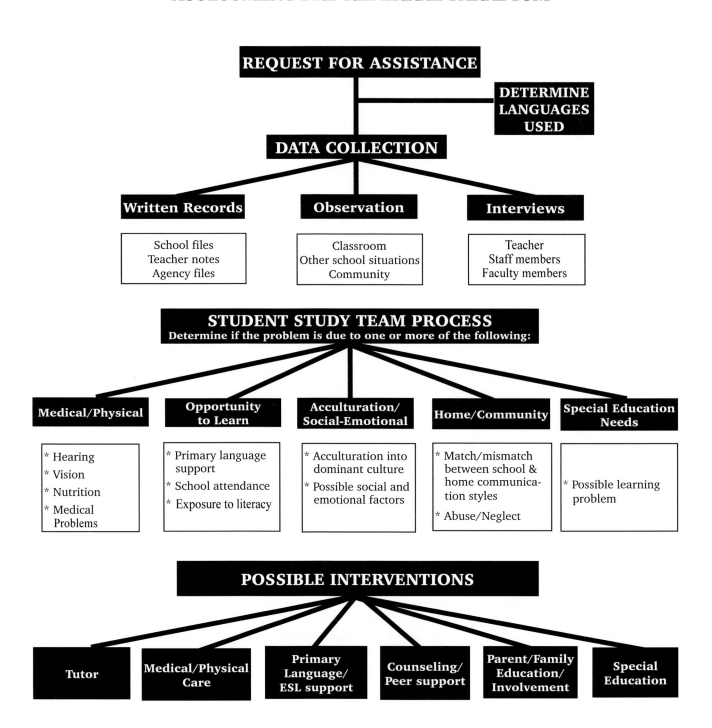

Reproducible Form 11.1
ENGLISH LANGUAGE LEARNER PRE-REFERRAL SCREENING
Developed by Celeste Roseberry-McKibbin, Ph.D., CCC-SP

Referring Staff Member:_____   Date:_____

Child's Name:_____ Gender M F   Date of Birth:_____ Age:____ Grade:____

Home Address:_____

Telephone/Email:_____

Place of Birth: Student _____Mother_____Father_____

Other current services:_____

INDIVIDUALS INTERVIEWED AND RELATIONSHIP TO STUDENT

Individuals can be interviewed when completing this form or they can complete it independently. Use a different ink color for each interviewee.

Teacher:_____   Parent:_____   Other (Interpreter, etc.):_____

_____

LANGUAGE BACKGROUND AND HISTORY

First language(s) student learned: _____

Persons language is spoken with: _____

When was the child first exposed to English? How was English used? Describe the circumstances.

_____

_____

		Typical Child Development:
Age when child spoke first word in the first language:	_____	First words at 12 months
Age when child started combining words (two-word phrases):	_____	Phrases at 18 months
Approximate number of words spoken by 24 months:	_____	200-300 words at 24 months

EDUCATIONAL HISTORY

Name of School	Years	Grade	Location	Additional Support Services

Comments about attendance:

HEALTH INFORMATION

Vision screenings—dates and results:_____

_____

Hearing screenings—dates and results:_____

_____

_____

Health concerns:_____

_____

PARENT/CAREGIVER CONCERNS

PREVIOUS TESTING INFORMATION

CURRENT CLASSROOM MODIFICATIONS, INTERVENTIONS (e.g., front row seating, tutoring)

Intervention	Dates	Progress Made

CLASSROOM LANGUAGE USE	High Concern				Low Concern
Oral Language	5	4	3	2	1
Answers simple questions	5	4	3	2	1
Communicates basic needs	5	4	3	2	1
Tells a simple story sequentially	5	4	3	2	1
Describes familiar events, objects	5	4	3	2	1
Reading	5	4	3	2	1
Functional Writing Skills (e.g., writing stories)	5	4	3	2	1
Written Language Structure	5	4	3	2	1
Math	5	4	3	2	1

Other: _____

Comments: _____

_____

SCHOOL SOCIAL INTERACTION	High Concern				Low Concern
Communicates ineffectively with peers	5	4	3	2	1
Often plays alone	5	4	3	2	1
Is teased/ridiculed by others	5	4	3	2	1
Is excluded from activities by peers	5	4	3	2	1
Rarely initiates with peers	5	4	3	2	1

LANGUAGE AND LEARNING PROBLEMS (compared to peers from a similar cultural and linguistic background who have had similar opportunities for learning)

	High Concern				Low Concern
Difficulty communicating in first language	5	4	3	2	1
Difficulty communicating in English	5	4	3	2	1
Difficulty learning in first language	5	4	3	2	1
Difficulty learning in English	5	4	3	2	1
Significantly behind academically	5	4	3	2	1
Family history of learning problems	5	4	3	2	1
Child learns more slowly than siblings	5	4	3	2	1
Consistently prefers gestures	5	4	3	2	1
Slow to respond to directions-home	5	4	3	2	1
Slow to respond to directions-school	5	4	3	2	1
Inappropriate responses	5	4	3	2	1
Difficulty staying on topic	5	4	3	2	1
Difficulty with basic routines	5	4	3	2	1
Appears disorganized, confused	5	4	3	2	1
Difficulty paying attention	5	4	3	2	1
Requires frequent prompts, or repetition to learn new information	5	4	3	2	1
Requires a high degree of structure	5	4	3	2	1
Motor problems (visual motor, gross motor, fine motor)	5	4	3	2	1

Comments: _____

_____

_____

ENVIRONMENTAL INFLUENCES AND LANGUAGE EXPOSURE

	Yes	No	Don't Know
Has the student's primary language been maintained?	____	____	____
Has the student had adequate opportunities to interact with peers who speak English?	____	____	____
Does the student have consistent literacy exposure outside of school?	____	____	____

SUMMARY OF INPUT FROM PARENT(S), TEACHER, AND OTHER PERSONNEL

_____A. Based on current information, this student is progressing appropriately and referral for further evaluation is not necessary at this time.
Comments:

_____B. Based on current information, there are concerns about this student's language skills, but additional information is needed. Please describe:

_____C. Based on current information, there are concerns about this student, but additional interventions in the general education curriculum are recommended. The student's progress should be monitored to ensure that these interventions are resulting in improved learning.

_____D. Based on current information, further assessment is recommended.

Type of assessment: _____

Personnel needed to conduct assessment(s): _____

OVERALL SUMMARY AND ADDITIONAL COMMENTS

Reproducible Form 11.2
Linguistic and Conceptual Development Checklist

Student's Name: _____ Date of Birth:_____ Chronological Age:_____

Language Spoken: _____ Person Completing Form:_____

Questions	Yes	No	Don't Know
❏ Has the child been regularly exposed to L1 literacy-related materials?	___	___	___
❏ Is the child's vocabulary in the first language well-developed?	___	___	___
❏ Was the child's L1 fluent and well-developed when s/he began learning English?	___	___	___
❏ Have the child's parents been encouraged to speak and/or read in L1 at home?	___	___	___
❏ Has the child's L1 been maintained in school through bilingual education, L1 tutoring, and/or other L1 maintenance activities?	___	___	___
❏ Does the child show interest in L1 maintenance and interaction?	___	___	___
❏ Is the English classroom input comprehensible to the child?	___	___	___
❏ Does the child have frequent opportunities for negotiating meaning and practicing comprehensible output in English?	___	___	___
❏ Has the child had frequent exposure to enriching experiences such as going to museums, libraries, etc.?	___	___	___
❏ Has the child's school attendance been regular?	___	___	___
❏ Has the child had long-term exposure to standard English models?	___	___	___

The more "yes" answers that are checked, the more likely it is that the child has a good conceptual foundation for language and academic learning. The more "no" answers that are checked, the more likely it is that the child has underdeveloped conceptual and linguistic abilities due to limitations within the school and/or home environment, language loss, limited English practice opportunities, inadequate bilingual services, or a combination of these factors.

of Education. Analyses were performed for a population-based sample of 9600 participating children and families. Expressive vocabulary delays by 24 months of age were found to be strongly associated with and predictive of children's receiving speech/language intervention at later ages. Morgan et al. concluded that expressive vocabulary delays at 24 months of age increase children's risk for needing speech/language services when they are older.

❏ At 24 months of age, children from any language background should have expressive vocabularies of at least 200 words and should be speaking primarily in short phrases. It is very important, as part of gathering the case history, to ask caregivers about this important linguistic milestone.

❏ The case history can be obtained from the student's parents or other available relatives who have some knowledge of the student's background. Uncles, aunts, siblings, and grandparents can provide valuable information, especially if they serve as the student's primary caretakers.

❏ Professionals can utilize the services of a trained interviewer who is fluent in both English and the student's primary language. Experienced professionals find that when parents can speak with someone from their own cultural background, they often feel more comfortable during the interview/case history gathering process.

❏ It is important to prepare carefully for interviews in which interpreters are used (Langdon & Saenz, 2016). The parents/interviewees must understand the purpose of the interview and the questions that are being asked.

❏ Some parents may feel that the case history questions are personal and, therefore, inappropriate. If parents understand why the questions are being asked, however, they will be more likely to answer questions without feeling uncomfortable.

Professionals should attempt to develop rapport with parents, create a comfortable atmosphere, and ask open-ended questions that will encourage parents to express themselves freely. I have found that parents often become overwhelmed when confronted with a large team of school professionals in a formal meeting. At times, parents speak most freely when they are in a small, informal setting with only one or two professionals and an interpreter present.

When gathering a case history, professionals must also consider the influence that poverty can have on a child's academic and linguistic performance. Answers to questions relating to the home environment often provide information about the socioeconomic status of the family. Moreover, a review of the children's school records may reveal specific types of assistance that the family may be receiving (e.g., Aid to Families with Dependent Children).

Tech Tie-In   *Gathering Case History Information*

This video includes helpful information related to the collection of case history information. Shao's teacher, a 3rd grade speaker of Cantonese and English, is concerned that Shao might have a language impairment. As part of the pre-evaluation process, I use the English Language Learner Pre-Referral Screening. I interview Shao's teacher, mother, and the Cantonese interpreter who has worked with him for the last months. Go to youtube.com and type in Celeste Roseberry (Love Talk Read). Then click on the video entitled *Assessment of ELLs with Language Impairment: Gathering Case History Through Interviews*

Paradis, Emmerzael, and Sorenson Duncan (2010) developed an outstanding case history questionnaire, the Alberta Language and Development Questionnaire (ALDeQ). This questionnaire helps professionals quantify multilingual children's language use, early milestones, and family history. It is a psychometrically valid measure that can be used with children and families from any cultural and linguistic group. The instrument is helpful in distinguishing between a language difference and LI.

Language Proficiency Variables

Before considering a special education assessment, it is important to deal with language proficiency issues. There are several steps involved in determining language proficiency and dominance:

1. Determine the student's primary language.
2. Determine language dominance.
3. Determine oral and written proficiency level in each of the languages spoken by the child.

Terms commonly used in discussions relating to bilingual students' language abilities are defined below:

- **primary language** - the language the student learned first and used most frequently in the early stages of language development. Information regarding language use in the home is best established through carefully conducted parent interviews and home language surveys.

- **dominant language** - the language spoken most proficiently by the student at the current time. The dominant language may change if there are changes in language usage patterns in the child's environment. Moreover, language dominance can vary depending on what aspect of language is assessed (e.g., syntax vs. vocabulary).

- **language proficiency** - the child's level of skill in the use of a particular language.

Whenever special education assessments are conducted, an important preliminary step is to find out the student's relative proficiency in the languages spoken. Schools often make use of individuals who do not have specialized training in language to administer these tests. However, professionals must be sure that language proficiency tests have been administered by trained personnel.

Measurement of a child's language proficiency should consist of three steps:

1. *Request that parents complete a language background questionnaire.* Language background questionnaires provide information about the languages used in the home.

2. *Conduct parent or teacher interviews.* Parent and teacher interviews provide information about the child's language use and proficiency in the home and classroom.

3. *Use information obtained from direct and indirect language measures.* Direct measures of proficiency in a child's two languages yield scores that can be helpful in identifying strengths and weaknesses in each language.

NONBIASED ASSESSMENT AND STANDARDIZED TESTS

Research over the years has consistently shown that many speech-language pathologists in the U.S. inappropriately use standardized tests in English to establish the presence of LI in ELLs (Arias & Friberg, 2017; Caesar & Koehler, 2007; Kimble, 2013; Kraemer & Fabiano-Smith, 2017; Kritikos, 2003; Roseberry-McKibbin, Brice, & O'Hanlon, 2005). Interestingly, this is a problem that also occurs in other countries (e.g., South Africa) (Mdlalo, 2017).

Despite the fact that this is not best practice and is frequently illegal, many professionals rely almost entirely on the use of standardized tests to evaluate the language abilities of ELL students and to plan intervention/service delivery. In fact, when speech and language evaluations are conducted, standardized tests are often the primary measure used in determining whether or not students qualify for special education intervention.

The procedures commonly used in determining students' eligibility for special education programs are shown in Figure 11.2. Professionals in many school districts are told that they must use standardized measures in determining students' eligibility for special education programs.

Reasons for reliance on standardized testing include the following:

1. legal considerations (e.g., percentile ranks and standard deviations used as cut-offs to determine special education eligibility)
2. time constraints (standardized tests are perceived as being faster to score and administer than informal measures)
3. caseload constraints (many schools have large numbers of students who are referred for testing due to academic difficulties)
4. convenience (standardized tests are often more automatic to administer than less structured, informal measures)

❏ Many public school professionals believe—incorrectly—that federal law in the U.S. requires the use of standardized tests to determine eligibility for special education services. However, to assess the heterogeneous ELL population in a nonbiased manner, other approaches are often necessary.

❏ Federal law allows for subjective and qualitative measures; norm-referenced tests are not required. However, because many professionals continue to rely heavily on the use of standardized tests to assess ELL students, this section addresses considerations in the use of these tests.

❏ If professionals choose to use standardized tests with ELL students, they need to be aware of the tests' potential legal, psychometric, cultural, and linguistic limitations in terms of validity and reliability. It is important to examine assumptions underlying formal tests.

FORMAL TEST ASSUMPTIONS

The development of standardized, formal tests has grown out of a framework that is Western, literate, and "middle class." These tests are often heavily biased against ELLs, especially those from low-socioeconomic status backgrounds. It is important for professionals to be aware of the underlying assumptions upon which formal tests are often based. These inherent assumptions are extremely important to consider when working with ELL students. These assumptions hold that students taking tests will do the following:

1. The students will follow the cooperative principle by performing to the best of their ability and trying to provide relevant answers.

2. The students will attempt to respond even when test tasks don't make sense to them.

3. The students will understand test tasks (e.g., fill in the blank, point to the picture).

4. The students will have the experience background necessary to perform the assessment tasks.

5. The students will feel comfortable enough with the examiner in the testing setting to give their best performance.

6. The students will verbally elaborate when asked to do so by an unfamiliar adult.

These assumptions can't be made with many of the ELL students who are referred for testing. For example, in some cultures, children are expected to greet unfamiliar events with silence or to be silent in the presence of an adult.

In sum, many ELL students have had no previous experience in a testing situation. Many have not had experiences that are consistent with the experiences assumed within the test design (e.g., verbally elaborating on a topic, filling in the blank). In addition, some ELL students do not perform optimally when the testing setting and/or examiners are unfamiliar to them and/or from a different ethnic background.

SOURCES OF BIAS IN STANDARDIZED TESTING

The bias in standardized tests can take many forms when these tests are being used with ELL students. Some of these forms of bias are described below.

Potentially Unfamiliar Items (Cultural and Linguistic Bias)

Cultural and linguistic bias occur when the examiner uses items and activities that do not correspond with the child's experiential base. Certain test items might be unfamiliar to ELL students, especially those who have immigrated to the United States. In addition, students from low-socioeconomic status backgrounds with limited life experiences and exposure may not recognize certain test items (Roseberry-McKibbin, 2013):

1. Various household objects (e.g,. blenders, microwaves)
2. Vehicles (e.g., off-road vehicles, subway trains)
3. Sports, especially those involving snow and cold weather. Sports such as football are not played in some countries.
4. Types of American weather and seasons
5. Musical instruments
6. Types of clothing (e.g., suspenders, galoshes, mittens)
7. Professions/occupations (e.g., computer programmer)
8. Historically related events & people (e.g. Thanksgiving, Christmas, Abraham Lincoln)
9. Foods (e.g., apple pie, yogurt, American fruits and vegetables)
10. American nursery rhymes, fairy tales (e.g., Cinderella, Humpty Dumpty)
11. Geography (e.g. New York, Midwest)
12. Games (e.g., tag, hopscotch, Monopoly)
13. Digital devices (e.g., computers, smart phones)

Items Translated from English

Translated versions of English tests are often used with ELL students. There are many problems inherent in the use of translated English tests.

1. Differences in structure and content between English and the primary language raise questions about the comparability of scores. Many words cannot be directly translated from one

language into another. For example, some Asian languages do not have pronouns; translating "she" or "he" or "it" into these languages is impossible. Also, the difficulty level of a specific word may differ in the two languages. For example, German has three different words for "the" that vary depending on the type of word that follows (e.g., *das Buch* = the book; *der Mann* = the man; *die Frau* = the woman). In Spanish, words for "the" vary depending on whether the following noun is singular, plural, masculine, or feminine. English test translations cannot test the student's knowledge of these important distinctions.

2. Normative data and information relating to the validity and reliability of the test cannot be used if a test is translated.

3. The test content may be culturally inappropriate for cultural populations not adequately represented in the test norming population.

Tests Developed in the Primary Language

Many professionals feel that they can obtain valid assessments of ELL students' language skills if they use tests specifically developed in the primary language. Tests developed for Spanish speakers, for example, are often assumed to be appropriate for all Spanish speakers. However, there may be problems even with these tests.

❏ One major problem is that much heterogeneity exists among populations that speak a particular language. For example, many dialects of Spanish exist, and Spanish-speaking children may come from such different countries as Cuba, Mexico, Puerto Rico, the Dominican Republic, and Spain. Words used frequently by Spanish speakers in one area of the U.S. may be rarely heard in other parts of the country.

❏ Another example is the Philippines, a country that has over 100 different mutually unintelligible languages and dialects. Therefore, a Filipino student who speaks Odionganon (the local dialect spoken in the town of Odiongan) can be expected to perform poorly on a test administered in Tagalog, a major national language.

❏ A second difficulty is that developmental data on languages other than English is limited. Some Spanish norms for articulation and language have been developed (e.g., Goldstein & Iglesias, 1996; Jiménez, 1987; Merino, 1992) but few easily-accessible established language development norms exist for languages other than English.

❏ There are also differences in the vocabularies and linguistic knowledge bases of students who are born in the United States and those who immigrate here at a later age. Thus, test norms based on students born and raised in Mexico are not valid for many Spanish-speaking students born and raised in the United States.

There have been efforts to develop valid, reliable measures in other languages. Liu et al. (2017) developed the Diagnostic Receptive and Expressive Language Assessment of Mandarin (DREAM). As mentioned in an earlier chapter, the Bilingual English Spanish Assessment (BESA) provides reliable assessment of language development in Spanish-English bilingual children between 4:0 and 6:11 years of age (Peña et al., 2014).

CONSIDERATIONS IN TEST SELECTION

Variables described as important to consider in selecting assessment instruments (Crowley, 2003; Roseberry-McKibbin & Hegde, 2016) are the following:

1. ***Purpose of the test***. Is the instrument used for screening or in-depth evaluation?

2. ***Construct validity***. What theory was used in the test's creation? Is one mentioned? Is it appropriate for the student being tested?

3. ***Appropriateness of test content.*** Professionals should have native speakers of the student's language review the test whenever possible. Field-testing can be helpful in evaluating the appropriateness of test items.

4. ***Adequacy of norms***. How was the standardization sample selected? Are the students being tested represented in the norming and standardization?

CONSIDERATIONS IN TEST ADMINISTRATION

Professionals must consider formal test assumptions and how these assumptions might negatively impact individual test-takers. There are ways in which professionals can alter the administration of standardized tests so that they are less biased against ELL students. By reducing bias, students are better able to show their true, underlying abilities.

Kohnert (2013) stated that professionals can use standardized tests in nonstandardized ways. If the administration and scoring of standardized tests is modified, it is important to describe these alterations in detail in the diagnostic report. The analysis of ELL students' responses on standardized tests can be helpful in identifying problems that may be indicative of LI.

Experts have suggested ways to alter test administration procedures to be more culturally and linguistically fair to ELLs (Paul et al., 2018; Rosa-Lugo et al., 2012; Wyatt, 2012):

Suggestions for altering test administration procedures include the following:

1. Provide instructions in both English and L1.

2. Explain to the child the reason for testing.

3. Change the pronunciation of test items to reflect the language or dialect of the child.

4. Rephrase confusing instructions.

5. Give extra examples, demonstrations, and practice items. Many tests just give the student a few demonstration items, and this frequently does little to help students understand the test tasks. I frequently give students at least five demonstration items before I begin testing.

6. Give the student extra time to respond.

7. Repeat items when necessary.

8. If students give "wrong" answers, ask them to explain and write down their explanation. Score items as correct if they are culturally appropriate. RECORD ALL RESPONSES.

9. Omit biased items that are likely to be difficult or confusing for students.

10. Continue testing even after the ceiling item on the test has been reached.

11. Devote more than one session to the testing.

12. Have a parent or other trusted adult administer test items under the professional's supervision.

13. If giving a timed test, consider how the child's culture views and prioritizes speed. If speed is not viewed as critical, you may wish to increase the time allotted for the completion of test items.

14. Use a "dual scoring" system in which correct answers in both the first language and English are counted in the total score.

Students may demonstrate a higher level of language proficiency for some skills in the first language and a higher level of proficiency for other skills in English. For example, young children often know "school" vocabulary (e.g., shapes, colors) in English and "home" vocabulary (e.g., body parts, certain foods) in the primary language. Thus, a dual-scoring or conceptual scoring system that uses answers in both languages to compute a total score is more reflective of a child's actual language knowledge than a system that only accounts for answers in one language or the other. Research using this type of scoring suggests that it can be helpful in reducing the number of children inappropriately-identified as having LI.

❏ Gross, Buac, and Kaushanskaya (2014) administered standardized vocabulary measures in English and Spanish to Spanish-English speaking children who were between 5 and 7 years of age. They found that conceptual scoring increased the portion of children who achieved vocabulary scores within the average range. Based on these results,. they concluded that conceptual scoring assists in ruling out vocabulary deficits, especially in typically-developing bilingual children.

❏ Holmstrom, Salameh, Nettelbladt, and Dahlgren-Sandberg (2016) assessed bilingual children who spoke Arabic and Swedish. For these children, combined Arabic-Swedish total scores were significantly higher than single-language scores. Holmstrom et al. concluded that use of this type of scoring system may reduce the over-identification of LI and the underestimation of lexical knowledge in bilingual populations.

Profile

A bilingual SLP was evaluating the language skills of Jose, Spanish-English student. She showed him a picture of a couch and asked him what it was. He replied "la cama" (bed). The SLP marked Jose's answer as incorrect, but later realized that the answer was correct in light of Jose's background. Jose's family lived in poverty, and in his home, the couch actually was his bed.

CONSIDERATIONS IN TEST INTERPRETATION

When professionals administer standardized tests, there are ways to interpret these tests that can effectively reduce bias:

1. Do not identify a student as needing special education based on standardized test scores alone. Use informal measures (described in the next chapter) to supplement standardized test scores.

2. Ascertain whether students' errors are typical of those observed among other students from similar backgrounds.

3. Review test results with family members and/or other persons from the student's background to gain additional insights that may be helpful in educational decision-making.

4. Interpret overall test results in a team setting. If professionals review and interpret results without consulting with other team members, errors may occur.

5. When writing assessment reports, be sure to include cautions and disclaimers about any departures from standard testing procedures. In addition, discuss how the student's background may have influenced test results.

Profile

Soua L., a shy kindergarten student from a Hmong family, was referred for a special education assessment. At the end of his kindergarten year, Soua was still designated as "Limited English Proficient." However, the special education team used standardized English tests to assess Soua's speech-language, cognitive, and academic skills. Each examiner commented about how Soua was unwilling to speak or make eye contact during testing. Soua's scores on each test were significantly below the norm for the sample tested, and Soua was labeled "disordered in oral and written language." He was then placed in both speech-language and resource services for "remediation."

The next year, a new speech-language pathologist came to the school and reviewed Soua's reports and IEP from the previous year. When it was time for Soua's annual review, the speech-language pathologist carried out a comprehensive pre-evaluation process that included gathering an extensive case history from the student's parents and re-evaluating his language proficiency in English and Hmong.

A home visit was conducted with a Hmong interpreter whom the family knew and trusted. Soua's parents shared that they had been in the U.S. for only two years and that they did not know English. They confided to the interpreter that they did not understand why Soua was receiving "extra help" but that they were grateful that he was "learning more English." Soua's parents said that he learned Hmong rapidly and easily in comparison with his five siblings, and that they had no concerns about his ability to learn or remember in the Hmong language. Soua's first-grade teacher stated that he was progressing well in class, and the interpreter shared that in his five years of experience working with Hmong students in the school district, Soua "looks normal to me when he speaks in Hmong—and he remembers everything I tell him."

Soua was dismissed from special education services but continued to receive support in Hmong from an interpreter who came into his classroom twice a week. Soua was also signed up for the after-school literacy program that allowed him to work in a small group with a tutor who helped ELL students become grade-level proficient in reading. Soua's teacher was given suggestions for supporting him in the classroom.

There are many hazards to using standardized, formal tests with ELL students. However, if professionals use these tests, they should be aware of potential forms of bias that may affect performance. If professionals are extremely cautious in the way they use standardized tests, and if they administer and interpret them in sensitive and nonbiased ways, the tests' results may help to provide part of the answer to questions regarding the presence or absence of LI.

SUMMARY

When ELL students are struggling in school, professionals must decide whether poor school performance can be attributed to language and/or cultural differences, environmental variables, or underlying language-learning disabilities (Pieretti & Roseberry-McKibbin, 2016).

Professionals must remember the following:

❏ Behaviors commonly observed among second language learners, such as transfer from the primary language, may be inappropriately viewed as signs of LI.

❏ Testing must conform to legal requirements and must be non-discriminatory.

❑ It is important to use a pre-evaluation process to obtain information about the student's linguistic and environmental background and to determine whether formal special education testing is truly necessary.

❑ The pre-evaluation process should consist of several components, including the classroom teacher's evaluation of classroom performance, a case history, and determination of the student's proficiency in the primary language and English.

❑ ELL students do not have LI if they demonstrate problems in English only; difficulties must be evident in both the primary language and English.

❑ Formal, standardized language tests do not provide a complete picture of the child's communication skills. Standardized tests have many limitations that need to be recognized and accommodated if these tests are used.

❑ Because of the bias inherent in standardized tests, it is appropriate for professionals who assess ELL students to avoid using norms from these measures to determine eligibility for special education programs.

If the identification of disabilities is based primarily on standardized test scores, many students will be misdiagnosed and inappropriately placed into special education. Remember that there is absolutely NO federal U.S. law requiring the use of norm-referenced tests to identify ELL students for special education programs.

Pre-evaluation procedures and nonstandardized, informal assessment methods provide information about the student's environment, levels of language proficiency and underlying language-learning ability. These methods are described in the next chapter.

STUDY QUESTIONS

1. Discuss the types of bias inherent in norm-referenced tests. Why is the use of test scores from these measures so inappropriate for the majority of ELL students?

2. Why is the pre-referral process so important when an ELL student is suspected of having a language impairment?

3. List five potential indicators of a language impairment in an ELL student.

MULTIPLE CHOICE

4. Which of the following statements are TRUE?
    A. The student's primary language is the language the student learned first and used most frequently in the early stages of language development.
    B. The student's dominant language is the language spoken most proficiently by the student at the current time.
    C. The term "language proficiency" refers to the child's level of skill in the use of a particular language.
    D. If a student is labeled "English proficient," it is then appropriate to administer formal standardized tests in English and use formal scores to determine special education eligibility.
    E. IDEA (2004) mandates that in order for a student to receive intervention for a "learning disability," there must be a severe discrepancy between intelligence and academic performance.

5. Which one of the following is FALSE about the *Every Student Succeeds Act*?

    A. English language proficiency is considered an academic indicator of accountability under ESSA.
    B. During their first year in the U.S., ELL immigrant/refugee students will need to take both math and reading assessments and have the results publicly reported. However, these first year scores won't count toward a school's rating.
    C. Under ESSA, individual states can choose their own short- and long-term goals. These goals must address proficiency on tests, English language proficiency, and graduation rates.
    D. In ELLs' second year, the state has to incorporate their test results for both math and reading, using some measure of growth.
    E. In the ELL student's fifth year in the U.S., proficiency in English is generally equivalent to that of a native English speakers and, therefore, norm-referenced English language tests can be used to identify disabilities.

6. An SLP is administering a standardized language test to an ELL student. Which of the following are acceptable ways to alter this test for the student, assuming that the SLP reports her alterations in detail in the diagnostic report?

    A. Repeat items.
    B. Give extra examples and demonstrations.
    C. Score the student's responses according to the norms provided in the test manual.
    D. Discontinue testing when the student reaches a ceiling.
    E. Give portions of the test on different days.

7. When teachers provide information about a student's classroom performance for language assessment purposes, they should include the following:

    A. Information about school social interaction problems
    B. Information about the student's classroom language use
    C. Impressions from classroom observations
    D. Information about language and learning problems (in both the primary language and English)
    E. Documentation about the student's personal habits (e.g., eating habits, hygiene, etc.)

8. Indicators of LI in an ELL student include the following:
    A. Family history of special education/learning difficulties
    B. Difficulty in learning language at a normal rate

    C. Lack of organization, structure, and sequence in spoken and written language; difficulty conveying thoughts

    D. A low level of proficiency in only one of the languages spoken by the student

    E. A low level of proficiency resulting from limited exposure to English

9. Rosalia is a fourth grade student who came to kindergarten speaking only Spanish. She is struggling in class, and her teacher is considering a referral for special education testing. A thorough case history, conducted with Rosalia's mother, indicates that Rosalia did not speak her first word in Spanish until she was 2 years old. Rosalia was slower to develop verbal skills in Spanish than her siblings. Because the school was reluctant to evaluate Rosalia for special education when she was in the early grades, she was given many non-special education "extras." These included participation in the after-school Homework Club, preferred seating in the classroom, individual assistance from a Spanish-speaking interpreter, and participation in the school's English as a Second Language program. Despite this extra assistance, Rosalia's performance in fourth grade is substantially below that of Spanish-speaking peers in both oral and written language skills. Her parents are concerned because none of their other children have struggled in school to the extent that Rosalia has. Which quadrant of the Diagnostic Pie would best describe Rosalia's status?

    A. Quadrant one

    B. Quadrant two

    C. Quadrant three

    D. Quadrant four

10. Masood is the son of immigrants from Saudi Arabia. He entered the sixth grade class at your school speaking primarily Arabic with very limited English. After four months in the all-English sixth grade classroom, Masood has friends but, predictably, is struggling academically. The classroom teacher is new and has no background in working with ELLs. She refers him for special education testing because his academic test scores are not commensurate with those of other ELLs who were born and raised in the U.S. A conversation with Masood's parents reveals that he reads and writes proficiently in Arabic. He performed well in Saudi Arabian schools. Masood's father is a doctor, and his mother is a full-time at-home mom who has devoted herself to raising her family—including doing a great deal of reading with Masood since early childhood. As stated, at school, Masood has friends and is well-liked by other students. He is picking up conversational English well, and is especially gifted in athletics. Which quadrant of the Diagnostic Pie would you select based on Masood's background?

    A. Quadrant one

    B. Quadrant two

    C. Quadrant three

    D. Quadrant four

ANSWERS TO STUDY QUESTIONS

    4. A, B, and C
    5. E
    6. A, B, and E
    7. A, B, C, and D
    8. A, B, and C
    9. C
    10. A

Chapter 12

Ecologically Valid Assessment: Practical Strategies

Outline

NONBIASED ALTERNATIVES TO STANDARDIZED TESTS

Problems commonly encountered when norm-referenced tests are used in the identification of culturally and linguistically diverse student populations were reviewed in the previous chapter. When assessing multicultural student populations for LI, many experts recommend the use of nonstandardized, informal measures, either alone or in conjunction with standardized formal tests (Mattes & Saldaña-Illingworth, 2009; Mdlalo, 2017; Pieretti & Roseberry-McKibbin, 2016). Students from culturally and linguistically diverse populations should never be identified as having language impairment (LI) based solely on scores from standardized, norm-referenced instruments.

As mentioned in the previous chapter, there is no federal U.S. law that requires the administration of formal, standardized measures in the special education assessment of students. When used within a team approach to assessment, informal, qualitative measures provide equitable, valid, and nondiscriminatory information about the student's development and actual use of language skills. By using a combination of formal and informal measures, school professionals are better able to identify those students who are truly in need of special education services (see Figure 12.1).

Data obtained from survey research has shown that many public school speech-language pathologists have concerns related to the use of assessment instruments in distinguishing language differences from LI (Arias & Friberg, 2017; Kimble, 2013; Kraemer et al., 2013; Roseberry-McKibbin et al., 2005). This chapter includes a review of informal, nonstandardized procedures and practical strategies for using these tools. Research-based, reproducible assessment tools are presented in this chapter that can be used with students from any language background. The information obtained from these tools will be helpful in identifying children with LI.

Advantages of Informal, Nonstandardized Assessment

Informal assessment measures circumvent the test bias issues that are inherent in the use of standardized, norm referenced measures and provide useful information to professionals that will not be obtained in a rigid, formal testing environment (Moore & Montgomery, 2018; Roseberry-McKibbin, 2016). Use of these measures benefits professionals in a variety of ways:

1. *Professionals are able to evaluate the student's functioning in real-life contexts.* Formal testing seldom taps these students' individualized, functional skills in their own environments. Using informal measures permits ecologically valid assessment, which considers the environment, home, and culture of the child and family.

2. *The assessment process can be individualized based on observed behavior, yielding data*

Tech Tie-In

Practical Assessment & Treatment Strategies for English Language Learners w/ Language Impairments
I created this 30-minute video for the American Speech-Language-Hearing Association (ASHA). To view this practical video, go to youtube.com and search for Celeste Roseberry (Love Talk Read)

Figure 12.1

TEAM APPROACH TO COMPREHENSIVE ASSESSMENT

ASSESSMENT WHEEL FOR ELLs

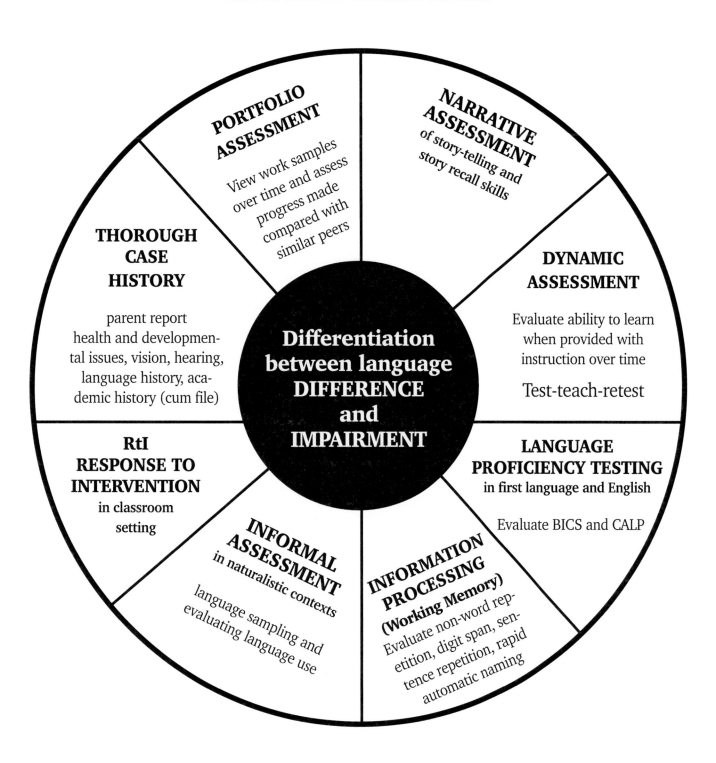

PORTFOLIO ASSESSMENT
View work samples over time and assess progress made compared with similar peers

NARRATIVE ASSESSMENT
of story-telling and story recall skills

THOROUGH CASE HISTORY
parent report health and developmental issues, vision, hearing, language history, academic history (cum file)

DYNAMIC ASSESSMENT
Evaluate ability to learn when provided with instruction over time
Test-teach-retest

Differentiation between language DIFFERENCE and IMPAIRMENT

RtI RESPONSE TO INTERVENTION
in classroom setting

LANGUAGE PROFICIENCY TESTING
in first language and English
Evaluate BICS and CALP

INFORMAL ASSESSMENT
in naturalistic contexts
language sampling and evaluating language use

INFORMATION PROCESSING (Working Memory)
Evaluate non-word repetition, digit span, sentence repetition, rapid automatic naming

that is helpful in distinguishing language differences from language impairment. If the diagnosis is LI, data from informal measures facilitates the identification of specific areas in which intervention is needed.

3. *Assessment data can be collected from multiple sources in a variety of contexts.* Synthesizing information from multiple sources helps professionals to make accurate diagnoses.

4. *Performance can be evaluated in relation to the demands of the curriculum.* For example, it is important to examine the extent to which the student has mastered the concepts necessary to understand lessons being taught within the classroom.

5. *Educational decisions can be based on how the student responds to instruction.* In contrast to standardized, norm-referenced tests which generally assess previously acquired knowledge (influenced by environmental experiences) at a specific point in time, informal measures make it possible to examine behavior in actual learning situations.

6. *Environmental variables can be identified that may cause a typically-developing ELL student to appear as though he has LI.* Poverty, lack of preschool experience, and limited exposure to books are among the many environmental variables that may affect the development of basic language skills.

General Strategies for Using Informal, Nonstandardized Assessments

When informal, nonstandardized assessment procedures are used, communication skills can be evaluated based on performance in a variety of settings over a period of time. These procedures make it possible to evaluate language in relation to children's previous experiences. They also make it possible to identify specific problems that are being experienced when efforts are made to teach language skills. Children who have "language impairment," will show evidence of difficulty learning even in situations where culturally and linguistically appropriate instruction is provided. By examining how children respond to instruction, speech-language pathologists and other professionals will be able to more accurately identify individuals who are truly in need of special education services (Mattes & Saldaña-Illingsworth, 2008).

When assessing culturally and linguistically diverse student populations in school settings, the following strategies are suggested:

1. *Collect assessment data in both languages if the child makes functional use of two languages.*

2. *Determine the child's level of language functioning and performance in the classroom setting.* A curriculum-based assessment is important to determine how the child uses language in academic contexts.

3. *Use a dynamic approach to assessment.* Evaluate the student's ability to learn over time when provided with instruction. This is highly preferable to a static approach in which the student is tested in one or two assessment sessions. Take advantage of the IDEA (2004) concept of Response to Intervention (RtI), described later in this chapter.

4. *Evaluate the student's ability to learn language.* Because so many students have had limited exposure to mainstream school concepts and vocabulary, they do poorly in formal testing situations. Thus, professionals should evaluate ability to learn rather than focusing only on identifying the student's current level of functioning. Students who have typical underlying language-learning ability but limited experiences will generally learn new language rules readily, while students with LI will have difficulty learning language rules. Students with disabilities

usually require more repetition in their instructional programs than students who are developing language in the typical manner.

5. *Evaluate communication holistically.* Focus on the functional aspects of language as the child uses language to communicate meaning and to meet the demands of various communication situations.

6. *Collect observational data in a variety of naturalistic contexts.* It is important to evaluate the student's ability to interact in everyday situations. The use of multiple observations in naturalistic settings makes it possible to obtain information about the child's overall communication behavior in a variety of situations. Professionals can observe students in the classroom, at recess, at lunch, in the library, in the home, and in other settings.

7. *Use questionnaires to obtain information from individuals who interact with the student.* Parents, teachers, and others can provide information about specific problems that the student is experiencing. The English Language Learner Pre-Referral Screening presented in the previous chapter can be used to collect valuable information about the student's communication functioning in daily contexts.

8. *Assess the student's ability to construct narratives and to remember stories that have been heard.*

9. *Use natural language samples.* These samples can be used to evaluate students' communication skills as language is used in various settings.

10. *Review the student's school performance records.* A review of the student's cumulative record file often yields helpful information. I find it especially salient to read teachers' comments on report cards. I look for themes over the years. For example, a pattern of teacher comments about difficulties with listening, speaking, reading, and writing is a strong indication that the student has LI.

The use of language samples, observational techniques, and informal assessment measures will increase the likelihood that students with LI are accurately identified and that culturally and linguistically appropriate programs of instruction are developed to meet their needs. These measures make it possible to plan intervention programs based on how the student functions in the classroom and in various social contexts.

In this chapter, informal assessment strategies are described that can be used in the identification of ELL students with LI. Specific research studies are cited that explain the scientific underpinnings for these practical strategies.

DYNAMIC ASSESSMENT OF LANGUAGE-LEARNING ABILITY

Theory Underlying Dynamic Assessment

Professionals who wish to evaluate language-learning ability must first understand the theory underlying dynamic assessment. Reuven Feuerstein, a Romanian philosopher/practitioner/scholar, developed the Theory of Structural Cognitive Modifiability. This theory was based on many years of experience working with low-functioning children from over 70 cultures. He worked with Holocaust survivors, children from concentration camps, and immigrants from Persia, Morocco, and the former Soviet Union, among others. Feuerstein's theory gave birth to the Learning Potential Assessment Device (LPAD). The major tenets of Feuerstein's theory and the LPAD are the following:

❑ Conventional tests and most other current methods of assessment are static measures that passively catalog children's current knowledge and measure their level of functioning at one point in time. These tests accept a student's current level of functioning as a predictor of how well the student will function in the future.

❑ The LPAD attempts to assess the child's "zone of proximal development" (Vygotsky, 1962) which shows what the child can achieve with active help from a more knowledgeable person such as an adult.

❑ The LPAD focuses on students' ability to profit from learning experiences when presented with instructional activities in which they are able to apply their problem-solving ability and to demonstrate that they can improve their performance. Thus, students may be able to demonstrate problem solving skills that probably would not become evident in a formal test situation. This approach makes it possible to observe performance in natural learning contexts and, therefore, provides useful information about the child's ability to profit from instruction.

❑ All children are modifiable.

❑ Adults must engage children in mediated learning or purposeful directed activities.

❑ Adults need to use instrumental enrichment (IE) or specific materials and exercises along with guidance and direction in activities.

❑ The LPAD itself can take several days and up to 25 hours to complete with an individual student. This is a very daunting proposition for professionals who must assess many students! However, professionals can utilize Feuerstein's principles to develop approaches to assessment that examine the student's actual functioning and ability to learn over a period of time.

❑ Dynamic assessment determines the capacity to learn rather than one's knowledge at a specific point in time. Dynamic assessment allows the examiner to observe how the student learns rather than focusing entirely on what the student already knows. Again, the student's learning process is emphasized.

❑ The underlying assumption is that during dynamic assessment, children with language differences will exhibit more modifiability than those with LI. If children have LI, they will typically show a small change in performance, a low post-test score, and poor learning behaviors. More effort will have to be expended to teach students with LI (Petersen et al., 2017).

❑ Diagnoses of LI are often made based on static assessment procedures in which test scores are obtained during one or two testing sessions. It was stated earlier that this is a less than optimal approach to testing. It was also stated that a major difficulty with static assessment is that the information obtained represents the child's performance at one point in time.

Tech Tie-In

 ASHA has a multimedia tutorial on dynamic assessment. This resource can be accessed at the link below:

http://www.asha.org/practice/multicultural/issues/Dynamic-Assessment.htm

❑ If testing is conducted once a year, the child's instructional objectives for an entire year are usually based on these results. In addition, static measures usually measure language knowledge, which can be impacted by environmental variables such as poverty and homelessness and linguistic variables such as lack of familiarity with English. Dynamic, ongoing assessment holds much greater promise for obtaining accurate measures of the abilities of ELL students (Ebert & Pham, 2017; Kraemer et al., 2013; Paul et al., 2018).

Strategies for Implementing Dynamic Assessment

1. **Graduated prompting**. Responses are elicited through use of increasingly specific prompts. For example, the examiner may begin by modeling a response ("This is a tiger."). The examiner may then present the model followed by an elicitation question ("This is a tiger. What is it?"). The examiner may also model with an object obstacle (withholding the object until the child attempts to produce the word). The level of prompting needed by the child determines the child's readiness to learn specific target items.

2. **Testing the limits**. The goal is to find out what children can do and what they know. For example, during testing, children may be provided with feedback, including explanations to help them understand why specific responses were incorrect. They may also be asked to explain how they arrived at some of their answers. This can help children understand why they are making mistakes so that they can self-correct.

3. **Test-teach-retest**. In this strategy, the initial testing is conducted to determine what the child knows and what the child does not know. Intervention focuses on teaching unknown items. Following a period of instruction, the child is re-tested to ascertain whether or not she has acquired the newly-taught information. How much change has occurred? How much support did the child need to acquire the new information? In other words, the child's modifiability is evaluated. Children with LI require considerably more support than peers from a similar cultural and linguistic background.

   The child can be evaluated for the ability to acquire any type of new information—rules of pragmatics, individual words, grammatical morphemes, etc. It is helpful if several typically developing peers from the same cultural and linguistic background are evaluated as well. In this way, the performance and overall modifiability of the child in question can be compared with that of these similar peers. Steps in the test-teach-retest approach are as follows:

   A. Test the child to see what she does and does not know. Find items/concepts she doesn't know.
   B. Teach these concepts to the child (e.g., new vocabulary, how to tell a story in sequence).
   C. Re-test the child to see if she has retained the information taught and is able to apply it (e.g., Is the child able to tell a story in sequence). Has there been a small or large change in performance?
   D. Evaluate how much effort it took to teach new concepts to the child. Did the examiner need to repeat concepts many times and provide multiple illustrations and examples because the child had difficulty retaining the information? Or did the child learn quickly and show ability to retain and apply the information taught in the short teaching sessions?
   E. Compare the child's performance to that of peers from a similar cultural and linguistic background.

Researchers believe that the *test-teach-retest* format holds the most promise for fair and accurate assessment of ELLs suspected of having LI (Fiestas, 2017; Grech & McLeod, 2012; Gutiérrez-Clellen & Peña, 2008; Paradis et al., 2011; Petersen et al., 2017; Wyatt, 2012). When using *test-teach-retest* to evaluate students' ability to learn, professionals should ask these questions:

❏ *How much structure and individual attention is needed for the student to acquire new language skills?* Students with LI usually need more prompts, modeling, and repetition than their peers.

❏ *To what extent does the student exhibit off-task behaviors or inappropriate responses during classroom activities?* Students with LI may give responses that are off-topic or inappropriate. Because their problems make learning difficult, they also may show off-task behaviors such as fidgeting, annoying other students, and generally not attending to task.

❏ *To what extent does the student require instructional strategies that differ from those that have been used effectively with peers?* Strategies that have worked effectively with typically-developing ELL students may not be effective with students who have LI and, therefore, these students require a more "customized" approach to instruction.

Children who have language differences will generally respond quickly and learn well in short teaching sessions. Conversely, children with LI will be more difficult to teach, require more examiner effort, and retain and apply the information less skillfully (Fiestas, 2017).

Recent research has found evidence of the value of dynamic assessment in identifying the learning needs of young children.

❏ Kapantzoglou, Restrepo, and Thompson (2012) examined whether dynamic assessment of word learning skills is an effective method for identifying bilingual children with LI. In this study, fifteen 4- and 5-year-old predominantly Spanish-speaking children with typical language development and 13 children with LI participated in a 30-40 minute session of dynamic assessment of word learning skills. A pre-test—teach—post-test design was used. Results of the study indicated that typically developing children were faster than children with LI in making associations between the semantic and phonological representations of the new words. The typically-developing children showed greater modifiability. Kapantzoglou and colleagues concluded that a brief dynamic assessment is a promising method for accurately distinguishing typically-developing Spanish-speaking children from those with LI.

❏ Petersen and Gillam (2013) investigated the predictive validity of a dynamic assessment designed to evaluate later risk for reading difficulty in bilingual Hispanic children who were at risk for LI. During their kindergarten year, 63 Hispanic bilingual children completed a dynamic assessment nonsense-word recoding task that yielded pretest—posttest scores in several areas. At the end of first grade, the same subjects completed criterion reading measures of reading fluency, decoding, and word identification. Petersen and Gillam concluded that the dynamic assessment used in their study yielded high accuracy for predicting word-reading ability in first grade. This study is very important because it showed that use of the dynamic assessment measure in kindergarten, which was simple to administer and took less than five minutes to complete, was highly accurate in predicting later difficulties with reading in first grade. Use of a dynamic assessment strategy such as this can help professionals engage in early identification of and thus intervention for at-risk students, preventing problems later.

❏ Petersen, Changthongthip, Ukrainetz, Spencer, & Steeve (2017) investigated the classification accuracy of a concentrated English narrative dynamic assessment for identifying LI in young Spanish-English bilingual children. They found that English narrative dynamic assessment results were highly accurate in identifying bilingual children with and without LI.

Response to Intervention (RtI)

As previously stated, RtI may be used as a form of dynamic assessment of a student's ability to learn when provided with instruction. This multitiered approach makes it possible to provide services and interventions to struggling students at increasing levels of intensity. In the classroom, this approach is ideal when providing small group instruction and side-by-side teaching.

RtI was mandated in the IDEA (2004) as a way of minimizing misidentification and over-referral of certain groups of students to special education. Today, researchers from many disciplines have recommended the use of RtI with ELL students suspected of having special education needs (Moore & Montgomery, 2018; Pieretti & Roseberry-McKibbin, 2016).

❑ RtI is an assessment and intervention approach that provides students with intense, high-quality, scientifically valid instruction through a three-level process that becomes progressively more individualized and intense (Roth, Dixon, Paul, & Bellini, 2013). Periodic assessment of the student's progress determines the appropriate placement level.

❑ RtI can be viewed as a pre-referral intervention designed to help general education teachers appropriately assess the needs of their underachieving students and provide effective instruction for these students.

❑ RtI builds on the idea that collaborative, systematic efforts help teachers provide effective intervention for students in the general education classroom. RtI focuses on helping teachers maintain responsibility for student achievement as opposed to viewing extra support in the classroom as a hurdle en route to a special education referral.

❑ With the advent of the Common Core State Standards, teachers are more pressured than ever to push decontextualized learning (e.g., understanding expository text) down to the kindergarten level. I have found that teachers sometimes feel so pressured that they refer ELL low achievers to special education, hoping that special education will boost the students' state test achievement scores.

❑ While this concern about raising test scores is certainly understandable, it is definitely not an acceptable answer to the challenges that teachers face in their efforts to improve learning. RtI has a much better chance of actually supporting ELL students who struggle academically because it is specifically geared to increasing these students' access to the curriculum.

As discussed previously, placement in a program for children with LI is warranted only when it is determined that a disability is the cause of the problems observed in the school setting. Problems resulting from limited exposure to English or environmental circumstances are not indicators of language impairment. Response-to-Intervention, a dynamic method for evaluating students' ability to learn over time when provided with instruction, facilitates the collection of information that has direct relevance to students' language learning needs. If students are provided with supportive learning opportunities and continue to progress much slower than peers from similar backgrounds, the need for special education services should be seriously considered.

Tech Tie-In

ASHA has developed comprehensive information about RtI and its application across a wide variety of settings.
http://www.asha.org/slp/schools/prof-consult/RtoI/

Profile

Lily, a Filipino ELL student, was referred to me by her third-grade classroom teacher because of learning difficulties in the classroom. Visayan was Lily's primary language. Based on what the teacher told me, I felt that Lily's difficulties should be discussed at a meeting of the Student Study Team.

The teacher met with the Student Study Team to discuss the specific problems that Lily was experiencing. Because of Lily's limited proficiency in English, the team recommended that she be provided with additional time to complete assignments and with help from a peer tutor. Front-row seating, the use of visual stimuli, and participation in an after-school homework program were also recommended. The team asked the teacher to implement these strategies for six months and to collect information to show how her performance compared with that of peers from similar backgrounds. The team was also able to recruit a Visayan-speaking parent volunteer to give Lily extra support (in her primary language) so that she could complete in-class assignments.

At the end of the six-month period, the Student Study Team met with the teacher to review Lily's progress. The data collected by the teacher showed that classmates far surpassed Lily in all areas of performance—math, reading, spelling, and social studies. Although Lily had been provided with targeted instruction, her progress, even with many added supports, was minimal in all areas.

A comprehensive special education evaluation was then completed using information collected by the speech-language pathologist, school psychologist, and resource specialist. Based on assessment data and information relating to how Lily responded to instruction, it was determined that she had a clinically significant learning disability and that limited proficiency in English was not the cause of her difficulties.

The services of a speech-language pathologist and resource specialist were recommended. At the IEP meeting, Lily's mother confided that she herself had difficulty in school while growing up in the Philippines. She was thankful that Lily would receive special help at school.

Portfolio Assessment

Portfolio assessment is a dynamic assessment process that can be used to obtain performance data in a variety of areas over a period of time. A portfolio is a box, folder, notebook, or other container that holds materials by and information about a student. Portfolios can be used in a variety of ways to identify learning needs and plan intervention programs:

❏ Portfolios provide a multidimensional view of students' development. Portfolios can contain language samples, student work samples in various subjects, and other examples of students' performance.

❏ Portfolios include information that can be used to track and evaluate students' performance over time. For example, if a first grader is struggling in September, the teacher may save several of her writing samples from September for the portfolio. Writing samples can be added from October, November, December, and January. In February, these samples can be laid side by side and evaluated to determine if progress has been made.

❏ Portfolios include information relevant to evaluating the effectiveness of instruction. If little change is seen in the student's performance, even with extra support, the team may suspect the possibility of an underlying LI. More in-depth assessment can then take place.

❏ Portfolios give professionals a better picture of students' abilities than that revealed by standardized tests. The information contained within portfolios shows students' functional use of skills that they are learning.

❏ Portfolios reflect the student's performance within the classroom curriculum and provide a picture of the types of educational opportunities that students have been given.

When ELL students are referred for testing, I often ask teachers to provide me with samples of their work over a period of time. It is always interesting to compare these samples with those obtained from peers who are showing typical progress in classroom learning activities. I have found that students with portfolio samples that show little evidence of growth over a period of time frequently end up qualifying for special education services when formal testing is completed.

ASSESSMENT OF INFORMATION PROCESSING/WORKING MEMORY

Children with LI frequently have difficulties with working memory. These difficulties underlie deficits in information processing skills, negatively impacting LI children's ability to quickly and efficiently process and remember information that they hear. Put differently, children with LI have underlying deficits in the temporal processing of auditory signals (Ratner, 2017).

Research has focused on the assessment of students' information processing/working memory skills as a way to circumvent problems associated with the bias in standardized tests that measure acquired knowledge (e.g., knowledge of vocabulary), especially in ELL students (Pieretti & Roseberry-McKibbin, 2016). According to Paradis (2016, p. 179);

> "....One approach [to assessment of ELLs] involves emphasizing the use of language-processing or memory-system measures in assessment, such as nonword and sentence repetition...The reasoning behind this approach is that processing measures would be less biased against bilingual speakers because they are targeting language learning capacity more than accumulated knowledge of particular words and grammatical constructions...."

❏ Assessment of ELL children's information processing/working memory skills is a very promising tool for differentiating language difference from LI (Roseberry-McKibbin, 2016). Essentially, children are asked to listen to a series of stimuli and repeat them back verbatim. For example, the child may be asked to do the following:

> "Say these numbers just like I do. Ready? 9-3-8-1."

The child responds by repeating the four numbers in the correct sequence.

Tech Tie-In

Assessment of ELLs with Language Impairment: Evaluating Ability to Follow Directions

In this video, Afeefa, the interpreter, ensures that the student understands the vocabulary used in the Token Test for Children. She administers the test in Arabic, the student's primary language, to evaluate her ability to follow directions when vocabulary is known and visual stimuli are present. Notice how the student hesitates, manifests latencies or delays, and needs repetition of simple directions. Go to youtube.com, search for Celeste Roseberry (Love Talk Read), and select the video title above.

❑ The assessment of information processing skills that rely on working memory makes it possible to circumvent the pervasive problem caused by the use of measures based upon background knowledge. (Kohnert, 2013; Oetting et al., 2016; Paradis, 2016; Santiago-Valles et al., 2016).

❑ Repeating a series of nonsense words, or "non-words," is especially difficult for many children with LI. For example, an examiner might say to a child, "I am going to have this puppet say three silly words. I want you to say them back just like he does: paedish, gothu, humplah. Now you say those."

❑ Professionals can assess memory by asking children to repeat strings of digits, nonwords (nonsense syllables), real words, and/or sentences.

Research has provided strong evidence that difficulties with working memory are characteristic of children with genuine, underlying language impairment (Boudreau & Costanza-Smith, 2011).

❑ Processing-based measures have been found to be more accurate in distinguishing between language differences and language impairment than information-based measures (Campbell, Dollaghan, Needleman, & Janosky, 1997; Dollaghan & Campbell, 1998; Jacobs & Coufal, 2001; Windsor, Kohnert, Lobitz, & Pham, 2010).

❑ Working memory tasks have been found to be effective in identifying LI in children who speak English and a variety of other languages:
  • Cantonese (Stokes, Wong, Fletcher, & Leonard, 2006)
  • French (Thordardottir et al., 2011; Thordardottir & Brandeker, 2012)
  • Italian (Dispaldro, Leonard, & Deevy, 2013)
  • Portuguese (Engle, Santos, & Gathercole, 2008; Fortunato-Tavares et al., 2012)
  • Spanish (Restrepo & Gutiérrez-Clellen, 2012; Windsor & Kohnert, 2004; Windsor, Kohnert, Lobitz, & Pham, 2010)
  • Vietnamese (Hwa-Froelich & Matsuo, 2005)

❑ In a study conducted in Brazil, children from low-income families scored lower on measures of vocabulary than did children from high-income families. These differences, however, were not observed on measures of working memory (Engle, Santos, & Gathercole, 2008).

❑ ELL children with language impairment have been found to demonstrate more difficulty on tasks that require them to repeat sequences of words, nonwords, and digits than children who do not have language impairment (Fazio, 1998).

❑ Children with LI have been found to score significantly lower than typically-developing children on nonword repetition tasks (Estes, Evans, & Else-Quest, 2007; Guiberson & Rodriguez, 2013; Kan & Windsor, 2010; Paradis & Sorenson Duncan, 2009).

Tech Tie-In

Differentiating Language Difference from Language Impairment Using Nonsense Syllables
In this video, I assess the information processing skills of a student with a potential language impairment using a task involving the repetition of nonsense syllables. This task tests working memory, an area that is commonly deficient in students with language impairment. Go to youtube.com, search for Celeste Roseberry (Love Talk Read), and select the video title above.

❏ Nonword repetition reduces bias in the assessment of ELLs with potential LI (Kapantzoglou, Restrepo, Gray, & Thompson, 2015).

❏ When nonword repetition tasks were used in assessment, the difference between typically-developing subjects and LI subjects increased as the complexity of the nonwords increased. Strings of long nonwords were difficult for LI subjects to repeat (Kan & Windsor, 2010). Children with LI, however, have been found to experience difficulty on nonword repetition tasks even if short words are used.

❏ Nonword repetition tasks can be used with children as young as two years of age (Wagner, Francis, & Morris, 2005) and performance on these measures can be effective in predicting the presence of LI in these children (Roy & Chiat, 2004; Chiat & Roy, 2007).

❏ Brandeker and Thordardottir (2015) found that the underlying mechanisms of nonword repetition in 2- and 3-year olds mainly rely on short term processes, not long term vocabulary knowledge. Nonword repetition was not impacted by previous language exposure.

❏ A valid and nonbiased screening for LI in young African American children can be created by including a measure of nonverbal cognition and a measure of nonword repetition (nonsense syllables) (Craig & Washington, 2004a).

❏ In a study of Portuguese-speaking immigrant children living in Luxembourg, Engel de Abreu, Baldassi, Puglisi, and Befi-Lopes (2013) found that the results of verbal working memory measures involving numbers (e.g., digit repetition) were relatively independent of cultural status and language of testing. Vocabulary, on the other hand, was strongly influenced by linguistic and cultural background.

❏ Swanson, Saenz, and Gerber (2006) used tasks such as digit repetition forwards and backwards as well as word memory to assess Spanish-speaking low-income children. They concluded that "…these measures are particularly well suited to identify children at risk for reading problems in their second language" (p. 262).

❏ In a study conducted in Canada, Paradis, Schneider, & Sorenson Duncan (2013) examined the effectiveness of using a parent questionnaire on first language development in conjunction with English language assessment instruments to distinguish between ELLs with and without LI. The parent questionnaire was found to be an effective tool for identifying children with LI. Children with LI also scored significantly lower than children without LI on all except one of the English language measures. Nonword repetition and tense morphology in English were found to be distinctive clinical markers of LI for children from a variety of language backgrounds.

Practical Assessment Implications for ELLs

When ELL children are given processing/working memory measures, their performance can be compared with that of peers from similar cultural, linguistic, and socioeconomic backgrounds. It is always important to use a variety of measures and to document performance over time.

The Comprehensive Test of Phonological Processing-2 (CTOPP-2), developed by Wagner, Torgeson, Rashotte, and Pearson (2013) has specific subtests that can be used when assessing ELL students with suspected LI.

1. *Memory for Digits* - measures the ability to repeat numbers accurately
2. *Nonword Repetition* - measures the ability to repeat nonwords accurately
3. *Rapid Digit Naming* - measures the ability to rapidly name numbers

4. *Rapid Letter Naming* - measures the ability to rapidly name letters

5. *Rapid Color Naming* - measures the ability to rapidly name colors

6. *Rapid Object Naming* - measures the ability to rapidly name objects

The CTOPP-2 was developed for use with individuals between the ages of 4 and 24. Issues relating to use of the CTOPP has been reviewed by various experts (see Paul et al., 2018). It is important for professionals to be aware that few ELLs participated in the norming sample of the CTOPP-2. By comparing a student's performance to that of typically-developing classmates from a similar background, however, processing difficulties may be identified that could be indicative of LI.

Profile

Tran, a Vietnamese 14-year-old high-school freshman, was referred for special education assessment. He had a history of learning problems dating back to kindergarten, but school personnel were concerned about mislabeling him. The student spoke Vietnamese as his dominant language and had limited proficiency in English. Thus Tran participated in non-special education support programs such as tutoring and ESL small-group work, but he was never evaluated for special education. His high-school teachers were concerned because Tran had greater difficulty remembering information than his Vietnamese peers. Several teachers confided that "I tell Tran something, and five minutes later he's forgotten it." Tran had few friends and was beginning to show signs of a clinically significant behavior problem. His parents were concerned because he had stated that he wanted to join a gang.

The speech-language pathologist, working with a Vietnamese interpreter, conducted a dynamic assessment screening to evaluate Tran's ability to learn. He found that Tran was slow to learn new information and concepts, even with repeated demonstrations and explanations in both English and Vietnamese. Tran was unable to repeat a sequence of more than four digits (immediate rote memory) in either Vietnamese or English. The interpreter conversed with Tran at length about various topics, and noted that he often gave inappropriate responses. Tran also never initiated topics during the conversation. The interpreter said that "When Tran tells me something, I don't know what he's talking about—he makes me confused." The speech-language pathologist concluded that a formal assessment of Tran's language skills was necessary.

There are several potential problems in the use of nonword repetition tasks with ELL students:

1. Professionals must be careful to use only stimuli that are phonologically familiar to the children being tested and that are consistent with their articulatory abilities. For example, the use of non-words with consonant clusters might make the task more difficult for Asian students whose languages do not contain these clusters. Young children might also have difficulty producing consonant clusters, even if those clusters exist in the primary language.

2. Even though processing/working memory tasks represent a culturally and linguistically nonbiased method of screening for LI, these tasks should always be used in conjunction with other measures.

3. Nonwords should not represent real words (e.g., *ganana* for *banana*) because any association with their lexical knowledge reduces the validity of the task as a measure of information processing (Wagner et al., 2005).

Reproducible Form 12.1 includes practical tasks that can be used when assessing ELL students who have been referred for speech and language testing.

Reproducible Form 12.1
INFORMATION PROCESSING TASKS FOR
ENGLISH LANGUAGE LEARNERS
Celeste Roseberry-McKibbin, Ph.D.

Child's Name:_____   Date of Birth:_____   Age:_____   Grade:_____
Date of Testing:_____   Primary Language:_____   Dominant Language:_____

    If the student speaks only the first language (L1), present these tasks in L1 only. If the student speaks L1 and English, administer the tasks in L1 first. Approximately one week later, administer the tasks in English and compare the results in the two languages. It is important to wait at least a few days between L1 and English administrations to reduce the likelihood of "practice effects" that might influence performance. Several typically developing peers should be selected from the classroom of the child who is being evaluated. Administer these same tasks to the peers and compare the performance of the child in question with that of these peers. If the child in question has substantially more difficulty than peers, there is a high probability that the child has some type of language impairment that underlies both L1 and English.

NONSENSE SYLLABLES

Instructions: Start by having the child repeat two nonsense syllables.

Example: dee — fay

Gradually increase the number of syllables to determine how may syllables the child is able to repeat in sequential order in a 10-item task. Sample syllables are listed below:

gah	ko	mo	vay
tay	kah	ni	vo
tah	dee	nu	beh
kay	fay	po	wu
ki (as in *kite)*	fi (as in *fight)*	sah	wah

Repeats 2 syllables	*Repeats 3 syllables*	*Repeats 4 syllables*	*Repeats 5 syllables*
___ 1.	___ 1.	___ 1.	___ 1.
___ 2.	___ 2.	___ 2.	___ 2.
___ 3.	___ 3.	___ 3.	___ 3.
___ 4.	___ 4.	___ 4.	___ 4.
___ 5.	___ 5.	___ 5.	___ 5.
___ 6.	___ 6.	___ 6.	___ 6.
___ 7.	___ 7.	___ 7.	___ 7.
___ 8.	___ 8.	___ 8.	___ 8.
___ 9.	___ 9.	___ 9.	___ 9.
___10.	___10.	___10.	___10.
Total Correct : _____	Total Correct : _____	Total Correct : _____	Total Correct : _____

WORD REPETITION TASK

Instructions: Ask the child to repeat sequences of real words, ranging in length from two words to five words. Do not present words containing sounds that are difficult for the student to produce. For example, do not present words containing /r/ if the student has not mastered production of this sound.

hill	ball	cat	shoe	dog	sun
hair	nose	face	bus	book	pen
fish	cup	bike	desk	chair	swing
slide	box	coat	car	lock	sky
wall	foot	sock	bread	ring	watch
grass	horse	pig	tree	sand	pants
dress	light	door	teeth	ear	mouth
heart	plate	spoon	fork	fence	yard
nurse	boat	mouse	glass	box	bed
phone	hat	pear	duck	pan	foot

Repeats 2 words	*Repeats 3 words*	*Repeats 4 words*	*Repeats 5 words*
___ 1.	___ 1.	___ 1.	___ 1.
___ 2.	___ 2.	___ 2.	___ 2.
___ 3.	___ 3.	___ 3.	___ 3.
___ 4.	___ 4.	___ 4.	___ 4.
___ 5.	___ 5.	___ 5.	___ 5.
___ 6.	___ 6.	___ 6.	___ 6.
___ 7.	___ 7.	___ 7.	___ 7.
___ 8.	___ 8.	___ 8.	___ 8.
___ 9.	___ 9.	___ 9.	___ 9.
___10.	___10.	___10.	___10.
Total Correct : _____	Total Correct : _____	Total Correct : _____	Total Correct : _____

PICTURE POINTING TASK

Instructions: Ask the student to point to familiar picture sequences consisting of two pictures, three pictures, four pictures, or five pictures. Use only pictures that the child can name. Say, "Point to ____, ____." ("Point to *car, bath;*" "Point to *spoon, ring, desk,*" etc.)

Two pictures	*Three pictures*	*Four pictures*	*Five pictures*
___ 1.	___ 1.	___ 1.	___ 1.
___ 2.	___ 2.	___ 2.	___ 2.
___ 3.	___ 3.	___ 3.	___ 3.
___ 4.	___ 4.	___ 4.	___ 4.
___ 5.	___ 5.	___ 5.	___ 5.
___ 6.	___ 6.	___ 6.	___ 6.
___ 7.	___ 7.	___ 7.	___ 7.
___ 8.	___ 8.	___ 8.	___ 8.
___ 9.	___ 9.	___ 9.	___ 9.
___10.	___10.	___10.	___10.
Total Correct : _____	Total Correct : _____	Total Correct : _____	Total Correct : _____

Summary of Observations:

Laing and Kahmi (2003, p. 51) emphasized that:

> The use of processing-dependent dynamic measures with ELL (English Language Learner) students is appealing for a number of reasons. They are not biased toward life experience, socialization practices, or literacy knowledge, and they are quick and easy to administer...It is very advantageous to use assessment measures that do not rely on a child's prior experience or world knowledge...Performance on non-word repetition and working memory measures has been found to be highly correlated with LI and second-language vocabulary acquisition in adults and children. *When children perform poorly on processing-dependent measures, there is a high likelihood that they will have some type of language-learning difficulty* (italics mine).

ASSESSMENT OF RAPID AUTOMATIC NAMING (RAN)

Students who have difficulty with written language (e.g., those diagnosed with reading disability) tend to perform poorly on Rapid Automatic Naming (RAN) tasks (Isoaho, Kauppila, & Launonen, 2016; Paradis et al., 2011; Roth, 2004; Wolf, Bowers, & Biddle, 2000). I have experimented with the use of RAN tasks with ELL students at the school where I work part-time. It has been my experience that students who have difficulty on RAN tasks often experience difficulty learning to read.

❏ The assessment of RAN has been found to be helpful in identifying deficits in naming speed and possible reading disorders in students from several language backgrounds (Isoaho et al., 2016; Wiig, Langdon, & Flores, 2001; Wiig, Zureich, & Chan, 2000).

❏ A recent study assessed and compared the predictive values of group membership for RAN and phonemic awareness in Dutch school children with and without reading disabilities (RD) or LI. Results of the study showed that those children with RD only were more affected by poor RAN skills than the LI-only group. Both groups showed difficulties with phonemic awareness (De Groot, Van den Bos, Van der Meulen, & Minnaert, 2015).

❏ Isoaho and colleagues (2016) found that Finnish children with LI had RAN difficulties that put them at risk for reading problems. RAN skills depend on lexical retrieval and nonlexical processing speed.

❏ RAN tasks are often used that require students to label the color and shape of objects in English. These tasks can be helpful in identifying disorders affecting the acquisition of literacy skills. More research is needed to validate the efficacy of using RAN tasks to assess disabilities affecting the ELL student's acquisition of reading skills.

Tech Tie-In

How to Use Digit Repetition to Assess for Language Impairment
Students with genuine, underlying language impairment have difficulty with information processing skills involving working memory. This 7-year-old girl can repeat three digits in the correct sequence with 100% accuracy, but is unable to repeat four digit sequences in both English and Spanish. Further evaluation is necessary to ascertain whether or not she has an underlying language impairment and needs special education services.

Go to youtube.com, search for Celeste Roseberry (Love Talk Read), and select the video title above.

Profile

Emilio A., a native speaker of Spanish, was referred for a special education assessment by his second grade teacher. She noticed that he struggled academically to a much greater degree than other Spanish-speaking students in her class, and was concerned about his progress. Retention was being considered.

I conducted an oral language screening, and found that Emilio's conversational skills in English were excellent. Although identification of written language disabilities is not the job of the speech-language pathologist at my particular school site, I decided to administer the RAN subtest of the CELF:4 to Emilio to see whether or not he might need to be referred for a possible disability affecting written language.

Emilio struggled mightily with the RAN. He skipped shapes, rubbed his eyes, and asked me to please stop administering this subtest. He showed visible signs of distress. He scored lower than would be expected for his age level. I referred Emilio to the site resource specialist and psychologist for further assessment. After a prolonged period of assessment in both English and Spanish, Emilio was diagnosed with a severe reading disorder. He now receives support from the resource specialist for reading and writing.

LANGUAGE SAMPLING

In assessing oral communication, many experts recommend gathering a spontaneous language sample in English and in the child's primary language (Arias & Friberg, 2017; Ebert & Pham, 2017; Jacobson & Walden, 2013; Moore & Montgomery, 2018; Paul et al., 2018; Wood, Diehm, & Callender, 2016). The SALT computer program (Miller & Iglesias, 2008) has measures specifically designed for Spanish speakers.

General Suggestions for Gathering a Language Sample

1. *Collect language samples in familiar contexts such as the classroom or home.* When a variety of locations are used, assessment yields a more accurate and representative picture of the student's language.

2. *Use a variety of conversation partners.* Conversational samples are often obtained in situations in which an adult "interviews" a child. Although these samples can be diagnostically useful, the information obtained may be quite different from that obtained when the student interacts with peers. Student interaction with peers is one of the most important sources of information regarding a student's use of language in social contexts. Samples can also be collected while students interact with siblings or parents. Samples of this type provide information about family interaction patterns, social relationships between peers, and so forth.

3. *Collect the sample in several different settings over a period of time.* It is recommended that three oral samples be obtained in which the communication partners interact for at least 10 minutes. Each sample should be obtained on a different day.

4. *Record the language sample for analysis.* Obtain an audio or video recording of the sample so that it can be transcribed accurately. Use of a smart phone or iPad is recommended.

5. *Ask a bilingual speech-language pathologist to evaluate the primary language sample.* If one is not available, knowledgeable professionals who speak the primary language can listen to the sample and give their impressions. Bilingual community members may need to be used if the services of a bilingual professional cannot be obtained. Ideally, at least

two native speakers should transcribe the sample. The information obtained should be discussed in detail with the bilingual speech-language pathologist.

6. *Ensure that the student is relaxed when a language sample is collected.* The student may verbalize very little if the person conducting the assessment is unfamiliar to him or her. The student may also experience anxiety if the testing is conducted in an unfamiliar environment. It is important to establish rapport with the student and to establish an environment in which the student feels comfortable. Children often verbalize more during interactions with familiar adults.

7. *Remember that students may be from cultures in which they are more accustomed to interacting with other children than with adults.* It may be necessary to observe a child interacting spontaneously with peers or family members to obtain language samples that show the child's true abilities.

8. *Analyze both content and form.* It is important to examine the student's morphosyntactic (grammatical) usage in both English and the primary language. However, professionals must also evaluate the student's communicative competence in various settings.

9. *Use wordless picture books to assess spontaneous story-telling skills.* The use of wordless picture books may be more appropriate for students between 5 and 8 years old than for older students (Ebert & Pham, 2017).

10. *Engage the child in playing a game of cards or playing a board game.* It can be very informative to observe the child's ability to learn new strategies, sequence, talk about the game, and take turns (Langdon & Saenz, 2016).

When analyzing language samples, remember that students with LI frequently demonstrate difficulty with verb tense morphology in the first language. Evidence of these difficulties has been found to occur on both structured tasks and in spontaneous speech (Blom & Paradis, 2013; Krok & Leonard, 2015).

❑ Children with LI were found by Blom and Paradis (2013) to use fewer tense-marked verbs than typically-developing children. The researchers argued that past tense use could potentially differentiate between typically-developing and LI children who spoke English as a second language.

❑ Danish-speaking children with LI had more difficulty producing past tense verbs than typically-developing peers on sentence repetition and completion tasks (Christensen & Hansson, 2012).

❑ Spanish-speaking children with LI were found to score lower than typically-developing children on six out of seven spontaneous speech measures that provided information relating to tense production in Spanish (Grinstead, Baron, Vega-Mendoza, Canti-Sanchez, & Flores, 2013).

❑ In a study conducted by Jacobson and Walden (2013), the analysis of narrative language samples obtained from Spanish-English sequential bilingual school-age children revealed that word morpheme omission errors in both languages were the best predictors of bilingual LI. The researchers concluded that these omission errors are significant as a clinical sign of LI.

Although structured tasks can be helpful in identifying specific problems that the student may be experiencing, some children perform poorly on these measures because of the way in which the tasks are structured. Language samples are likely to provide more valid results because they reflect the child's actual use of language in meaningful communication contexts. By collecting spontaneous language samples in the primary language and English, instructional goals can be developed that are relevant to the child's specific needs.

Reproducible Form 12.2 is an informal measure of oral language skills, designed for use with ELL students. Use of this form facilitates the collection of language samples in any language. The form may be modified, as necessary, for use in assessment.

Evaluating Language Use

Evaluating language use via a language sample is a highly recommended technique. When analyzing a language sample, ask persons who are familiar with the child's L1 to assess grammatical and overall structural accuracy and complexity.

It is also important to evaluate the child's ability to communicate meaning effectively. Assessment personnel should observe and analyze student interactions in natural communication situations with peers from similar cultural and linguistic backgrounds (Pieretti & Roseberry-McKibbin, 2016).

If LI is suspected, problems in the functional use of language need to be documented based on observations of the student in the classroom, on the playground, and in other natural speaking situations. The following behaviors may be indicative of LI:

❑ Nonverbal aspects of language are culturally inappropriate.

❑ Student does not express basic needs adequately.

❑ Student rarely initiates verbal interaction with peers.

❑ When peers initiate interactions, student responds sporadically.

❑ Student replaces speech with gestures and communicates nonverbally when talking would be more appropriate.

❑ Peers give indications that they have difficulty understanding the student.

❑ Student often gives inappropriate responses.

❑ Student has difficulty conveying thoughts in an organized, sequential manner that is understandable to listeners.

❑ Student shows poor topic maintenance.

❑ Student has difficulty with presuppositions (providing background information that the listener needs in order to understand the topic of the conversation).

❑ Student fails to provide significant information to the listener.

❑ Student has difficulty taking turns appropriately during communicative interactions.

❑ Student perseverates on conversation topics.

❑ Student fails to ask questions appropriately.

❑ Student fails to answer questions appropriately.

❑ Student needs to have information repeated, even when that information is easy to comprehend and expressed clearly.

❑ Student often echoes what is heard.

Reproducible Form 12.2
INFORMAL MEASURE OF ORAL LANGUAGE SKILLS FOR ELL STUDENTS
Celeste Roseberry-McKibbin, Ph.D.

Child's Name:_____ Date of Birth:_____ Age:_____ Grade:_____ Gender: M F

Date of Testing:_____ Primary Language:_____ Dominant Language:_____

Language of Assessment:_____ English Proficiency Level: _____

Background Information: _____

_____

_____

Task A: Giving Personal Information

1. What is your name?

2. How old are you?

3. What grade are you in?

4. Where do you live?

5. Tell me about your family.

6. What do you like to watch on TV? Tell me about it.

7. What do you like to do at school?

8. Tell me about your friends.

9. What is your favorite game? Tell me how you play it.

10. What is your favorite book? Tell me about it.

Task B: Labeling Objects and Giving Functions

Ask the student to name each item and to describe what it is used for.

	What do you call this?	**What do you do with it?**
1. book	_____	_____
2. chair	_____	_____
3. shoe	_____	_____
4. pencil/pen	_____	_____
5. table	_____	_____
6. clock	_____	_____

Task C: Making Comparisons

1. How is a car different from a bicycle?

2. How is a car like a bicycle?

3. How is a shoe different from a hat?

4. How is a shoe like a hat?

Task D: Solving Simple Problems

1. You see a fire in a house. What should you do?

2. You are tired because you have been working all day. What should you do?

3. You lose your friend's ball. What should you do?

USE OF NARRATIVES AND STORY-RETELLING

Many researchers have recommended that language evaluations include an assessment of the students' ability to construct narratives and retell stories (e.g., Ebert & Pham, 2017; Fiestas, 2017; Fiestas & Peña, 2004; Mills, 2015; Petersen et al., 2017; Rezzonico, et al., 2016; Wong, Au, & Stokes, 2004).

Cultural Considerations

Mainstream U.S. culture favors topic-centered narratives characterized by a linear flow of events with a clearly delineated beginning, middle, and end. There is usually a limited number of main characters, a problem that occurs, and a resolution to that problem. Most standardized tests are scored based on criteria that require use of a topic-centered style when telling stories. In this style, as discussed in chapter 4, there is structured discourse on a single topic, elaboration upon the topic, and lack of presupposed shared knowledge. There, however, are cultural differences in rules for narrative construction and story-telling that must be taken into account when evaluating students' narrative skills.

❏ The topic-associating style is typically used by working class African Americans. Lengthy narratives are common and stories may be embellished with exaggeration, jokes, slang, and metaphors (Champion & Mainess, 2003). Traditional examiners may view students who use this style as being disorganized because the topic-associating style is characterized by presupposition of shared knowledge, lack of consideration for detail, and structured discourse on several linked topics.

❏ On the other hand, Japanese children may tell stories in a style that is exceptionally succinct in comparison to how children from other cultural and linguistic backgrounds tell stories. Many Japanese value discourse that is implicit. Their discourse tends to rely heavily on the empathy of the listener (Gutiérrez-Clellen & Quinn, 1993).

❏ When Spanish-speaking children tell stories, they tend to focus on descriptive information related to personal relationships and family (Mahecha, 2003).

❏ There are cultural differences in the stylistic and creative features that children employ when producing narratives based on wordless picture books. Gorman, Fiestas, Peña, and Clark (2011) found that African American children included more fantasy in their stories, Hispanic children named their characters more often, and White children made more references to the nature of relationships between the story characters.

These examples illustrate the importance of taking children's backgrounds into account when evaluating narrative skills. It is important to use culturally appropriate stories that are within the student's realm of experience.

Clinical Implications

Recent research with students from different language backgrounds has shown that evaluation of narrative skills in the first language can be effective in differentiating typically-developing students from those with LI. When professionals evaluate students' narrative skills, it is important to examine *macrostructure* and *microstructure* (Ebert & Pham, 2017; Fiestas, 2017; Rezzonico et al., 2016).

❏ Macrostructure can be thought of as the frame for the story and relates to the child's ability to (1) tell a thematically coherent story, (2) plan and tell sequences of events, (3) provide the setting and characters, and (4) make inferences about characters' motivations.

❏ Microstructure can be thought of as details within the story frame that contribute to the complexity of the story. It includes features relating to productivity (e.g., number of words, number of utterances), lexical diversity (e.g., number of different words), and linguistic complexity (e.g., sentence length).

❏ Soodla and Kikas (2010) examined the macrostructure in the narratives of Estonian children between 6 and 8 years of age; LI children were compared with typically-developing children. The typically developing children had superior skills in starting stories when compared with LI peers. The typically developing children also provided more story information than LI peers.

❏ To et al. (2010) examined the narrative skills in school-age Cantonese-speaking children (ages 4-12) using a story re-tell procedure. The researchers found that syntactic complexity was especially vulnerable in Cantonese-speaking children with LI. Stories told in Cantonese by LI subjects were less complex syntactically than those told by children without LI.

Narrative language skills can be assessed as students tell familiar stories, retell stories, and create their own stories. Use of wordless picture books can be very effective. When using iPad apps, I often turn off the sound of the narrator's voice and ask the student to tell the story. Frequently, stories on iPad apps have "moveable parts" (called "hotspots") that students can actually manipulate. This active engagement in the process is highly motivating. Several of my favorites, which have had positive responses from students ages 3-18 years old, are *The Monster at the End of this Book, Miss Spider's Tea Party,* and *The Tale of Peter Rabbit.*

Reproducible Form 12.3 provides professionals with a practical checklist that can be used as a starting point when evaluating the narrative skills of ELL students. As stated on the checklist, students must be evaluated in the first language and English (if possible) and their performance should be compared to that of peers from similar cultural, linguistic, and socioeconomic backgrounds. Reproducible Form 12.4 includes several simple stories that include familiar information; students can be evaluated to determine how well they remember both major and minor details.

ASSESSMENT OF ASSOCIATED MOTOR BEHAVIORS

Experts have indicated that students with underlying language and learning impairments tend to demonstrate difficulties with associated motor behaviors (Nelson, 2010; Paul et al., 2018; Santiago-Valles et al., 2016). In my work as a public school speech-language pathologist, I have noted that students who have problems in the following areas are often later identified as having special education needs:

1. Poor coordination or awkwardness

2. Difficulty copying information from the chalkboard

Tech Tie-In

How to Screen a Child for Fine and Visual Motor Difficulties
The child in this video has challenges with finger-to-thumb apposition and struggles to copy shapes. When asked to write sentences to dictation, she omitted words and generally struggled to write. In cases like this, I refer the student immediately to the psychologist and resource specialist so that they can determine if there is a need for special education intervention.
Go to youtube.com, search for Celeste Roseberry (Love Talk Read), and select the video title above.

Reproducible Form 12.3
BRIEF NARRATIVE ASSESSMENT CHECKLIST
Celeste Roseberry-McKibbin, Ph.D.

Child's Name:_____ Date of Birth:_____ Age:____ Grade:____ Gender: M F

Date of Testing:_____ Primary Language:_____ Dominant Language:_____

Language Observed:_____ English Proficiency Level: _____

Evaluated by:_____

Compared with peers from a similar cultural, linguistic, and socioeconomic background, the following are areas of concern during narrative tasks:

Behavior	High Concern				Low Concern
Has difficulty initiating the story	5	4	3	2	1
Uses decreased syntactic complexity	5	4	3	2	1
Uses decreased quantity of information	5	4	3	2	1
Has difficulty sequencing events	5	4	3	2	1
Appears disorganized	5	4	3	2	1
Does not make information comprehensible	5	4	3	2	1
Does not include major details of story	5	4	3	2	1
Cannot remember major details upon questioning	5	4	3	2	1
Cannot remember minor details upon questioning	5	4	3	2	1
Gives irrelevant comments, explanations	5	4	3	2	1

Comments and Summary of Findings:

Reproducible Form 12.4
COMPREHENSION OF NARRATIVES
Celeste Roseberry-McKibbin, Ph.D.

Child's Name:_____   Date of Birth:_____   Age:_____   Grade:_____   Gender: M F
Evaluated by:_____

These paragraphs can be read in the child's L1. If the paragraphs are also read in English, it is best for the English reading to occur approximately one week after the first language reading. Answers in both languages can be compared. Responses should be written down verbatim.

Story 1

The children liked their teacher, Ms. Rodriguez. She was very nice to them. Everyone wanted her birthday to be a special day. Ms. Rodriguez' birthday was on a Friday. Josie brought her flowers. Ernesto's mom brought a cake. Bobby's dad brought ice cream. At 11:30 in the morning, after math lessons, the children sang the Happy Birthday song to Ms. Rodriguez. Everyone got cake and ice cream. Ms. Rodriguez had a very happy birthday!

What was the teacher's name? (Ms. Rodriguez)   _____

What was the special day? (Ms. Rodriguez' birthday)   _____

Ms. Rodriguez' birthday was on what day of the week? (Friday)   _____

What did Josie bring Ms. Rodriguez? (flowers)   _____

Whose mom brought a cake? (Ernesto's)   _____

What did Bobby's dad bring? (ice cream)   _____

What time did the children sing the Happy Birthday song to
Ms. Rodriguez? (11:30)   _____

What lessons did the children finish before singing the
Happy Birthday song? (math)   _____

Story 2

Josie liked to watch TV. Her mom and dad had a nice, big TV in the living room. Josie's favorite things on TV were cartoons and the Disney channel. She got to watch cartoons and the Disney channel on Saturday and Sunday. Her parents did not let her watch TV on school nights because she had to do her homework. Josie was always excited when Saturday and Sunday came. She really enjoyed watching TV and eating ice cream while she watched.

What did Josie like to watch? (TV)   _____

Where was the TV? (living room)   _____

What were Josie's favorite things on TV? (cartoons)   _____

When did she get to watch TV? (on Saturday and Sunday)   _____

Why did she not get to watch TV on school nights? (homework)   _____

When Josie watched cartoons, what did she eat? (ice cream)   _____

Story 3

One Monday morning, the children were playing at recess. There were about 200 of them on the playground. They had 15 minutes for recess. Joshua and Maria wanted to play tetherball. There was a long line of kids waiting to play tetherball, so they went over to the slide. Joshua let Maria go down the slide first. When she got to the bottom, her foot hit something sharp. It really hurt her. Joshua came down the slide and helped Maria walk over to the yard duty teacher. It turned out that Maria was wearing sandals, and she had pricked her foot on a sharp stick that was on the playground. The yard duty teacher went and made sure there were no more sharp sticks on the playground. She also told Maria that she might want to wear tennis shoes in the future so that her feet would not get hurt when she was playing.

When were the children playing at recess? (Monday morning)   _____

How many of them were on the playground? (200)   _____

How long did they have for recess? (15 minutes)   _____

What was the first game Joshua and Maria wanted to play? (tetherball)_____

When the tetherball line was too long, where did they go? (slide)   _____

What happened to Maria when she got to the bottom of the slide? (her foot hit something really sharp)

_____

What did Joshua do? (came down the slide and helped Maria walk over to the yard duty teacher)

_____

What was Maria's problem? (she was wearing sandals, so the stick hurt her)

_____

What did the yard duty teacher do? (went and made sure there were no more sharp sticks on the playground; told Maria to wear tennis shoes in the future)

_____

3. Poor handwriting

4. Clumsiness and poor balance

5. Difficulty manipulating small objects

6. Awkward finger-to-thumb apposition (quickly touching the thumb to each finger in succession)

7. Difficulty with self-help skills such as tying shoes and buttoning shirts

Speech-language pathologists and other personnel who observe any of these behaviors should be aware that these behaviors are commonly observed among children who need special education services. Research, however, is needed relating to the clinical utility of these behaviors when assessing ELLs from cultural and linguistically diverse backgrounds.

USE OF INTERPRETERS

Schools today often use the services of interpreters for assistance in assessment, intervention, and family conferencing. The term "interpreter" is used in this chapter to refer to a bilingual individual who translates written information or who facilitates communication between speakers who do not speak the same language. The role of the interpreter may include translating forms, administering tests, interviewing parents, translating for parents and teachers, and so forth. Finding interpreters is often not an easy task, especially if there are few people in the community who speak the target language. Interpreters can often be located by contacting local churches, high schools, universities, community health centers, the Red Cross, embassies, international associations, and other organizations that provide services in the local community (Wyatt, 2012).

Family members can be used effectively as interpreters in some situations. It is often difficult to use family members, however, in situations requiring that test items be administered in a predetermined format. Sometimes family members tell the child the answers or show signs of being upset if the child has difficulty performing specific tasks.

Characteristics of Interpreters

Criteria for the selection and use of interpreters have been described in the literature (Langdon & Saenz, 2016; Riquelme & Rosas, 2014; Rosa-Lugo et al., 2012; Wyatt, 2012). These criteria include (most importantly) the characteristics that interpreters must have to be used effectively in assessment.

1. Interpreters must be trained for their roles.

2. Interpreters must have excellent bilingual communication skills. They must possess good oral and written proficiency in both English and the primary language.

3. Interpreters must understand their ethical responsibilities. They must be able to maintain confidentiality at all times. They must also be honest about their abilities and limitations.

Tech Tie-In

Screening Sight Word Recognition as a Possible Indicator of Reading Disability
As an SLP, I sometimes evaluate a student's ability to read sight words. If the student struggles, I refer the student to the Resource Specialist and psychologist so that they can determine if there is a reading disability. This video shows my use of an interpreter to translate my directions into Dari, so that a 10-year-old child can understand them. Go to youtube.com, search for Celeste Roseberry (Love Talk Read), and select the video title above.

4. Interpreters must act in a professional manner. It is important for them to be able to function on professional teams. Interpreters must understand the importance of punctuality, impartiality, responsibility, and professional dress.

5. Interpreters must be able to relate to members of their cultural group. Some interpreters have grown up in circumstances quite different from those of the students and families with whom they work. Others may speak a different dialect than the students and their families. Interpreters should have the ability to relate to students and families and should be able to establish rapport.

6. Interpreters need good short-term memory skills so that they can record information and report what they learn from contacts with parents and students.

7. Interpreters should help facilitate communication between families and professionals by explaining how cultural differences might be impacting an interaction.

School districts should provide funding so that interpreters can be paid for their services. Interpreters take their jobs more seriously when compensation is provided.

Immigrant Insight   Amrit, daughter of Indian immigrants, speaker of Punjabi

You have to be so careful when you select an interpreter to speak with Indian families. If the interpreter is of a lower caste than the parent of a child who is higher caste, the parent will become angry and refuse to listen to what the interpreter has to say. The easiest way to tell which caste someone is from is by looking at the person's last name. Ask another Indian who you know on a more personal basis, who will be happy to help you figure out which caste the interpreter and the child's family are from.

Training Interpreters

When interpreters are being trained, it is optimal for school districts to work together to provide the training. This type of collaboration can reduce costs and promote cooperation between districts.

The training of interpreters will vary depending on the nature of the interpreters' responsibilities. The following areas are recommended for inclusion in the training of interpreters:

1. Characteristics of speech-language disorders and learning disabilities

2. Information about first and second language acquisition

3. Guidelines for distinguishing language differences from language impairment

---

Tech Tie-In

Dr. Cate Crowley of Columbia University has a terrific website with helpful assessment information, including reviews of currently-published tests, demonstration videos, and more. Go to http://www.leadersproject.org/ for free access.

4. Special education terminology relevant to their roles in working with family members

5. Role of the interpreter on the team

6. Goals of special education testing

7. Procedures for administering tests

8. Cultural differences and their impact on assessment

9. Strategies for interacting with families

10. Use of assessment results in placement decisions

11. Legal requirements and professional ethics

Use of Interpreters in Assessment

The professional who is using the services of an interpreter in assessment has important ethical responsibilities. It is important for the professional to do the following:

1. Recognize the limitations of translated tests.

2. Allow the interpreter only to carry out activities for which training has been provided.

3. Involve others in training the interpreter when appropriate.

4. Make sure that the "permission for assessment" form specifies that the services of an interpreter will be used during the assessment.

5. Be sure to specify in the assessment report that the services of an interpreter were used.

6. Provide the interpreter with background information about the student who is to be tested.

7. Prepare the interpreter for each testing session and debrief the interpreter afterwards.

8. Show the interpreter how to use tests and make sure that the interpreter feels comfortable with the testing. Some interpreters come from cultures in which it is not appropriate to admit that something has not been understood. It is imperative that the professional makes certain that the interpreter truly understands the assessment tasks.

9. Allow the interpreter time, before the student arrives, to organize test materials, read instructions, and clarify any areas of concern.

10. Ensure that the interpreter does not protect the student by hiding the extent of the student's limitations/disabilities.

11. Demonstrate the administration of tests.

Profile

Prima, Indian speech-language pathologist from California

We have a lot of Indian families in my district. Often, parents won't sign an IEP which permits their children to receive special education services such as speech-language therapy. It's considered a disgrace for a child to have a communication disorder. It is especially bad if the interpreter in the IEP meeting is from their neighborhood. Families don't want anyone to know that there is "something wrong with their child," especially a neighbor.

The professional needs to be sure that the interpreter participates only in activities for which training has been provided. Family members should be informed that an interpreter will be used in assessment. It is important to prepare the interpreter for each testing session and to provide feedback following the assessment. Langdon & Saenz (2016) recommended the process of B. I. D.: (1) briefing, (2) interaction, and (3) debriefing. Interpreters should be observed during the testing sessions to prevent the following problems:

1. Recording the assessment data incorrectly

2. Prompting the student or giving clues

3. Using too many words

4. Giving directions that are too brief or too complicated

5. Over- or under-using reinforcement

It is important to remind the interpreter to write down all behaviors observed during testing, even if the behaviors seem extraneous to the immediate task. Interpreters should watch for the following behaviors in students being tested:

1. Response delays (latencies)

2. Use of gestures to replace words

3. False starts, word repetitions

4. Perseveration

5. Confusion

6. Inattention, distractibility

7. Language and articulation errors

I have found it helpful to ask experienced interpreters how the student they just assessed compared with other students from similar cultural and linguistic backgrounds. For example, a question might be, "Based upon your five years of working in Elk Grove Unified School District with 400-500 Tagalog-speaking students, how would you evaluate Cresandro's performance in comparison to these other students? When compared with other Tagalog speakers, does Cresandro stand out to you as having an inordinate amount of difficulty with talking, remembering, or listening?" Anecdotally, I have found that if an experienced interpreter states that the student in question is having difficulties beyond those of similar peers, the student almost always turns out to have LI based on objective measures. Talking with experienced interpreters has been tremendously helpful.

Use of Interpreters as Interviewers

I have interviewed interpreters to obtain their viewpoints about common problems encountered when conducting interviews in the schools. Several interpreters stated that professionals often spoke for too long during meetings without pausing, and thus the information was difficult to remember and convey. Interpreters also stated that they were frequently called at the last minute and put into meetings or other situations with no preparation at all.

1. *Provide training to interpreters to ensure that they have the skills necessary to explain the special education process to families.* Families who are not familiar with the educational system in the United States may believe that special education is appropriate only for children with severe physical or mental disabilities. As previously stated, one immigrant summarized commonly held beliefs about disabilities by saying, "In my country you are either normal, lazy, crazy, or retarded. We don't have all these categories like the U.S. does."

2. *Meet with the interpreter prior to the meeting to discuss the questions that will be asked.* The interpreter must understand the interview questions completely and know how to record the family's responses.

3. *Make sure that a professional is present at interviews with family members to ensure that the appropriate information is communicated and that concerns expressed by family members are addressed.* The interpreter's responsibility is to facilitate communication between school professionals and family members. If appropriately trained, interpreters can be a valuable resource to school professionals in both assessment and intervention. The material presented in Langdon and Saenz (2016) is excellent and highly valuable for professionals interested in training and using interpreters.

4. *Make an audio-recording of the interview if at all possible so that the family's responses can be reviewed with the interpreter in detail.* Some families, however, may object to having their responses recorded in this manner.

It is recommended that the following guidelines be followed during the actual interview:

1. Ask the interpreter to sit as close as possible to family members.

2. Introduce family members to everyone at the meeting. The parents should hear each person's name and understand each person's role as it relates to the student.

3. Explain the purpose of the meeting.

4. Speak in short units, avoiding slang and professional jargon.

5. Encourage the interpreter to translate the family's words without paraphrasing them.

6. Look at the family rather than the interpreter when speaking.

7. Observe the nonverbal behaviors of the family during the interview.

8. Allow opportunities for family members to ask questions.

9. Provide written information when appropriate.

10. Record the interview if the family is comfortable with the use of a recording device.

Profile

Jacky C. was referred to me by his first grade teacher. She said that he wasn't learning optimally; that there were attention and behavior issues; and that she wondered if he might have a language impairment. I screened Jacky, whose English conversational skills were excellent. In his file, there was no history of language delay in Cantonese. His mother, Tao, came to the school and met with me. She cried for an hour, and I tried in vain to comfort her. She said that her husband gambled away all her earnings, and let Jacky stay up so late that he was always tired at school the next day. Tao had been a computer consultant in Hong Kong, but in the U.S., she was unable to find a computer job due to her limited English skills. She worked in a cookie store, where customers were frequently rude and condescending.

Nothing I said or recommended helped Tao feel better. Fortunately, the Chinese interpreter came in unannounced. Tao lit up and they talked animatedly for several minutes. Tao stopped crying and she was all smiles as she left. The Chinese interpreter told me that Tao had agreed to go with her to a local Chinese church, where she could receive some support and advice from other Chinese parents about how to help her son succeed in school.

SUMMARY

It is important for professionals in today's schools to utilize informal, nonstandardized assessment methods and measures that are tailored to the needs and backgrounds of individual students. These methods and measures include dynamic assessment, assessment of information processing/working memory skills, language sampling, use of narratives and story-telling, assessment of motor behaviors, and utilization of interpreters to assist in the assessment process. When professionals assess ELL students in an appropriate, individualized, and nonbiased manner, the diagnosis of language difference vs. LI will be much more straightforward. As a result, the placement of these students into educational settings will be much more clear-cut, appropriate, and consistent with their needs.

STUDY QUESTIONS

1. Many professionals use the services of interpreters in the assessment of ELL students. List and describe four characteristics that you would look for in choosing an interpreter to assist in the assessment process.

2. Summarize the research regarding information processing/working memory as it relates to assessment of LI. How might professionals apply the results of this research to the assessment of ELL students with LI?

3. Describe three informal procedures that the professional can use to obtain valid, nonbiased information about the performance of ELL students with suspected LI.

MULTIPLE CHOICE

4. When professionals utilize the services of interpreters during meetings, these professionals should do the following:

   A. Look at the interpreter rather than the family when speaking.
   B. Speak in short units, avoid slang, and refrain from using professional jargon.
   C. Encourage the interpreter to paraphrase the family's words for ease of translation.
   D. Allow opportunities for family members to ask questions.
   E. Provide written information when appropriate.

5. Advantages of informal testing include the following:

   A. This type of assessment is generally ecologically valid and considers the environment, home, and culture of the child and family.
   B. Data obtained can be evaluated in relation to the demands of the classroom curriculum.
   C. This type of assessment allows professionals to evaluate the student's functioning in real-life contexts.
   D. Specific standards are specified for scoring each response.
   E. Specialized training is not needed to interpret the results.

6. Which one of the following is NOT a red flag for possible clinically significant difficulties with narrative skills?

   A. The student uses a lower quantity of information.
   B. The student has difficulty sequencing events.
   C. The student appears disorganized.
   D. The student does not conclude narratives with a "moral of the story."
   E. The student does not include major details from the story.

7. When obtaining a language sample from an ELL, the SLP needs to keep the following in mind:

   A. Difficulties with verb tense are not a red flag for LI; these difficulties are found even in typically-developing children in the primary language.
   B. Playing cards and board games can be an effective way for the SLP to observe turn-taking and other language skills.
   C. Some students perform better if their skills are evaluated in settings where peers are present.
   D. A thorough language sample will involve having a student memorize a short poem and recite it back as perfectly as possible to assess working memory.
   E. Wordless picture books can be used; these are most appropriate for students between the ages of 3 and 6 years of age.

8. You are evaluating a student from Argentina who may have LI. You are conducting the evaluation in both Spanish and English. Which of the following are indicators that the communication problems observed are caused by LI?

   A. The student has difficulty conveying thoughts in an organized, sequential manner that is understandable to listeners.
   B. The student fails to provide significant information to the listener.
   C. The student often echoes what is heard.

D. The student shows poor topic maintenance.

E. The student fails to ask and answer questions appropriately.

9. Rithy is a 4-year-old girl from a Cambodian immigrant family who came to preschool speaking only Khmer. Preschool teachers are concerned because Rithy, after six months of consistent preschool English exposure, speaks very little. They wonder if they should refer Rithy to the speech-language pathologist for an evaluation for a possible LI. Which of the following would be appropriate to consider in an evaluation?

A. Conducting a detailed interview with Rithy's parents (via a Khmer-speaking interpreter) to ask for information about Rithy's language development in Khmer

B. Using standardized English vocabulary tests and comparing Rithy's performance with that of the norming sample

C. Asking Rithy to repeat nonword sequences presented by the interpreter and comparing her performance to that of several typically-developing Khmer peers

D. Keeping Rithy's drawings and "writing" samples over a period of several months and evaluating whether or not Rithy is showing progress in these areas

E. Evaluating Rithy's knowledge of the alphabet and her ability to recognize simple English sight words

10. Which informal measures are supported by research as being appropriate for use with ELLs from a wide variety of cultural and linguistic backgrounds?

A. The ability to sing familiar songs in the first language and English

B. Language samples

C. Assessment of narrative skills

D. Having students read paragraphs in English and answer questions about what they have read

E. Assessment of information processing skills

ANSWERS TO STUDY QUESTIONS

4. B, D, and E
5. A, B, and C
6. D
7. B and C
8. A, B, C, D, and E
9. A, C, D
10. B, C, E

Part 3

Intervention for Students with Special Needs

Chapter 13

Foundations of Effective Service Delivery

Outline

- Laws Impacting Service Delivery to ELL Students
- Incorporating Multiculturalism into Education
- Non-Special Education Service Delivery Options
- Instructional Continuum for ELL Students with Special Needs
- Determining the Language of Intervention
- Writing Collaborative IEP Goals
- Working with Families
- Encouraging Parent Involvement in Learning Activities
- Fostering Family Literacy
- Conclusion

As illustrated by the statistics presented in previous chapters, the population of ELL students in U.S. schools has increased dramatically year after year. Nearly 75 percent of American classrooms include at least one English Language Learner (ELL), and these students make up approximately 10% of American public school students (Sparks, 2016). Approximate population increases that have occurred in the U.S. since 1980 are listed below for specific languages, based on information reported by the Accredited Language Service (2017):

1. The number of speakers of Spanish has increased by 210%.
2. The number of speakers of Tagalog and Chinese has tripled.
3. The number of speakers of Korean, Arabic, and Russian has quadrupled.
4. The number of speakers of Vietnamese has increased by 510%.

Individuals who speak multiple languages are an important asset in a world in which bilingualism and biculturalism are increasingly valued. It is imperative that the educational needs of ELL students be met to the fullest extent possible to prepare them for adult life and to maximize their educational, social, and vocational potential. In this chapter, we examine foundational concepts that relate to (1) service delivery to ELL students whose needs can be met within the general education curriculum and (2) service delivery to ELL students who qualify for special education assistance because of an underlying language impairment (LI). Because special education personnel such as speech-language pathologists (SLPs) are increasingly working with general education personnel to serve at-risk students, it is imperative to discuss principles and strategies that apply to all ELLs (Pieretti & Roseberry-McKibbin, 2016).

First, it is important to examine federal laws and policies that impact service delivery to ELLs in America's public schools. At the present time, there are three such laws/policies: (1) Individuals with Disabilities Education Act, (2) Every Student Succeeds Act (ESSA), and (3) Common Core State Standards.

LAWS IMPACTING SERVICE DELIVERY TO ELL STUDENTS: FACTS AND IMPLICATIONS

Most people are keenly aware that federal/state policies and the health of the national economy are key factors in determining resource allocation. Policy makers around the U.S. are attempting to determine ways to restructure education, especially special education. Many people feel that special education has become so expensive that new strategies for serving these students are a high priority.

There is a trend toward streamlining special education in many school programs, although many special educators are opposed to this trend. The number of students with special education needs increases as the population increases, but limited funding is available for special education programs to help these students.

Individuals with Disabilities Education Act

When Congress passed IDEA in 1975, it pledged (under IDEA Part B) to fund up to 40% of the average per-pupil expenditure for each special education student. However, today the federal government only funds 14.8% of that amount. If this funding continues at the current rate, Congress will not meet its promise to fully fund IDEA before the year 2045. Many school districts have personnel shortages and the professionals currently working in schools have large student caseloads. Early intervention programs have been implemented in many school districts to reduce the likelihood that students will need special education services.

❏ The Individuals with Disabilities Education Act (IDEA, 2004) specifically focused on prevention and early intervention (pre-referral services) for struggling students in general education classrooms, with the goal being to reduce the number of students who are eventually referred to special education.

❏ There is a strong emphasis on providing support to children who are experiencing difficulty developing basic reading skills, especially in the early grades. Schools may use up to 15% of their funding for early intervention with these students.

❏ If too many students from a certain group (e.g., ELL students) are placed into special education, states are asked to account for this placement and are required to provide comprehensive, coordinated, early intervention programs for these students.

Every Student Succeeds Act (ESSA)

As stated in the previous chapter, the ESSA is designed to provide equal opportunities for all students to learn, and has important implications for students with limited English language proficiency (Editorial Projects in Education Research Center, 2016; Migration Policy Institute, 2017; U.S. Department of Education, 2017).

❏ Under ESSA, individual states can choose their own short- and long-term goals. These goals must address proficiency on tests, English language proficiency, and high school graduation rates.

❏ States (rather than the federal government) make critical decisions about school improvement and how to intervene with students who are struggling.

❏ English language proficiency is considered an academic indicator of accountability under ESSA.

❏ The ESSA broadens access to early childhood education. It has expanded the previous national education law by calling for nationwide, high quality preschool.

❏ Other components of ESSA include a standalone program for parent engagement, reservations for arts education, gifted and talented education, and Ready to Learn television.

Common Core State Standards

The development and implementation of Common Core State Standards has had a profound impact on educational programs throughout the country. Whether or not schools should have a common set of standards for all students has been the topic of much debate. In many school districts, special education professionals are under pressure to teach skills that are too cognitively demanding for their students. These standards will be addressed in greater detail in the next chapter, as they pertain to intervention for ELLs who require special education programs.

INCORPORATING MULTICULTURALISM INTO INTERVENTION

There are many reasons for incorporating multicultural materials and methods into regular and special education curricula and activities.

❏ Children who are centered in and proud of their cultural heritage tend to be more motivated and show greater academic gains than children whose culture is de-emphasized and suppressed.

❏ Exposure to a multicultural curriculum promotes understanding of other groups and potentially reduces race-related conflict.

❏ Multiculturalism prepares students for workplaces in which they will be part of a multi-ethnic workforce and interact with colleagues from a variety of cultural and linguistic backgrounds.

Strategies for Incorporating Multiculturalism

Suggested strategies for incorporating multiculturalism in instructional programs are listed below:

1. Show interest in students' home language, country, and culture. For example, because I serve many Hispanic students, I often ask them to tell me about their trips to Mexico. In Sacramento, we have many immigrants from the former USSR; I often ask students to tell me about home countries such as Ukraine, Russia, and Siberia.

2. Learn a few words of a student's language, and use those words. This can mean a great deal to the ELL students and their families. I will never forget the Russian-speaking middle school students who were so thrilled when I learned to say "thank you" and "goodbye" in Russian. My Hispanic parents have been very appreciative of my attempts to communicate in Spanish.

3. Reduce students' anxieties as much as possible. A relaxed learner is an effective learner. During initial English language instruction, stress can be reduced by allowing a silent period in which students are not required to respond verbally.

4. Make sure that students know that you are there to help them and that you want them to succeed. Give students special attention when possible. I sometimes let students come to my "speech room" before or after school for some one-to-one attention and conversation.

5. If nobody in the classroom speaks the student's language, assign an English-speaking peer buddy to assist the student.

6. Encourage students to use their primary language in various contexts at school and also in contexts outside of school.

7. Represent languages of the various cultural groups in the school community by having signs in key areas (e.g., front office, auditorium) in these languages.

8. Display objects and pictures representing various cultures. Create classroom or therapy room bulletin boards that display pictures of and information about people from diverse backgrounds and cultures.

9. Provide and read books written in a variety of languages in which diverse cultural groups are represented. I have the book *Rainbow Fish* in English and Tagalog. The students I serve love to see the Tagalog words and listen to me read in Tagalog. It conveys the fact that knowing several languages is "cool."

10. Give all students sustained exposure to multicultural activities. Don't just incorporate sporadic, token activities into intervention.

11. Present thematic units in which students learn about specific cultural groups or even a specific country. In the Discovery Club at a local school, the students study one country a month. Bulletin boards, stories, foods, and other items increase students' awareness of cultural differences, and guest speakers from the country being studied share information and answer questions. If a large number of students at the school come from particular countries (e.g., India, Vietnam, Mexico), activities focusing on these countries are especially valuable.

12. Present a comparative study of folktales. For instance, read the story of Cinderella and ask the librarian for books with parallel stories in other cultures. Read, compare, and discuss the similarities and differences in the stories. The American and Kuwaiti versions of Cinderella, for example, have been used with young children in this country to promote cultural understanding and peace education (Al-Jafar & Buzzelli, 2004). Comparative folktales support narrative development and increase students' metalinguistic skills (Paul et al., 2018).

13. Teach students words, phrases, and songs in various languages.

14. Have students read (either silently or aloud) a biographical sketch about a culturally and linguistically diverse leader or role model. In an earlier chapter, I shared information relating to ways in which an African American student (receiving language therapy) and I studied the quotes of Dr. Martin Luther King. I recently discussed the important contributions of Caesar Chavez during therapy sessions with a Hispanic teenager.

15. Celebrate the holidays of various cultures. Food, dance, and music can be included in the celebrations. Students can even plan and carry out festivals in which families are involved.

16. Have students interview their families and explore their family trees, characteristics of their home countries, and the family's reason for coming to the U.S. Students can write a report based upon this. In my college course, Communication Disorders in Multicultural Populations, students were asked to interview relatives who are immigrants to the U.S. Many of these students reported how deeply touched they were by the sacrifices these individuals had made.

17. Have students use the Internet to conduct research about countries in which they are interested. One American child I worked with was fascinated with China, so we logged onto the Internet and found information and pictures about China. He enjoyed this activity and asked many questions. Browsers such as Google (http://www.google.com), MSN Search (http://search.msn.com), and Yahoo! (http://www.yahoo.com) can be useful.

18. Use maps of the U.S. and of the world so that all students can see where their families and the families of other students have come from.

One afternoon while working in an elementary school speech and language program, I asked individual students to discuss where their ancestors came from, and used a globe to help the students identify their exact countries of origin. One multiracial girl said proudly, "My ancestors are from China, Korea, and Africa." An African American boy said with great pride, "My ancestors are from Africa!" The White boy in the group paused, thought a minute, and said, "And my family is from....Sacramento!" Much can be learned about how students perceive their world and the world of others by engaging them in conversations about their family history and way of life.

Profile

A university student of mine, Fernan T., generously gave me permission to share his story. Fernan moved to the U.S. with his family from the Philippines when he was 10 years old. Fernan stressed that he felt like such an outsider coming to an American school and shared that no one showed a personal interest in him. He was under pressure to learn English as fast as possible so that he could translate for his parents in day-to-day situations and help them interact with U.S. agencies and society in general. (To this day, Fernan takes his parents to all their doctors' appointments and translates for them.) Fernan's parents stressed to him that education is the way out of poverty. His parents have a high school education; Fernan is the first person in his family to go to a four-year college.

He stated that upon beginning to attend an American school as a 10-year-old old, he noticed how disrespectful American students were; he commented about the relative lack of structure in American classrooms as compared to those in the Philippines. When Fernan read aloud in class, his classmates laughed at his accent—so he stopped talking altogether for a few years. He watched the television show "The Wonder Years" in order to learn English and expose himself to standard models. Friends asked him to play football with them, which is actually kickball/soccer in the Philippines. When the football hit Fernan in the face, he realized that football in the U.S. meant something different!

Fernan stressed that it would have made a world of difference to him if even one person—teacher or fellow student—had cared about him personally and taken a little extra time to talk with him. He said it would have been so great if someone had learned even a few words in Tagalog and expressed interest in his life in the Philippines.

NON-SPECIAL EDUCATION SERVICE DELIVERY OPTIONS

Although it is tempting for many general education teachers to refer struggling ELLs to special education as a first resort, it is important to remember that non-special education options are available for meeting the needs of students who require support in the first language and English. The over-identification of ELLs for special education continues to be a problem in the U.S., and thus professionals need to be fully aware of all non-special education options that can support these students (Kapantzoglou et al., 2016; Moore & Montgomery, 2018; Pieretti & Roseberry-McKibbin, 2016).

There is a continuum of options to support ELLs in schools. The availability of each option is often driven by individual states' policies and laws. Ideally, ELLs would experience maintenance bilingual education in which they are provided with strong support to continue development of their first language as they acquire skills in English.

❏ **Maintenance bilingual education classrooms**:

1. Instruction is presented in the primary language and English.

2. The activities promote the development of proficiency in both the primary language and English.

3. The goal is to foster English development and simultaneously nurture and develop the primary language.

❏ **Transitional bilingual education classrooms**:

1. Initial instruction is in the first language.

2. The focus is placed on transitioning students into all-English classrooms as quickly as possible.

❏ **Sheltered English classrooms** (stand-alone classrooms):

1. The instructional program focuses on making subject-matter instruction in English comprehensible to limited English speakers from diverse language backgrounds. For example, in a Sheltered English classroom, there may be students from 8-10 different language backgrounds.

2. The English-only curriculum emphasizes visuals, demonstrations, activities relevant to students' experiences, student-to-student interaction, adaptation of materials, and use of supplementary materials. The teaching pace is slowed down and there is a considerable amount of repetition.

3. Curriculum activities are included to teach subject matter content (e.g., math and social studies), to develop the second language (English), and to promote mastery of academic skills.

4. Students are often grouped by their English language proficiency so that lessons can be tailored for different levels.

5. The instruction aims to develop intrinsic motivation and learner autonomy.

❏ **English as a second language (ESL) pull-out**:

1. Students are pulled out of the classroom and brought to a separate room to learn English.

2. ESL instruction is usually presented once or twice a week in a small group for 30-45 minutes.

❏ **"Sink or swim" all-English classrooms** (least optimal situation):

1. The student is given no support in the first language.

2. No ESL pullout is available.

3. The student must keep up academically with monolingual English-speaking peers with no additional support.

Immigrant Insight   Romina, speaker of Tagalog, daughter of Filipino immigrants

When we came to the U.S., I was in sixth grade. I spoke perfect English, with little or no accent at all. I remember being taken out of class to take a test. The person asked me a series of questions about pictures and had me tell what was happening in the story. Next thing I knew, I was being placed in remedial classes! I was very confused because I already knew everything being taught. I was the only person getting an "A" on all the tests, and my classmates always asked me for help. I remained stuck in remedial classes in grades six through eight.

One day in eighth grade biology (still remedial), my teacher handed out a sheet of biology terms. My teacher was supposed to go over the terms with the class, but she saw that I finished it right after she had passed it out. She was confused, and asked me how I already knew the terms. She said "What are you doing in here?" and I told her I didn't know. The teacher talked to my mom, and the teacher fought with the counselor about my placement in remedial classes. My teacher knew I needed to be in mainstream classrooms. When the fourth quarter of eighth grade started, I was switched into mainstream classrooms. Because of this, when I transferred to high school, I took regular education classes and was no longer forced to attend remedial classes. I took Honors and Advanced Placement classes in high school, and graduated with honors!

INSTRUCTIONAL CONTINUUM FOR ELL STUDENTS WITH SPECIAL NEEDS

In the past, ELL students were often referred immediately for special education testing if they demonstrated problems learning in the classroom. The students were tested and then labeled as having disabilities and were subsequently placed into special education. Teachers, feeling relieved that the students were now in "special ed," believed that the students' progress was now a "special education issue" and no longer their responsibility. For those teachers, it was "back to business as usual." The problem was handled. This paradigm is illustrated in Figure 13.1.

Sometimes ELL students' disabilities were not severe enough for them to be eligible for special education—especially in the early elementary years. These students needed services and extra support, but they were too high-functioning to merit an IEP and services from special education personnel. Frequently, these students were in a "wait to fail" mode. As they progressed through the primary grades, their performance became so low in comparison to that of their peer group that, technically, they ended up qualifying for special education. A child could fail several grades before testing revealed a severe discrepancy between his academic performance and his intellectual ability. This discrepancy or wait-to-fail model frequently resulted in students having low self esteem, behavior problems, academic failure, and even limited vocational opportunities in adult life.

Response to Intervention

In response to this situation and to the challenges and mandates of IDEA (2004), many schools started implementing a response-to-intervention (RtI) model (mentioned in previous chapters). RtI emphasizes the greater role of the general education teacher in scaffolding instruction for students who are struggling in the classroom. RtI is being implemented nationally, and the goal is to prevent failure and help all students benefit from appropriate instruction. In addition, RtI may reduce the stress placed upon special education personnel by reducing the number of inappropriate referrals for testing.

As mentioned in the previous chapter, RtI makes it possible to evaluate a student's ability to learn when provided with instructional activities. As illustrated in Figure 13.2, today's emphasis on RtI (Response to Intervention) has made a greater continuum of options available for all students who struggle in the classroom setting—including ELL students.

❏ A major tenet of RtI is that students' progress is monitored, and there is increasingly intense and differentiated instruction based on student need. Usually the learning activities occur in the general education classroom and an effort is made to present scientifically-based instruction.

❏ Ongoing professional development for school professionals is important to help them implement RtI successfully. RtI makes it necessary for teachers in the general education curriculum to provide high-quality instruction and scientifically-based interventions that support each child who is struggling to keep up academically.

❏ Teacher Assistance Teams (TATs) provide peer support and coaching for teachers of struggling students. In some schools, these teams go by other names such as Student/Teacher Assistance Team (STAT) or Student Study Team (SST). A referral to special education is made only after a number of alternative teaching strategies and methods have proven to be ineffective in improving academic skills. Data collected related to the effectiveness of attempted instructional strategies is used to determine whether or not special education testing is necessary.

RtI is now part of a continuum of services for students that is divided into five levels (see Figure 13.2). The first three levels apply to students who receive all instruction within the general education curriculum.

Figure 13.1

Traditional, "Non-Collaborative" Special Education Services

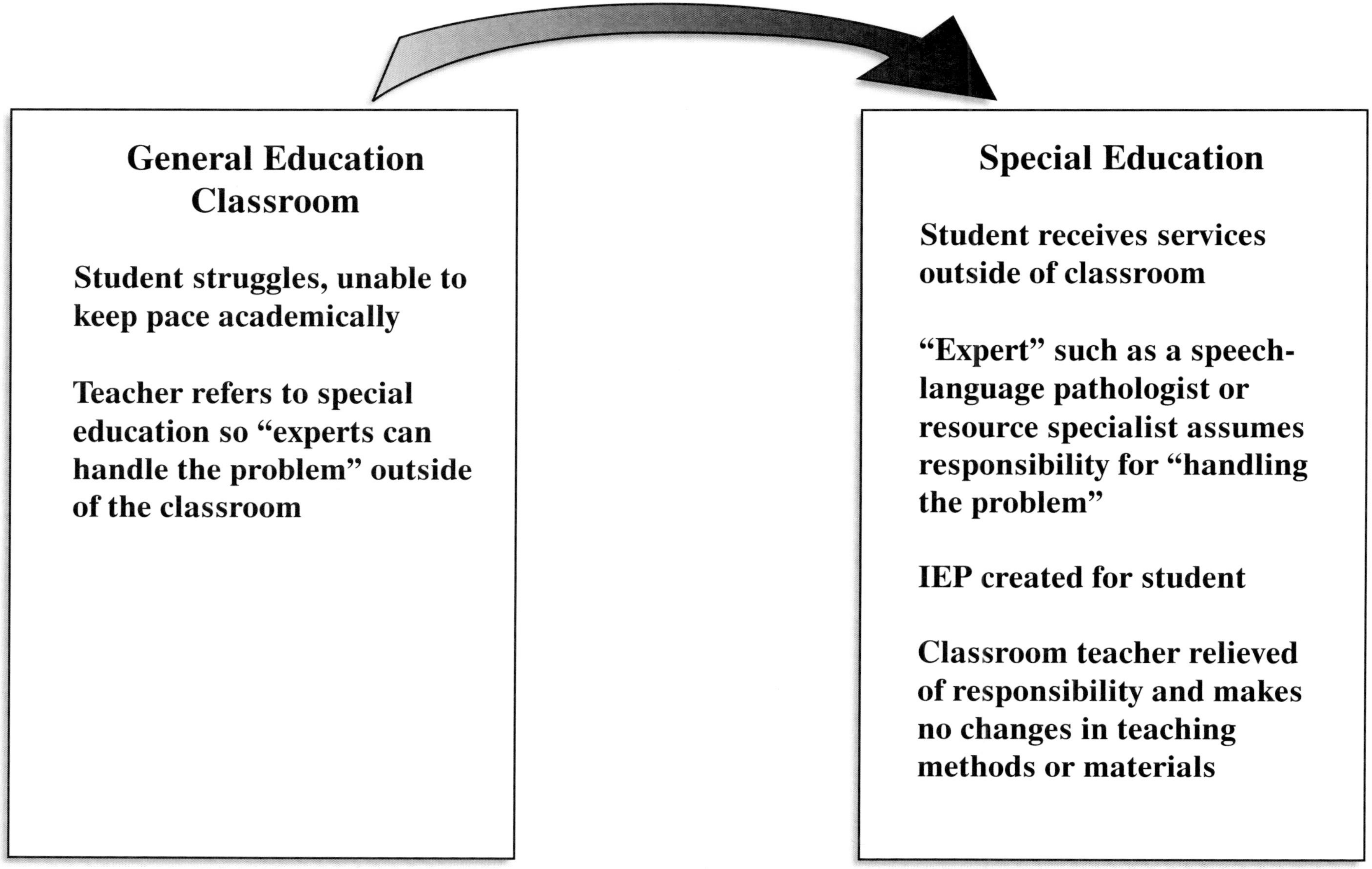

General Education Classroom

Student struggles, unable to keep pace academically

Teacher refers to special education so "experts can handle the problem" outside of the classroom

Special Education

Student receives services outside of classroom

"Expert" such as a speech-language pathologist or resource specialist assumes responsibility for "handling the problem"

IEP created for student

Classroom teacher relieved of responsibility and makes no changes in teaching methods or materials

Figure 13.2

Instructional Continuum for English Language Learners

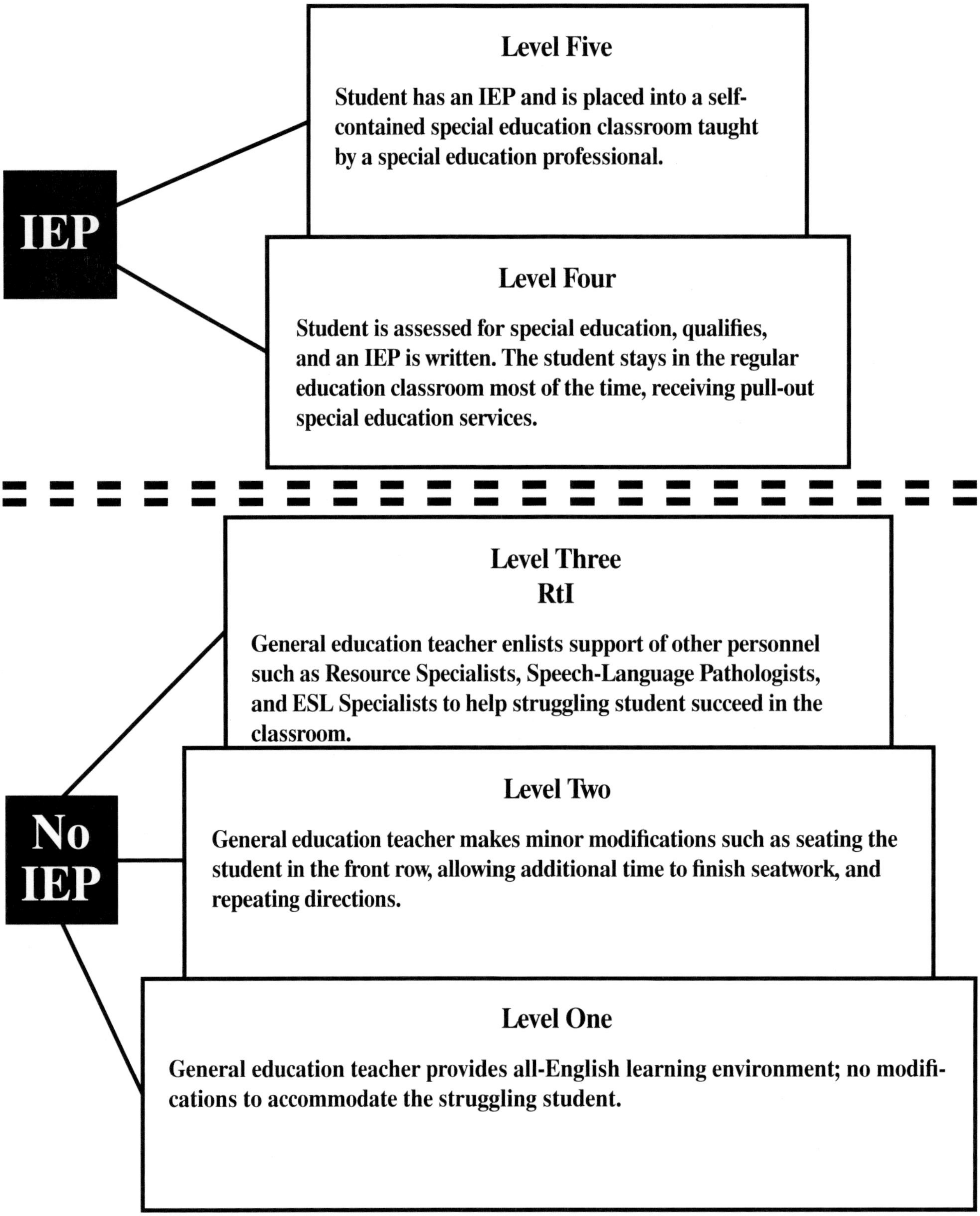

IEP

Level Five

Student has an IEP and is placed into a self-contained special education classroom taught by a special education professional.

Level Four

Student is assessed for special education, qualifies, and an IEP is written. The student stays in the regular education classroom most of the time, receiving pull-out special education services.

- -

Level Three
RtI

General education teacher enlists support of other personnel such as Resource Specialists, Speech-Language Pathologists, and ESL Specialists to help struggling student succeed in the classroom.

Level Two

General education teacher makes minor modifications such as seating the student in the front row, allowing additional time to finish seatwork, and repeating directions.

No IEP

Level One

General education teacher provides all-English learning environment; no modifications to accommodate the struggling student.

❑ *Level One of the Instructional Curriculum*. At this level, the teacher does not modify curriculum materials or strategies for any students who are experiencing difficulties in class. They are left to flounder, and frequently do. Fortunately, this is becoming less common as general education teachers must take greater ownership of the progress of all students, including those with limited proficiency in English.

❑ *Level Two of the Instructional Curriculum*. At Level Two, the general education teacher incorporates generic modifications to support struggling students. These modifications commonly include such strategies as assigning a peer buddy, having the student in question sit in the front of the class, giving the student extra time to complete assignments, and others. Teachers work by themselves; no other professionals are called in for support. Figure 13.2 illustrates Level Two interventions that were recommended to teachers at the elementary school site where I work.

❑ *Level Three of the Instructional Curriculum*. This is the "Response to Intervention (RtI)" level of the instructional curriculum. At this level, the classroom teacher employs diagnostic or clinical teaching. In this approach, teachers provide instruction and collect data to ascertain whether or not the strategies and materials being used are successful in boosting students' academic performance. Speech-language pathologists, resource specialists, and other special education personnel may come into the classroom to directly support struggling students (Hale, 2017). Listed below are examples of instructional modifications that are often helpful when ELL students experience difficulty learning in the classroom:

1. Group students by level of English proficiency.

2. During specific periods of the day, have students go to classrooms where they can be provided with instruction that is geared to their level of English language proficiency.

3. Have special education teachers come into the classroom so that they can observe students and participate in the instructional activities.

4. Try using different instructional strategies if students do not meet expected performance levels. The goal is to provide explicit, differentiated instruction that addresses the identified learning needs of students. Maintain records showing how students perform when different instructional strategies are attempted.

5. Review progress with the Teacher Assistance Team (TAT) based on the data obtained.

Figure 13.3 illustrates an approach used at an elementary school where I worked. This curriculum adaptation plan is used to support classroom teachers as they try to meet the needs of students who are struggling in the classroom setting. This approach can be used at Level 2 or Level 3.

Speech-language pathologists are becoming increasingly more involved in RtI, especially as part of language/literacy teams that attempt to increase the literacy skills of struggling students. Rather than pulling out students a few times each week for therapy, an increasing number of students are receiving classroom-based language intervention. When speech-language pathologists go into classrooms and work in a collaborative manner with teachers, many students make progress and do not need to be referred for "testing." By interacting with students and teachers during learning activities in the classroom, ELL students who simply need more exposure to English often can be distinguished from ELL students who have a disorder that affects their ability to acquire language skills.

Although RtI offers much promise, problems often occur during implementation. In a survey that was returned by 583 speech-language pathologists, the majority of respondents indicated their

Figure 13.3

General Education Individual Curriculum/Instruction Adaptation Plan

* =Typically an accommodation   ^ =Typically a modification

*Quantity	***Time**	***Level of Support**
▲ Reduce verbal input to 1-2 instructions. ▲ Check frequently for understanding. ▲ Ask student to paraphrase information.	▲ Provide wait-time. ▲ If student does not respond, repeat, reword, rephrase information and/or question.	* Preferential Seating * Peer buddy * Collaborative learning groups ▲ Individual or small group instruction when possible
*Input	**^ Difficulty**	***Output**
Use visual aids such as pictures, objects and manipulatives. Provide multiple models of expected response. Provide multi-modal instruction. State the student's name before asking him/her a question.	Prior to launching a lesson, determine the underlying skills that are required. Probe to determine the student's comprehension of those concepts as a foundation to beginning your approach to the lesson. To improve auditory attention, memory, comprehension, and note-taking abilities, scaffold response using cloze procedure in which student writes in 1 or 2 words to complete a note that has been prepared by the instructor. The teacher then writes the key word in the blank on an overhead as student says it.	Encourage student to reauditorize, visualize and to repeat information silently. Encourage student to ask a question regarding information presented. Encourage student to draw a picture to illustrate a concept or vocabulary word. Increase the number of opportunities during instruction that the student has to respond verbally using academic language.
*Participation	**^ Alternate Goals**	**^ Substitute Curriculum**
Pre-teach concept individually or in a small group prior to large group instruction. Provide opportunities for student to answer questions that he has mastered aloud in class. In order to continually check for understanding, ask for a brief 1-2 word response. The teacher provides 2 possible answers. The last answer offered by the teacher is the correct response.	Narrow instructional focus and expected response to 1 or 2 concepts that are the most dissimilar and that will provide the most auditory and visual contrast. (e.g. The instructor may teach auditory discrimination between words in which the long vowels *ee* and *ou* are present, in order to maximize visual and auditory cues.)	Differentiate instruction by teaching underlying weak or missing skills. Provide patterned practice with concepts that have not been mastered.

Developed by Barbara Koski. Adapted with author's permission.

*   Grades based on above Adaptation Plan
▲   Rationale/Evidence for Adaptation Plan

_____

_____

_____

_____

acknowledgement of the important role of RtI, but more than 80% viewed implementation as a challenge. These challenges included funding, training, additional personnel, planning time, and administrative leadership. However, many survey respondents did state that they appreciated the fact that students who were not identified for special education were receiving help and support (Sanger, Mohling, & Stremlau, 2012).

When making decisions regarding program placement, RtI makes it possible to eliminate problems that are inherent in the use of a discrepancy model and provide information that is relevant to classroom performance and the individual student's instructional needs.

❏ A major problem with the discrepancy model is that discrepancies between performance and ability often are not evident in the early school grades. When RtI is used, eligibility for special education services is based on how the student responds when high-quality, intensive, culturally and linguistically appropriate intervention is provided. RtI facilitates the early identification of students who may need special education services.

❏ When RtI is used, student performance can be evaluated based on how it compares with that of students from similar cultural and linguistic backgrounds.

❏ RtI is a dynamic approach to assessment that makes it possible to determine eligibility for special education services based on how students perform over time during actual learning activities. Students who continue to struggle and show treatment resistance (lack of ability to profit from additional support) after being provided with high-quality, intensive intervention (Level 2 and Level 3) are likely to have disabilities and should be referred for special education evaluations. Speech-language pathologists, school psychologists, and other professionals who participate in the assessment must make sure that culturally and linguistically appropriate measures are used to determine eligibility for special education services.

Students who are identified as having LI should receive direct services in the least restrictive environment. Therefore, students should be pulled out of the general education classroom only to the extent to which their learning needs cannot be met within that setting.

Options for ELL Students who Qualify for Special Education

A variety of options are available for ELL students who are found to qualify for special education after participating in RtI programs:

1. Consultative, collaborative service provisions in which ELL students remain in the general education classroom and the teacher receives assistance from special education personnel, ESL teachers, and/or bilingual staff members

2. Pull-out services in English (or, ideally, bilingual intervention) conducted one to two times a week in the specialist's room

3. Placement in a regular bilingual education or Sheltered English classroom with support from special education

4. Monolingual English special education classroom (hopefully with primary language support using a bilingual teacher, tutor, etc.)

5. Bilingual special education classroom

Many monolingual English-speaking speech-language pathologists feel inadequately trained to serve ELL children who have limited proficiency in English (Arias & Friberg, 2017). If, however, classroom teachers, parents, special education professionals, and bilingual/ESL specialists work in a collaborative manner, ELL students with special needs can receive appropriate instructional services.

Profile

DETERMINING THE LANGUAGE OF INTERVENTION

When providing speech and language intervention to ELL students who have been identified as having LI, decisions need to be made relating to the language of instruction. When working with a child from a Spanish language background, for example, should instruction be provided in English, Spanish, or both languages? The development of language skills in English is important, but it is also important for students to become proficient in the language of the home.

❏ School support for the development of English and the home language is important for the social and emotional well-being of students and will increase the likelihood that these students achieve academic and vocational goals (Pieretti & Roseberry-McKibbin, 2016).

❏ Bilingual language approaches to intervention are often necessary to teach LI students effectively and result in improved communication skills in both the first language and English (Genesee, 2016; Goodrich et al., 2013; Gorman, 2012; Gutiérrez-Clellen et al., 2012; Lugo-Neris, Jackson, & Goldstein, 2010; Paradis et al., 2011; Pham, Ebert, & Kohnert, 2015; Pham, Kohnert, & Mann, 2011; Restrepo, Morgan, & Thompson, 2013; Riquelme & Rosas, 2014; Rosa-Lugo et al., 2012; Simon-Cereijido, 2015).

❏ Mendez, Crais, Castro, and Kainz (2015) examined the performance of Latino Spanish-speaking preschoolers who were learning English. Group 1 was taught vocabulary in English only, while group 2 was taught new vocabulary in both English and Spanish. Children taught in both languages had significantly higher scores in both Spanish and English than children taught in English only. In fact, the children taught in English only showed a slower rate of English oral language development.

❏ Duran, Hartzheim, Lund, Simonsmeier, and Kohlmeier (2016) conducted a meta-analysis of current research, analyzing the results of 26 studies. They concluded that research supports the efficacy of bilingual language intervention for children with LI and those who are at risk for LI.

Factors to consider when providing bilingual intervention include the following:

1. *What language is used in the home?* If the primary language is not developed or reinforced in the school setting, the student may lose the ability to interact with people in the home who speak only that language. As discussed elsewhere in this book, there are many ramifications to this situation. Spontaneous, close, emotionally authentic relationships are more likely to occur if parents and children are able to interact in the language that they feel most comfortable speaking. If students lose their skills in the first language and parents speak little or no English, the quality of the parent-child connection is likely to be negatively affected. I have personally encountered situations in which grandpar-

ents, who spoke only the first language and were greatly involved in their grandchildren's lives, lost their special relationship with their grandchildren as the grandchildren's first language was gradually replaced by English.

2. *Do the parents wish for the student's primary language to be maintained?* Sometimes parents wish for their children to learn English as quickly as possible, and they may feel that intervention should be provided in English only. Other parents wish for the primary language to be maintained and developed.

3. *Does the student wish to use and maintain the primary language?* The student's attitudes and motivation are of utmost importance.

4. *What resources are available for conducting treatment in the primary language?* Ideally, therapy should be conducted by a bilingual speech-language pathologist who speaks English and the child's first language. If no such professional is available, the SLP can work in a collaborative manner with an interpreter or bilingual paraprofessional who speaks the child's first language fluently.

Speakers of the student's first language can often provide assistance by working as tutors. Suggested strategies for finding speakers of languages other than English who can provide the needed assistance are listed below:

1. Recruit high school and/or college students from various language backgrounds. Give these students credit/units for tutoring. For example, a high school Vietnamese student might receive independent study credit or community service hours for tutoring a younger Vietnamese child.

2. Seek help from local religious and/or community organizations. Religious organizations are often looking for ways to reach out to their local communities, and their members will often gladly volunteer to tutor students in school settings. Many communities have churches and religious organizations that represent various cultural/linguistic backgrounds. In some communities, for example, there are Samoan churches in which many members speak both Samoan and English. Members of churches that offer services in Vietnamese, Spanish, Russian, or other languages can offer valuable assistance.

3. Recruit retired bilingual individuals. Many retired persons are active and have children and grandchildren of their own. Some communities have Foster Grandparents, a group devoted to children who need their support.

4. Contact the Red Cross and other charities to find out if they have access to multilingual individuals who might be willing to serve as tutors.

5. Contact various branches of the legal system (police, courts) to locate bilingual interpreters and others who may be able to provide assistance.

6. Contact businesses that have community service requirements for their employees; bilingual employees can serve as tutors to fulfill their community service requirement.

7. Use peer tutors from the student's classroom or school. Older Spanish-speaking students, for example, can assist younger Spanish-speaking students during reading activities.

Immigrant Insight   Camilla, university senior, speaker of Spanish,
                            daughter of immigrants from Medellin, Colombia

My parents brought us to the U.S. for a better life. My sister was killed in Medellin by a drunk driver and there were witnesses, but he was the son of a powerful drug lord and the lawyers were paid off to dismiss the case. Drug lords threatened to kill my parents because they tried to take the drunk driver to court. One of my brothers died at 18. In the boys' school he attended in Colombia, students learned how to use machine guns. After school they would form gangs and rob people. My brother and all his high school friends are dead.

When they left Colombia with us for good, my parents told my younger brother and me that we were going to Disneyland, so all we had in our suitcases was enough for a Disney trip. I was 7 when we arrived in the U.S.

I was so happy to be here! My parents came to Granite Bay, California, and lived in a house with nine other people. They became housekeepers. They cleaned house for a dentist who gave me and my brother free dental care.

I didn't know any English, and learned it mostly by reading books. My parents were told "Don't speak any Spanish at home." So they didn't. I was thrown into the deep end—all-English classrooms in school. From grades 4-12, I spent a lot of time with my American friends and learned my social English from them. In high school, I decided I wanted to speak fluent Spanish, so I asked my parents to spend time speaking Spanish with me. I'm so glad they did because my Spanish is fluent today. We love living here, and my parents have made a wonderful life for my brother and me.

WRITING COLLABORATIVE IEP GOALS

Writing goals and objectives for IEPs is often a challenge, especially if the student speaks two languages. However, there are certain general principles that professionals can follow when writing IEPs for ELL students who need special education services:

❏ In writing objectives, an emphasis should be placed on measurable outcomes (also called "benchmarks").

❏ The special educator may be a monolingual English speaker who is unable to provide direct services to the student (if the student's English is very limited). Thus, as previously stated, the professional may need to work with a first language speaker to develop and present the instructional activities. This should be stated specifically in the IEP.

❏ Goals related to oral communication need to emphasize overall communicative competence rather than isolated skills.

❏ Goals should focus on teaching both content and strategies for learning.

❏ Special educators should collaborate in developing objectives to avoid fragmentation in service delivery. The current emphasis on collaboration between professionals in general and special education programs makes it imperative to write IEP goals with a collaborative emphasis.

❏ IEP goals and objectives, in many states, must be written so that they relate directly to the content of the classroom curriculum.

❑ Many speech-language pathologists write IEP goals and objectives based on the English Language Arts requirements of the Common Core State Standards.

Tech Tip

How to Build Literacy Through Talking About Pictures in a Book
Many parents feel intimidated because they can't read in English. In this video, Zehra demonstrates that it is possible to successfully build children's literacy skills through an engaging conversation about pictures in a book. Talking about pictures builds children's oral language, literate language, and engagement with print materials. Zehra talks about the pictures in both Turkish and English, codeswitching with ease as she interacts with the girls.
Go to youtube.com and type in Celeste Roseberry (Love Talk Read). Click on the video with the title above.

WORKING WITH FAMILIES

Basic Principles

It is important for professionals to encourage families to participate in their children's educational programs. The goal of working with families is to empower them. In order to empower families, it is important to consider the cultural, social, and familial contexts that affect their lives. School professionals need to remember that language acquisition occurs within sociocultural contexts and is facilitated through daily family routines, interactions, and parent-child conversations (Kummer, 2012).

❑ It should be emphasized to parents that being bilingual is a great asset in our society. Many parents, in my experience, believe that schools do not support use of the primary language at home.

❑ Parents need to be reassured that bilingualism is a desirable goal. Bilingualism and biliteracy should be promoted because they provide economic, intellectual, and social benefits. Professionals should never suggest that only English should be spoken at home.

❑ Portfolios with examples of a child's work over time should be shared with parents when discussing the student's progress.

❑ Pictures showing students as they participate in various school activities should be shared with parents to help them understand what is being taught at school and what is happening in the special education setting.

Tech Tip

How to Talk with Your Child During Daily Routines
Caregivers often believe that they need to spend a considerable amount of time to provide language stimulation for their children. But in this video, Amy interacts with her daughter in Hmong and English while doing regular household chores. A rich and stimulating language environment is provided for her child during their daily routine!

Go to youtube.com and type in Celeste Roseberry (Love Talk Read). Click on the video with the title above.

Education and Support Programs for Parents

Support groups can be highly effective in helping multicultural families. Efforts should be made to recruit multicultural individuals or families that are familiar with the nature of school programs. These individuals can form support groups for families from similar backgrounds.

❑ As has been previously stated, multicultural family members often feel more comfortable if they can interact with others from their own culture when the learning needs of their child are being discussed. If support groups are not available, families may benefit from talking to even one other person from their cultural group. Schools can set up parent information networks to help parents share information with and support one another.

❑ Schools can sponsor programs to help immigrant parents and their children become accustomed to the "school culture" and its educational practices. Programs designed to reach out to parents have been described in the literature (American Institutes of Research, 2017a; Coelho, 2012; Kummer, 2012). These programs can help families with basic needs and also provide an introduction to the U.S school system and curriculum.

❑ Schools can create a parent center that has social workers, paraprofessionals, and others who help parents meet their basic needs. Interpreters in this center can help parents negotiate the school's expectations.

❑ By holding monthly meetings in the evening, many parents who work during the day will be able to participate. Individuals from the parents' culture can attend these meetings to answer questions about U.S. schools and the services that are available to students.

❑ Topics discussed in parent programs might include the following:

1. School routines for students that are common within U.S. schools (e.g., standing in line and taking turns)

2. Role of the parent in helping students with homework (American schools' emphasis on parental involvement)

3. Extracurricular activities

4. Discussion relating to the emphasis on competition and individual achievement in U.S. school programs

5. Information about the programs that are available for students with special needs

Profile

Victor G., a third grader from a migrant Mexican family, was placed into a speech-language intervention program after being assessed by a bilingual Spanish-speaking clinician. The speech-language pathologist spent many hours putting together a comprehensive "homework packet" with activities designed to build Victor's expressive and receptive language skills in Spanish. When Victor's parents were presented with the homework packet, his father said, "We live in our car. Do you have any suggestions for how we might implement these ideas given our current living situation?"

Informing Parents About Free Enrichment Programs for Children

Various types of extended learning programs may be available for children at their schools or in the local community. These programs offer valuable opportunities for children to develop language and literacy skills.

❏ Parents should be encouraged to enroll their children in before- and after-school programs, Saturday classes, and summer school. Participation in these programs can boost school achievement.

❏ Parents should be encouraged to support their children's participation in after-school homework clubs. Parents who work long hours may not be able to spend time with their children after school. I have been privileged to participate in after-school homework clubs that offer children both academic and social support.

❏ Enrichment programs such as Early Head Start and Transitional Kindergarten (TK) provide young children with valuable learning experiences. In California, children who participated in Transitional Kindergarten scored higher in language development, math, and literacy than students who did not have this experience (American Institutes for Research, 2017b).

Profile

Phuong, a Vietnamese kindergarten student, was referred to me for testing because of a possible stuttering problem. During the evaluation, he was found to stutter frequently in English.

A meeting was set up with Phuong's father to discuss the child's stuttering difficulties. The father requested that a Vietnamese interpreter be present at the meeting.

During the meeting, the father shared with the interpreter that his wife had abandoned the family. He was struggling to care for his five children and to survive. The father reported that Phuong stuttered in Vietnamese and English, and that his siblings teased him about the problem. Mr. L. said that the teasing caused Phuong to feel "sad."

The interpreter sympathized and explained that services were available in the school to remediate the fluency problem. The father was very relieved and expressed gratitude that something was going to be done to improve his son's speech. He had been unaware that the school offered services to help his child.

The program placement meeting ended positively with me giving suggestions (through the interpreter) for home carryover. The father indicated that he was interested in participating in a home program.

ENCOURAGING PARENT INVOLVEMENT IN LEARNING ACTIVITIES

When professionals interact with and learn about the student's family background, suggestions can be tailor-made for that family. The following suggestions can help parents to participate actively in their child's learning activities.

1. Encourage parents to volunteer in their child's classroom for several hours each week if their work schedule permits. Volunteering helps parents understand how to work with their children at home and increases their overall understanding of what is happening in the classroom. Parents who do not speak English can carry out activities such as collating and stapling papers while observing the classroom instruction. Because I grew up in the Philippines, I was unfamiliar with my son's school curriculum here in the U.S. I was privi-

leged to volunteer weekly in his classrooms throughout his elementary years. Being in the classroom, listening to the teacher, and observing the routine was extremely enlightening, and I became more familiar with what my son was required to do to succeed in school.

2. Encourage parents to visit the student's classroom. Many parents feel intimidated by their lack of English skills or their modest educational background. These parents need to be welcomed and reassured that they have an important role to play.

3. Encourage parents to share folk tales, home recipes, and cultural experiences with the student.

4. Encourage parents to view short videos that show students participating in language stimulation activities. Speech-language pathologists and other school professionals can provide these videos (Palafox, 2017). The parents can watch these videos as much as they want—whenever they want—for ideas about how to stimulate their children's language at home.

5. Encourage parents to develop the student's proficiency in the primary language by presenting a language-rich environment in which the child is exposed to oral and written language.

6. Encourage parents to view the child's homework regularly and to offer encouragement and support whenever possible. I spoke with a Hispanic school psychologist who had helped many low-income Hispanic families raise children who graduated high school and went on to college. She maintained that it is very important for parents to be physically in the vicinity when children are doing homework. The physical presence of parents when homework is being completed encourages and inspires children to stay on task and to be successful in school.

Profile

Ameet S., a kindergarten student from an East Indian family, was first enrolled in a speech and language intervention program in preschool. The family spoke Punjabi at home. Ameet had been placed in a speech and language program because his performance on English language tests was "below the norm for his age." The first speech-language pathologist who worked with Ameet never examined the student's background and, therefore, was unaware that Ameet had spoken only Punjabi until the age of 3 years.

I "inherited" Ameet in my elementary school caseload when he started kindergarten. After learning about his language background, his progress in the classroom was evaluated. The teacher reported that Ameet was making good progress in learning English.

I found that Ameet's progress in English language learning was adequate and that he did not have a language impairment. His mother said that Ameet's use of Punjabi had developed quite well. She had never understood why Ameet was in a remedial program and was relieved to learn that these services were being discontinued. I encouraged Ameet's mother to continue to develop his Punjabi skills at home so that he could grow up to be a fluent bilingual.

Tech Tie-In

For specific, practical ideas for intervention with culturally and linguistically diverse young children and their families, go to this link:

https://www.pluralpublishing.com/publication_cicdddt.htm

The early intervention series by Karanth, Roseberry-McKibbin, and James (2017) has a wide variety of easy-to-implement, practical ideas for stimulating language, fine motor, gross motor, and social skills in at-risk young children.

FOSTERING FAMILY LITERACY

It is crucial for professionals to do as much as possible to foster literacy in students' homes. Rather than targeting only the student for literacy development, professionals should include the entire family.

❏ Parents should be encouraged to stimulate the language of younger children, even infants and toddlers. In many cultures, babies and small children are provided with a great deal of love, physical affection, and emotional warmth; however, caregivers do not talk to or read with them.

❏ Parents should be made aware of how important it is to provide language stimulation beginning early in infancy (Roseberry-McKibbin, 2018). If talking to and reading with infants and small children is culturally not congruent for parents, older siblings can be trained and encouraged to do this.

❏ Professionals can help parents learn to respond immediately and positively to their children's attempts at communication. Marklund, Marklund, Lacerda, and Schwarz (2015) studied 1;6-year-old Swedish-speaking children with large and small vocabularies and found that parental speed of response to children's communication attempts is strongly related to vocabulary size in young children.

Specific Literacy-Building Strategies for Families

Current statistics show that in the U.S., 44 million adults are unable to read a simple story to their children. Six out of 10 households do not buy a single book in a year, and three out of four people on welfare can't read (Literacy Project Foundation, 2017). Because diverse families are especially vulnerable to poverty, it is critical for professionals to encourage family literacy. Recent research has focused on helping parents support their young children's vocabulary development in the primary language (Hammer et al., 2017; Simon-Cereijido, 2015).

Hammer et al. (2017) analyzed data from the Early Childhood Longitudinal Study—Birth Cohort, a nationally representative data set that is maintained by the U.S. Department of Education. Analyses were performed for a population-based sample of 9,600 children and families. Important findings related to vocabulary development were the following:

1. Children who were late talkers at 24 months of age were three times more likely than typically-developing children to have low vocabulary scores at 48 months of age.

2. Socioeconomic status played a major role, with poverty being a substantial contributor to low vocabulary.

3. Having a low vocabulary prior to school entry more than tripled the odds of low reading and math scores in kindergarten.

4. Children entering school at 5 years of age who had been late talkers were more likely to have low math and reading scores and also a greater likelihood of behavior problems.

5. Participation in child care for 10 or more hours a week led to improvements in children's vocabulary. Programs such as Early Head Start can be instrumental in providing this support for at-risk children.

Hammer et al. concluded that it is urgent for professionals to help parents foster their young children's early development through engaging in high quality interaction with them and creating cognitively stimulating home environments. Moreover, providing high quality child care for low-SES children can be very beneficial in boosting vocabulary. Programs such as Early Head Start can be instrumental in providing this support for at-risk children.

Based on a systematic research review, Duran et al. (2016) found that the following interventions were effective in helping young dual language learners who were at risk for language impairment:

1. bilingual preschool instruction

2. supplemental early literacy and language programs delivered in a bilingual format

3. individualized vocabulary instruction using home language bridging techniques

4. parent storybook reading in the home language using specific language scaffolding techniques

The research studies summarized below provide evidence that exposure to books and literacy-related activities in the home helps young children develop important literacy-related language skills:

❑ Pratt, Justice, Perez, and Duran (2015) conducted a study of print-focused intervention for Spanish-speaking children with LI in southeastern Mexico (Yucatan). Parents were asked to read one book to their children three times a day for a one-week period. During the reading activities, parents used simple print awareness strategies such as pointing to and discussing upper- vs. lower-case letters, asking children the names of the letters, identifying simple words, etc. This simple home intervention was found to substantially increase children's print and alphabet knowledge.

❑ Caesar and Nelson (2014) examined the feasibility of a home-school partnership for improving the emergent literacy skills of Spanish-speaking children between 2;6 and 5;2 years of age. They found that integrating parent-generated content into classroom language intervention activities resulted in higher early literacy assessment scores in both English and Spanish.

❑ Hamer (2012) found that the number of picture books in the home is positively linked to children's overall development of language skills, including vocabulary and reading skills. Many parents, however, do not have the financial resources to buy books, as they can afford only to provide basics such as food, shelter, and clothing for their families.

❑ Bitetti and Hammer (2016) examined the effect of the home literacy environment (HLE) on the English narrative development of Spanish-English bilingual preschool-first grade children from low-income backgrounds. They found that the more often mothers read with their children, the greater the children's narrative growth. Many of the families, however, had few books.

Tech Tip

Learn the Signs—Act Early
This is a new online resource available to parents who speak English, Spanish, Arabic, Korean, Vietnamese, Somali, and Portuguese. This website helps parents understand typical developmental milestones and when they should be concerned about their children's language development.

https://www.cdc.gov/ncbddd/actearly/milestones/milestones-in-action.html

It is important for schools to provide families with books that can be used in the home. I have worked with others to collect and donate over 180,000 children's books to ELL and low-income children in the greater Sacramento area of California, and to developing nations around the world. The recipients have included children who have been neglected and abused, children with a parent who has been incarcerated, etc. (Roseberry-McKibbin, Ibarra, & Kahrobaei, 2017). Our program, Love-Talk-Read, encourages parents to love, talk with, and read to their children daily. Table 13.1 lists simple strategies for starting your own book collection.

Due to recent technological developments, direct face-to-face interaction is often being replaced by the use of cell phones and the sending of text messages. Evidence has been found that the incidence of expressive language delays and behavior problems is higher among individuals who make frequent use of handheld communication devices such as cell phones (Ma, Van den Heuvel, Maguire, Parkin, and Birken, 2017; McDaniel & Radesky, 2017; Nelissen & Van den Bulck, 2017). Frequent face-to-face verbal interaction between parents and children is important for the development of oral communication and appropriate social interaction skills.

Suggestions for Parents

Professionals can help foster family literacy by doing the following:

1. Provide parents with resources that help them understand milestones of typical language development (Lewis, 2017). In this way, they can bring their children for early intervention if needed.

2. Provide information to help parents find quality reading materials that are inexpensive. Places to find these resources include flea markets, used book stores, library sales, garage sales, etc.

3. Tell parents about the local library and its services, hours of operation, etc. Librarians can be invited to meet parents. My colleagues and I have found that often, parents who have immigrated from developing countries do not know that U.S. libraries allow one to check out books for free with a library card.

4. Tell parents about local adult literacy services such as literacy volunteer programs and local adult classes. Some cities have adult literacy classes that include children; parents and children learn together and strengthen parent-child bonds.

5. Invite parents to literacy events such as book fairs.

6. Encourage parents to promote the development of literacy using functional writing tasks such as making lists, composing letters, and discussing print in the environment.

7. Encourage students to read to their parents. In this way, literacy is enhanced for both students and parents.

8. Help parents to discourage "screen time" for their babies and young children as much as possible. Research is increasingly supporting the finding that increased screen time for babies and young children is correlated with delays in expressive language and development of literacy skills in elementary school and beyond (American Academy of Pediatrics, 2017; ASHA, 2017).

9. Create book bags and give students dual-language books as well as CDs with stories that can be read in both English and the first language.

10. Encourage parents to read to their children as much as possible. It is ideal if parents can read to their children in the primary language of the home. This builds children's first lan-

---

Table 13.1

Practical Strategies for Collecting Children's Books

1. Place a large, attractive, marked box in a central location that is easy for people to locate.

2. Make the collection time-limited (e.g., 4-6 weeks).

3. Create a short flyer explaining why books are being collected and who they will be shared with. On the flyer, include the phone number or email address of a contact person.

4. If possible, donate the books locally to groups of children that your audience of donors will be motivated to help. For example, the books collected by the Orangevale Rotary go to the Orangevale Food Bank. Books collected by moms in Davis go to Head Starts in Davis. People are most enthusiastic if books stay in the local area and "connect" to them in some way.

5. Be sure to pick up the books on a regular basis. Don't let that box overflow and make a mess!

6. Challenge your group to collect a certain number (e.g., 100-500 books). People love a numerical goal.

7. Keep reminding people—announcing the book drive only one time will not be sufficient.

8. At the end of the book drive, celebrate with a treat! Share information about where the books went. If possible, share pictures of children who have received the books.

For more information, visit lovetalkread.com

---

guage literacy skills, which serve as a foundation for eventually becoming biliterate in the first language and English.

11. Let parents know that if they do not read, they can look at books with the children and discuss the stories in the primary language. Wordless books with attractive, relevant pictures are often effective (Palafox, 2017). Parents can use wordless books to help their children become familiar with at least some literacy conventions such as turning pages, holding a book right-side up, identifying the front and back of a book, etc.

12. Teach parents the acronym "CARE" and explain how they can use it when sharing books with their children:

    Comment about the pictures — The big red dog is hungry and wants something to eat.

    Ask questions — When do you think that the dog's owners are going to feed him?"

    Respond — When children make comments and ask questions, respond.

    Extend —   Child: "The big red dog is eating now."
    Parent: "Yes, the big red dog is eating now because his owners came and gave him some food."

13. Teach literate parents how to use print-referencing behaviors to enhance their children's literacy skills (e.g., "Show me the longest word on this page." or "Which word begins with the letter 'A'?") (Roseberry-McKibbin, 2018).

Tech Tip   *How to Read to Your Child with CARE*
Though Joseph is only 2 years old, notice how his father Dao engages him by CARE: Comment, Ask questions, Respond, Extend. Dao codeswitches between Hmong and English. Notice how Joseph responds to both languages. When Joseph says something, Dao adds words. He also asks Joseph questions and waits for Joseph to answer.

Go to youtube.com and type in Celeste Roseberry (Love Talk Read). Click on the video title shown above.

---

14. Create a short DVD that can be given to parents to take home and watch. This DVD can model print-referencing behaviors and other literacy strategies for parents to implement during reading activities at home.

15. Provide parents with short videos of their children doing language stimulation activities at school (Palafox, 2017). Encourage the parents to carry out similar activities at home.

Profile

Pa X., a fifth-grade student from a Hmong refugee family, was referred to me for testing. Pa's reading skills were at approximately a first- or second-grade level, and she was failing in many fifth grade subjects. She told me that she lived in a small home with 17 relatives and that she slept on the dining room floor with her cousins. At age 11, Pa was thinking about marriage because getting married at age 15 is common in some Hmong families. Our challenge at school was to help the family understand the importance of improving Pa's academic performance. The family seemed to be more concerned about Pa's mothering skills. After all, she would be married in a few short years and her life would be spent bearing and raising children, and caring for her husband.

CONCLUSION

When professionals provide intervention and instruction to linguistically and culturally diverse ELL student populations, they need to keep in mind the following foundational principles:

❏ On the national level, IDEA (2004), Every Student Succeeds, and the Common Core State Standards have had a major impact on regular and special education. Part of this impact is the development and implementation of Response to Intervention, or RtI, which provides early intervention and support to struggling students. A major goal of RtI is to help students succeed in the regular classroom setting without special education.

❏ As mandated by federal law, the only ELL students who can be placed in special education are those who have been identified as having an underlying LI or other disabilities based on data obtained from culturally and linguistically appropriate assessment instruments and procedures.

❏ ELLs who do not qualify for special education can be served using a variety of other options within the general school program; ideally, bilingual education programs make it possible to maintain and nurture the primary language while English is being learned.

❏ Multicultural activities and materials should be incorporated into the curriculum by professionals in both general and special education programs. The goal is twofold: first, affirm and support ELL students; second, educate mainstream students about multicultural issues as they prepare to enter a diverse workforce in adulthood.

❏ IEPs need to be collaborative in nature with goals appropriate for the student's cultural and linguistic background. In many school districts, IEPs must]include goals and benchmarks that align with the Common Core State Standards and promote the growth of academic skills.

❏ When students are served in special education programs, instruction should be provided using activities that are culturally relevant—the background experiences of the student must be considered.

❏ Professionals must promote opportunities for families to participate in planning and implementing programs for students. It is especially important to help foster family literacy.

When planning special education programs for ELL populations, it is important to consider the student's unique and individual background, interests, and goals, as well as the concerns of the family. The resources available in the educational environment also need to be considered. Through effective collaboration, the services currently available for ELL students both with and without LI can be much improved.

Tech Tie-In

For suggestions and information about how to start and maintain your own book collection, please see the following resources:

Website: Lovetalkread.com

Facebook: Love Talk Read

YouTube: Celeste Roseberry Love Talk Read

Twitter: @love_talk_read

Instagram: lovetalkread

STUDY QUESTIONS

1. Summarize the mandates of IDEA (2004) and ESSA. What has been the impact of these laws on the way that schools serve students?

2. Describe three ways to help families become involved in their children's education (either regular or special education).

3. List four sources for obtaining tutors who can work with ELL students in their primary language.

MULTIPLE CHOICE

4. To promote multiculturalism, general education teachers and speech-language pathologists can:

   A. Present thematic units in which students learn about specific cultural groups or even a specific country.
   B. Have students interview their families and explore their family trees, characteristics of their home countries, and the family's reason for coming to the U.S.
   C. Expose all students to ongoing multicultural activities and materials.
   D. Use a comparative study of folktales from American culture and students' cultures of origin.
   E. Show interest in students' home language, country, and culture.

5. Which one of the following is NOT advisable when working with family members?

   A. Inviting them to come to the school to talk about their language and culture
   B. Helping them find places to purchase or borrow books at little or no cost
   C. Emphasizing to parents that they do a disservice to their child if they speak the primary language at home
   D. Encouraging students to read to their parents
   E. Conducting programs that will help parents understand and adapt to the U.S. school system

6. Response to Intervention involves:

   A. Immediate referral for special education testing if a child is having academic difficulties
   B. The use of Teacher Assistance Teams so that teachers of students who are struggling in the general education curriculum can turn to teams of fellow teachers for support and ideas for classroom interventions
   C. Greater involvement of speech-language pathologists, especially in the area of increasing the literacy skills of struggling students
   D. Ensuring that parents come to the school daily to provide 1:1 help for their struggling children in classroom settings
   E. Re-writing IEPs every three months to ensure that intervention programs are successfully building the classroom skills of children who qualify for special education

7. When considering which language to use in intervention programs for children with LI, professionals must think about the following question(s):

   A. Does the student wish to maintain his primary language?
   B. Does the student speak a language that is considered prestigious by the community?
   C. Does the student have a high level of intelligence?
   D. Is the classroom teacher a native speaker of the child's primary language?
   E. Does the child have younger siblings who might be affected by recommended changes?

8. Which of the following are possible options for ELL students who qualify for special education?

   A. Placement in a monolingual English special education classroom with primary language support from a bilingual teacher, tutor, etc.
   B. Pull-out services (speech-language intervention, learning disability program, or both) in the primary language
   C. Bilingual special education classroom
   D. Pull-out services in English with primary language support
   E. Consultative, collaborative program implementation

9. You are working with children of migrant farm workers who speak Spanish only in the home. The parents are loving, diligent people who work hard to provide the basics of life for their children. However, they are so tired after a long work day that it is quite challenging for them to provide additional stimulation for their children (e.g., reading books, doing homework). Which of the following might be appropriate suggestions for supporting these families as they try to provide more opportunities for their children?

   A. Connect them with migrant family parents whose children are succeeding in school, and have support groups so that families can receive information and help from members of their community.
   B. Tell parents who speak even a little bit of English that it is best to speak English at home, not Spanish, so that their children will develop a solid linguistic foundation.
   C. Give them free children's books and provide suggestions for looking at these books with their children.
   D. Don't give books to parents who lack literacy skills.
   E. Encourage parents to allow their children to participate in after-school programs in which homework support is available.

10. You are working with Izolda, a 9-year-old girl from a Russian-speaking home. She has been tested in both Russian and English, and has qualified for speech-language and resource services because of LI. Which one of the following will NOT be important to remember as the team writes the IEP benchmarks?

   A. IEP benchmarks must correspond with Common Core State Standards.
   B. Goals should focus on learning strategies, but not on content, as focus on content is inappropriate for ELLs.
   C. Special education personnel should collaborate to try to ensure that services are not fragmented.
   D. Goals related to oral communication need to emphasize overall communicative competence.
   E. In writing objectives, an emphasis should be placed on measurable outcomes or benchmarks.

ANSWERS TO STUDY QUESTIONS

   4. All of the above
   5. C
   6. B and C
   7. A
   8. A, B, C, D, and E
   9. A, C, E
   10. B

Chapter 14

Practical Strategies for Intervention

Outline

- A Holistic Approach to Collaborative Instruction
- Structuring the Environment for ELLs with Language Impairment
- Teaching Compensatory Strategies
- Increasing Social Skills
- Evidence-Based Strategies for Vocabulary Development
- Building Literacy Skills
- Conclusion

As stated in the previous chapter, English Language Learners (ELLs) present professionals with a rich resource for the citizenry of our future. Our shrinking world increasingly values bilingual, bicultural individuals. When an ELL student is identified as having language impairment (LI), it is important to work to support that student as much as possible. Our overall goal for ELLs with LI is to help them maximize their potential so that they can become happy, productive, educated contributors to society (Brice, 2013; Roseberry-McKibbin, 2016).

In this chapter, specific strategies are recommended to help professionals achieve this goal. The holistic strategies approach to intervention is described in detail. Practical suggestions are included for structuring the environment, facilitating the development of social skills, teaching vocabulary, and building other critical language skills.

Strategies are also included to build literacy skills and to help students with LI achieve grade level performance in curriculum standards. Throughout this chapter, the use of technology is incorporated as it relates to increasing students' overall communicative competence. Clearly, recent technological developments can be used in a variety of ways to help ELL students with LI develop the language and literacy skills necessary for success in academic and social contexts.

A HOLISTIC APPROACH TO COLLABORATIVE INSTRUCTION

Foundational Principles

When general and special education professionals work with ELL students who have LI, listening, speaking, reading, and writing are often viewed as areas of language that should be taught separately. Moreover, each of these areas is often broken down into a series of skills that are taught in isolation. This artificial separation of "sub-skills" or "sub-areas" results in instruction that is often reductionistic and skill-specific.

Listening, speaking, reading, and writing can be taught simultaneously, using a **holistic-strategies approach** to instruction. The holistic-strategies approach integrates the best attributes of current, research-based approaches into a comprehensive model of teaching and learning.

❏ In the holistic-strategies approach, the various components of language are seen as synergistic in that they develop simultaneously as students learn within meaningful contexts. These components of language rely on cognitive underpinnings.

❏ The holistic-strategies approach is a conceptual framework that combines:

1. Vygotsky's social interactionism theory of language development (children learn language in meaningful social contexts from more experienced partners in order to communicate in their world);

2. an emphasis on literacy development;

3. the belief that one must undergird intervention for language skills with specific activities that address underlying metalinguistic and cognitive processing strategies;

4. the assertion that it is important to develop academic and social language;

5. the premise that building vocabulary is a key foundation for academic and social language success;

6. the belief that we must incorporate principles of the Universal Design for Learning (explained later);

7. the overall philosophy that it is necessary for professionals to collaborate to help students succeed educationally by meeting expectations as set forth in national laws and policies such as the Common Core State Standards (National Governors Association Center for Best Practices, 2010). The holistic-strategies approach is illustrated in Figure 14.1.

Common Core State Standards

The Common Core State Standards, enacted in 2010, have been adopted by 42 out of 50 states (several states adopted and then repealed the standards). These research-based standards in math, English language arts, and other subject areas have several major goals: (1) to create globally competitive citizens in the 21st century, (2) to prepare students for college, (3) to create critical readers who "read deeply," and (4) to help students become responsible citizens who use evidence for deliberation.

Throughout this chapter, the Common Core State Standards will be referred to as they relate to intervention for ELLs with LI. Educators have experienced many challenges and much frustration in their efforts to link all activities, materials, and outcomes to curriculum standards that are often cognitively demanding for special needs students.

❑ The primary goal of the Common Core State Standards is to create students who are ready to succeed in a twenty-first century, globally competitive society. Unlike No Child Left Behind (2002), there are no fiscal or other punitive consequences in the standards; thus, the standards represent a fresh opportunity for professionals to support ELLs in their growth.

❑ Speech-language pathologists have an opportunity to incorporate academic language goals into their IEPs for students with special needs; this increases the relevance of the speech-language pathologist's job in school settings (Moore & Montgomery, 2018).

❑ Basically, the standards require shifts in three areas: (1) building knowledge through content-rich nonfiction, or expository (informational) text, (2) reading, writing, and speaking grounded in evidence from text (not personal feelings or experiences), and (3) regular practice with complex text and academic language.

❑ For ELL students with LI to succeed in achieving the Common Core State Standards to the greatest extent possible, they must have strong language knowledge and adequate cognitive processing skills. Unfortunately, implementation of the Common Core State Standards has often led to "one-size-fits-all" approaches to instruction that can be highly detrimental to students with special learning needs. A holistic strategies approach is essential if these students are to experience success in school programs that require teachers to target specific curriculum standards.

Tech Tie-In

A helpful iPad app that I use is called *Common Core Library,* created by WAGmob Simple 'n Easy. If a speech-language pathologist is writing an IEP goal, s/he can go to the Speaking and Listening Standards (for example) and use any of the standards that are appropriate for the IEP. Curriculum-relevant goals are included such as, "The student will participate in collaborative conversations with diverse partners about grade 2 topics and texts with peers and adults in small and larger groups." This can easily be written as an IEP goal for an ELL with LI.

Figure 14.1

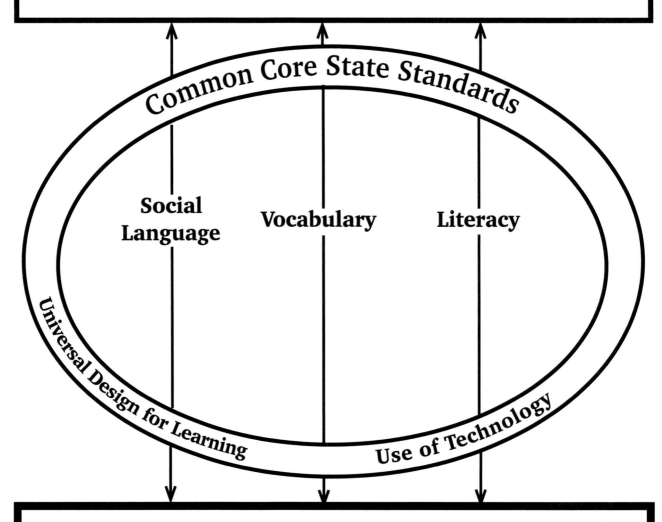

General English Language Arts areas within the Common Core State Standards are presented in Table 14.1.

Strengthening Cognitive Processing Skills

Selective attention, processing speed, and working memory are cognitive processing skills that often need to be strengthened in ELL students who have language impairment. This chapter integrates strategies for improving working memory and overall cognitive skills that can be used with ELL children who have LI.

❑ Teaching cognitive processing strategies can promote development of both the first language and English in ELL students with LI (Ebert & Kohnert, 2009; Ebert, Pham, Disher, & Payesteh, 2014; Ebert, Rentmeeser-Disher, & Kohnert, 2012).

❑ Strengthening the child's underlying learning system by improving working memory, processing speed, and selective attention provides a foundation that will facilitate the development of language skills (Boudreau & Costanza-Smith, 2010; Gillam & Gillam, 2014; Montgomery, Magimairaj, & Finney, 2010; Owens, 2016).

❑ It is also important to modify children's learning environments (e.g., the classroom setting) so that demands on working memory are more manageable. By making modifications that reduce cognitive load, students will be able to process incoming information more effectively.

STRUCTURING THE ENVIRONMENT FOR ELL STUDENTS WITH LANGUAGE IMPAIRMENT

Student performance often improves when simple modifications are made within the environment. The strategies below incorporate the principles of Universal Design for Learning (Center for Universal Design for Learning, 2015; Roth, Dixon, Paul, & Bellini, 2013). According to these principles, all learners need the following:

1. *Multiple means of representation.* Students must be presented with various methods to access the curriculum (e.g., professionals using digital textbooks, SmartBoards, tablets and apps, visuals, and others).
2. *Multiple means of expression.* Students' performance should be demonstrated through various methods and modalities such as oral and written expression, performing and visual arts, web-based projects, etc.
3. *Multiple means of engagement.* Students should be engaged and motivated in a variety of ways. Activities are needed to help students sustain effort and show persistence, maintain interest, and demonstrate self-regulation related to instructional activities.

Strategies for Structuring the Environment

1. *Use preparatory sets.* When preparatory sets are used, learners with special needs will know what to expect because their environment has been structured for them. For example, instead of starting an activity with no explanation, the professional might say, "Today we will share, read a story, and practice our sounds. What will you do?" If the student responds correctly say, "That's right - share, read a story, and practice our sounds."

2. *Limit clutter and excessive visual stimuli in the environment.* Many classrooms and therapy/resource rooms include beautiful collections of student art projects, work centers, pet cages, etc. While these rooms are colorful and attractive, they are often distracting to learners with special needs. These students often respond best in an environment that is attractive but very uncluttered and "plain." Because special needs students have difficulty

Table 14.1

English Language Arts Common Core State Standards

READING STANDARDS

Literature
Key Ideas and Details
Craft and Structure
Integration of Knowledge and Ideas
Range of Reading and Level of Text Complexity

Informational Text
Key Ideas and Details
Craft and Structure
Integration of Knowledge and Ideas
Range of Reading and Text Complexity

Foundational Skills
Phonics and Word Recognition
Fluency

WRITING STANDARDS

Text Types and Purposes
Opinion Pieces—Organizational Structure
Informative/Expository Tests
Narratives

Production and Distribution of Writing
Development and Organization
Revising and Editing

Research to Build and Present Knowledge
Research

SPEAKING AND LISTENING STANDARDS

Comprehension and Collaboration
Collaborative Discussions
Main Ideas and Supporting Details
Ask and Answer Questions for Information

Presentation of Knowledge and Ideas
Oral Presentations
Demonstrate Fluid Reading
Speaking in Complete Sentences

LANGUAGE STANDARDS

Conventions of Standard English
Standard English Grammar
Capitalization and Punctuation
Conventions of Standard English
Consult reference materials

Knowledge of Language
Choose Words and Phrases for Effect
Spoken and Written English Conventions

Vocabulary Acquisition and Use
Unknown and Multiple-meaning Words and Phrases
Literal and Non-literal Meanings
Acquire and Use Accurately Grade-Appropriate Words

screening out extraneous stimuli, they are distracted by items and events that do not distract most students.

3. *Set up an area of the classroom as the "office."* Some classroom teachers use an area of the classroom called the "office." This area has nothing on the walls; there is a little carrel that blocks off the rest of the classroom. Students are able to work in the office without visual distractions. Students who are susceptible to auditory distractions can wear headphones to block out noise.

4. *Wait until the room is quiet before presenting important information.* Students who have difficulty concentrating and remembering information will experience even more difficulty if the room is noisy.

5. *Reduce auditory distractions.* In many rooms, phones ring, people come in and out, and students talk freely. Learners with special needs can be highly distracted in such situations. Research shows that noise limits expressive vocabulary growth in children (Riley & McGregor, 2012); processing information in a second language under less-than-ideal listening conditions is especially a risk factor for ELL students with LI (Nelson, Kohnert, Sabur, & Shaw, 2005). These students tend to do their best work in quiet, organized environments.

6. *Speak at an appropriate loudness level.* Research has shown that when teachers speak at a level that is 15-30 decibels above their regular volume level, all children benefit—especially ELL students at risk for struggling in the classroom setting (Eriks-Brophy & Ayakawa, 2000). In some settings, teachers use FM units successfully for the benefit of students (Wilson, Marinac, Pitty, & Burrows, 2011). A teacher's use of an FM unit can improve the signal-to-noise ratio of the classroom, making the teacher's voice stand out in situations where background noise is present.

Strategies for Making Environmental Language Input Comprehensible

1. *Present new information in small "doses."* Frequent modeling and repetition may also be needed for learning to occur. Thus, each step of a task may need to be presented a number of times before these students are able to grasp the information being taught. Repetition and hearing information in smaller chunks can make incoming information more comprehensible.

2. *Review previously learned material daily.* Reviewing what has been taught previously reduces the likelihood that students will forget what they have learned.

3. *Check frequently for comprehension.* Students may be embarrassed to admit that they do not know specific information. In some cultures, it is inappropriate to admit not knowing something. Thus if a student indicates that he or she has comprehended something, we should check to make sure that comprehension has, in fact, occurred.

4. *Use a multimodal instructional approach in which visual and gestural cues are presented frequently.* Suggestions for accomplishing this are the following:

    A. Write assignments on the board.
    B. Use pictures, maps, diagrams, and various objects.
    C. Accompany oral presentations with gestures and facial expressions.
    D. Use visual organizers, clusters, and mental mapping to help organize information for the student.
    E. Incorporate interactive technology so that students hear, see, and physically interact with information being presented.

5. *Teach beginning students the names for common objects in the classroom.*

6. *Modify spoken instructions.* Helpful modifications include the following:

    A. Talk slowly enough for ELLs to process the information.

    B. Pause frequently to avoid "overloading" students with information.

    C. Use students' names to direct and maintain their attention.

    D. Use short sentences and phrases.

    E. Avoid the frequent use of long words.

    F. Explain new slang or idiomatic speech.

    G. Enunciate words clearly (e.g., "Did you eat?" instead of "Jueet?").

    H. Emphasize key words through increased volume and slightly exaggerated intonation.

    Example: "Now we will look at the calendar. The calendar shows us the days of the week."

7. *Rephrase and restate information to facilitate comprehension.* For example, the teacher might say, "Today we are going to read a chapter in our math books and do the problems on page 10 of the math workbook. Again, we will take our math books and read a chapter. We will then do the problems on page 10 of the math workbook."

8. *Seat students who speak the same language together, especially if one student speaks English with enough proficiency to help others.* The advanced student can then explain complicated directions and other information in the primary language.

9. *Allow additional time for special needs students to process information.* Learners with special needs often take longer to process information than students who are learning in the typical manner. Thus, professionals need to give these students time to answer, think, etc.

10. *Seat learners with special needs in the front of the classroom to minimize distractions.*

11. *Break down assignments into small components.* Students with special learning needs take longer to complete assignments and may become overwhelmed if given work that will take a long time to complete.

When intervention strategies such as those described above are used, the likelihood is increased that the instructional input will be comprehensible to ELL students who have LI.

Profile

Mr. J., a fifth-grade teacher, complained that "these bilingual special education kids in my class are driving me nuts. I want to put them somewhere else—just not in my classroom!" The only other fifth-grade teacher in the school was a recent college graduate with no previous teaching experience. The principal, therefore, told Mr. J. that he needed to try different instructional strategies with the ELL special education students.

During lunch one day, Mr. J. asked the speech-language pathologist (SLP) for suggestions, emphasizing that "these ideas better not take too much time—I'm already busy enough." The SLP offered to come and observe Mr. J's class and did so the following day. She noticed that Mr. J. used no visuals and that he spoke rapidly when presenting instructions to the students. He expected students to respond the first time he presented an instruction, and he rarely repeated instructions. The room was noisy and the SLP herself found it difficult to focus on what Mr. J. was trying to say.

The SLP offered to do a demonstration lesson, and Mr. J. accepted this offer. The SLP asked the students to participate in an experiment in being as quiet as possible. She told the students that a lesson would be presented and that a prize would be given to students at the quietest table. During the lesson, the SLP used the smartboard and other visuals when presenting the lesson. She also repeated key concepts several times in a slow speaking voice. Mr. J. reported at lunch the next day that the students told him they really enjoyed the lesson.

Mr. J. tried implementing the strategies demonstrated by the SLP. A few weeks later, he reported to her that the ELL special education students had "really turned a corner" academically. Mr. J. realized that he could implement changes to meet the needs of these special students.

TEACHING COMPENSATORY STRATEGIES

A major premise of the holistic-strategies approach is that ELLs with LI need to acquire STRATEGIES to learn. We stated that ELLs with LI especially need to be taught strategies that help boost working memory skills as a foundation for increasing language knowledge (Pieretti & Roseberry-McKibbin, 2016).

Strategy 1: Write down information and instructions in a notebook. This activity facilitates the development of organizational skills and helps the student to recall information presented during class. Students may also take notes on an iPad, iPhone, or Google Chrome device.

Strategy 2: Focus on key words and write them down. Many students will need explicit direction to help them focus their attention so that they can write down key words.

Sample instructions:

"Listen. I am going to write a sentence. You tell me what the most important words are. Don't worry about listening to all the little words. Just tell me what the most important words are."

Stimulus sentence: I went to the store to buy some milk.
Teacher: Which are the most important words?
Student: I, store, buy, milk.
Teacher: That's right: I - store - buy - milk. These are the important or key words that we need to remember.

The professional can also ask the student to name the little words in the sentence. After presenting sentences, short paragraphs can be used for this activity. This procedure is especially helpful for older students who need to take notes during lectures and have difficulty separating content (key) words from function (smaller, less important) words.

Strategy 3: Use visualization to help students form mental pictures of information.

Sample instructions:
"We are going to learn how to make pictures in our mind. Think of watching a TV show or a movie. You see a picture on a screen. Who has seen a movie or TV show lately? Tell me what you saw."

"Leo, tell us about your kitchen at home. (Child describes the kitchen). Leo, are you standing in your kitchen right now? No, you are here at school. Then how could you tell us about your kitchen? (pause) You just saw a picture in your brain, didn't you? We are going to learn how to make pictures in our brains to help us remember information."

During instructional activities, students should be encouraged to form mental pictures of what they are learning. For example, encourage students to see color, size, shape, texture, sound, movement, background, and other aspects of their mental pictures (Bell, 1991). Detailed visualization helps children remember new information that they see and hear. The more detail, the better!

Tech Tip

Intervention for English Language Learners with Language Impairment: Using Visualization

English Language Learners with language impairment often benefit from using visualization as an adjunct to listening and reading. Visualization, or creating mental images, facilitates comprehension of and memory for information. Here I work with a bilingual Hmong-English student to enhance his visualization skills.

Go to youtube.com and type in Celeste Roseberry (Love Talk Read). Click on the title above.

Strategy 4: Teach students metacognitive strategies to help them become more efficient learners. Metacognitive strategies include monitoring the success of one's current learning efforts, planning ahead so that learning time can be used efficiently, and being aware of one's own learning style and learning strategies. For example, the professional might say to a student:

> "The teacher just said that the class has 30 minutes to do the summary at the end of chapter 5 of your language arts book. There are five questions in the summary. How many minutes do you have to answer each question? That's right—6 minutes. We know that it can be hard for you to focus with noise around you, so we are going to ask Mr. Johnston if you can do the summary in the office. Let's get the things you need for this assignment: your book and two pencils." (15 minutes later) "How are you doing? OK, you have answered two questions. We have four questions to go and 15 minutes to answer them. Let's review what you have already written and then focus on finishing up."

Strategy 5: Use reauditorization/silent rehearsal. The students are told that when they hear something (e.g., directions), they are to repeat what they hear verbally at first, and later on quietly to themselves.

> *Example:*
> Do what I say:
> Touch your nose, eyes, and ears. I said, nose - eyes - ears.
> I want everyone to repeat after me—nose - eyes - ears (wait for students to respond verbally)
> Now, what did I say to touch? That's right—nose - eyes - ears. You remembered the words because you said them. Let's try another one.
>
> I went on a trip, and in my suitcase I put a dress, shoes, and shampoo.
> I want everyone to repeat after me—dress - shoes - shampoo (wait for students to respond)
>
> > Now we are not going to use our voices; we are going to repeat the words quietly in our heads. Listen:
> >
> > > I am going to the store, and I need to get milk, eggs, and apples.
> > > Now say it quietly in your head: "milk, eggs, apples" (pause for several seconds)
> > > What am I going to get at the store? (students answer)
> > > Good! You said the words quietly in your head, and you were able to remember what I said. In the classroom when the teacher is talking, I want you to take important things she is saying and say them quietly in your head. This will help you remember what you hear.

Many students profit from this strategy. The professional should encourage students to repeat items out loud at first to ensure that the strategy is working. Then move quickly to silent rehearsal.

Strategy 6: Pay careful attention to the speaker by maintaining eye contact during classroom activities in which the teacher is speaking. Professionals can say, "When the teacher is talking, I want you to look at his eyes and think about what he is saying. Do not look around you at other kids or think about other things. Look in the teacher's eyes and pay attention to him." This seems very simple, but I have found through clinical experience that it can have instant and sometimes dramatic results.

The holistic-strategies approach will be most effective when students receive direct and explicit teaching and opportunities for the rehearsal of appropriate strategies to enhance working memory for information presented. Professionals should monitor carryover of strategy use into the classroom and other settings. Professionals can work in a collaborative manner with parents, teachers, and other school professionals to ensure that students are being encouraged to use appropriate strategies for learning and remembering information.

Profile

Rosario A. immigrated to the U.S. from the Philippines with his family when he was in fourth grade. The teacher referred Rosario to the special education team because, in her words, "Rosario is SO quiet in class, and I can never get him to raise his hand and answer questions. Also, Rosario copies other students' work and can't seem to complete assignments on his own. I wonder if he needs some special education assistance."

The SLP, who had grown up in the Philippines, observed Rosario in class. There were 35 students in the somewhat noisy classroom, and Rosario sat quietly in the back, never volunteering any information. In addition, Rosario was observed trying to get other students to help him with a difficult math assignment. The SLP shared with the teacher that being quiet and respectful in class was expected in the Philippines, and that corporal punishment was sometimes used there for students who "got out of line." In addition, she shared that Filipino students frequently help one another with assignments rather than working on classroom tasks independently.

Rather than being evaluated for special education, Rosario was placed into the after school Homework Club, where he received help from older peer tutors who worked individually and in small groups with younger students. A sixth-grade Filipino student was assigned to work with Rosario and three Filipino students from other classrooms in a cooperative, informal, interactive, and friendly situation in the school library. After six months, the teacher reported that Rosario had made excellent gains and that he was even raising his hand occasionally in class to ask questions.

INCREASING SOCIAL SKILLS

In the holistic-strategies approach to learning, professionals help students become more effective communicators in their daily environments. Many ELL students in both general and special education programs need to enhance their communicative competence in their daily interactions. They especially need to increase their skills in topic initiation and maintenance. Reproducible Form 14.1 includes a "Communication Skills Quiz" that students can use to evaluate their own communication. Students should be asked to respond "yes" or "no" to each question. When presented to a small group, cultural differences can be discussed as they relate to specific items.

Reproducible Form 14.1

A COMMUNICATION SKILLS QUIZ FOR STUDENTS

Student's Name:_____   Date:_____

___1.   I greet people when I see them by smiling and saying "hi."

___2.   I listen to people without interrupting.

___3.   I apologize when I have to interrupt.

___4.   I try to be interested in what people say.

___5.   I try to take time to listen when people want to talk to me.

___6.   When people ask me questions, I try to answer as best I can.

___7.   When I talk, I try to talk as clearly as possible so other people will understand me.

___8.   During conversations, I take turns talking.

___9.   During conversations, I try to talk about what other people are talking about instead of bringing up new things in the middle of someone else's sentence.

___10.   If I don't understand what someone says, I ask the person to please repeat what was said.

___11.   If someone doesn't understand me, I repeat what I said more clearly.

___12.   I try to look at people when I talk to them.

The Speaking and Listening Standards in the Common Core State Standards emphasize teaching students to follow the rules of discourse and to use formal and informal English according to what is dictated by each social situation. Examples of curriculum standards are presented below:

Sample Grade 2 Standards:

[Students will] participate in collaborative conversations with diverse partners about kindergarten topics and texts with peers and adults in small and larger groups.

[Students will] follow agreed-upon rules for discussions (e.g., listening to others and taking turns speaking about the topics and texts under discussion.)

Sample Grade 6 Standards:

[Students will] adapt speech to a variety of contexts and tasks, demonstrating command of formal English when indicated or appropriate.

It is recommended that professionals work in a collaborative manner to ensure that students practice effective interpersonal communication skills in a variety of communication contexts. The following target behavior, for example, can be practiced in a variety of situations within the school environment.

Target Behavior: The student will demonstrate effective interpersonal communication skills in daily settings as observed by professionals who work with the student on a regular basis.

Objectives/Benchmarks:

1. The student will greet others by smiling and saying "hello" when appropriate.
2. The student will listen to others without interrupting. If an interruption is necessary, the student will say "excuse me."
3. The student will answer questions appropriately and promptly.
4. The student will take turns during conversation.
5. The student will ask for clarification when he or she does not understand something.
6. If a listener shows confusion, the student will clarify what was said by giving explanations.
7. The student will maintain appropriate eye contact with others during communication.
8. The student will demonstrate knowledge of appropriate use of formal and informal English in a variety of social and academic situations.

If students can master these basic social skills, they will be able to make friends easily and will also generate frequent opportunities for interaction with both adults and peers. Professionals in both general and special education programs can role-model these behaviors and actively teach students how to use them. We can begin teaching effective social skills as early as preschool.

❑ An excellent resource for supporting social skills in young children is *Kimochis: Seven Keys to Communication Effectiveness* (Dodge, 2010). *Kimochis,* or plush toys conveying feelings, are accompanied by a program that teaches seven keys to successful communication (e.g., "choose words that help instead of hurt"). The program is well suited to young ELLs with LI especially because it is tactile and very easy to teach, learn, and generalize to a variety of environments.

❑ ELL students who have language impairment may need support in learning the basic routines of a school classroom. Professionals should help these students carry out basic classroom routines. This will facilitate the development of social skills. For example, students should be taught to raise their hands, to speak only when called upon, and other "basics" to help them fit into the classroom setting. (Roseberry-McKibbin, 2015).

❑ For older students, technology can be used to improve social skills. Posnick-Goodwin (2013) described one high school in which students created Facebook pages to post compliments about other students or teachers. This activity led to a reduction in cyberbullying and helped students to develop friendships. Activities such as this are ideal for older ELLs with LI, who are often shy and reluctant to interact verbally with others.

EVIDENCE-BASED STRATEGIES FOR VOCABULARY DEVELOPMENT

General Principles

The holistic-strategies approach emphasizes the importance of building students' content knowledge or conceptual foundation within meaningful contexts. The Common Core State Standards place a major emphasis on vocabulary development, a major area of concern for ELLs in general.

Upon entry to kindergarten, many ELL students are already far behind their peers in English word learning, and this gap widens as they progress through school. ELLs know fewer English vocabulary words than monolingual English speakers, and they know less about the meaning of these words (Green, Stockholm, Cearley, & Sheffield-Anderson, 2015). Thus, even typically-developing ELLs need to accelerate their learning just to catch up.

The need for vocabulary development is even more important for ELLs with LI. For example, the research of Sheng, Peña, Bedore, and Fiestas (2012) with LI and typically-developing Spanish-speaking children showed that 65% of the LI group had semantic deficits in comparison to 14% of typically-developing students. Many bilingual children with LI had sparsely linked semantic networks.

Bilingual intervention programs have been found to facilitate both native- and second-language vocabulary development in children with LI (Restrepo et al., 2013). By providing opportunities to learn vocabulary in the primary language, children acquire language strategies that will be helpful in learning English. Developing rich vocabulary skills positively impacts a number of areas (Tattersall, Nelson, & Tyler, 2015). A recent study found, for example, that larger L2 (English) vocabulary contributed to ELLs' greater use of complex sentences (Paradis, Rusk, Sorenson Duncan, & Govindarajan, 2017).

It is recommended that the following strategies be followed when teaching vocabulary:

1. Teach vocabulary that the child needs to know to function effectively in both social and academic contexts. In addition to learning social vocabulary, students who are learning English as a second language need to develop their knowledge of vocabulary relevant to the content of the classroom curriculum (Green et al., 2015). As stated, vocabulary relating to Common Core State Standards is especially important.

2. Teach vocabulary to ELL students with LI through **multiple exposures** to words and **active engagement** in learning these new words (Beck, McKeown, & Kucan, 2013; Crowley, 2012; Green et al., 2015). Storkel, Komesidou, Fleming, and Romine (2017) stated that for children with specific language impairment, 36 exposures to a new word was ideal to promote word learning.

3. Teach vocabulary in the child's primary language first and then in English. This is the fastest, most efficient way to facilitate bilingual vocabulary growth (Ford, 2017).

4. When teaching new vocabulary words to ELLs with LI, present receptive language activities first. That is, the development of comprehension should be emphasized prior to asking children to produce new concepts verbally. Many ELL students feel uncomfortable in situations that require them to begin speaking immediately. It is ideal for professionals to present receptive vocabulary activities first and follow these by expressive activities that are hierarchically sequenced based on their complexity.

5. When teaching new vocabulary words, begin by presenting concrete, contextualized learning experiences (e.g., going to a zoo to see animals). If these concrete experiences are not possible, symbols or representations (e.g., pictures, objects) are the next best choice for teaching new concepts. An effort should be made to accompany vocabulary teaching with as many concrete pictures, objects, and hands-on learning experiences as possible.

6. Present activities that are accompanied by adult mediation in conversational contexts whenever possible. Rich, interactive, cognitively complex conversational experiences with adults are beneficial for both monolingual and ELL children with LI (Ford, 2017; Karanth, Roseberry-McKibbin, & James, 2017b).

Specific Activities for Developing Vocabulary Skills

Professionals can boost the learning of new vocabulary by presenting activities such as the following:

1. Have students talk about the meaning of new words that they are learning. Students, for example, can paraphrase the dictionary definition of the words.

2. Have students connect new words to something they already know. For example, students in one therapy group were trying to learn the meaning of the word *booth*. A student finally connected this word to a burrito stand that she was familiar with.

3. Have students demonstrate their knowledge and ability to use words in a variety of ways. Students, for example, can act out word meanings, draw pictures representing their meanings, use words in sentences, and give examples of contexts in which the words are used.

Reproducible Form 14.2 can be used to help students elaborate upon new vocabulary words that they are learning. I have used this form successfully with ELL children and teenagers who have LI.

Total Physical Response (TPR; Asher, 2007) is a highly successful and enjoyable activity for building the vocabulary skills of early English learners. In TPR, students learn new vocabulary by listening and carrying out bodily movements as instructed by the professional. Children feel comfortable participating in the activities because they are not required to speak. TPR supports long-term comprehension of the material that students are learning. A typical TPR lesson for teaching body parts is presented below:

Professional: Touch your nose (professional alone touches her nose).

Professional: Touch your nose (professional and students all touch their noses).

Professional: Touch your nose (students alone touch their noses).

Reproducible Form 14.2

I'm a Vocabulary Genius

My word is _____

This word has _____ syllables. Write the syllables in the boxes below:

This word is a (circle one)

NOUN	**VERB**	**ADJECTIVE**	**OTHER**
Person, Place,	Action	Describing	_____
Thing, or Idea	Word	Word	

In my own words, this word means

_____

_____

I can write a sentence using this word:

_____

_____

This type of activity is especially beneficial in the early stages of learning English when many children feel uncomfortable speaking the language. Professionals can add more words or commands as students' abilities increase. Students can also give commands for other students to follow. Other examples of activities that can be used to build vocabulary skills are presented in Table 14.2.

Tech Tip

How to Conduct Curriculum-Based Therapy for Students with Language Impairment

In this video, I teach Tier 2 vocabulary, focusing on words that are important because they are used within many different subject areas. I also incorporate morphological and phonological awareness into the lesson. Using this simple activity, I am able to target a number of areas!

Go to youtube.com and type in Celeste Roseberry (Love Talk Read). Check on the title shown above.

Teaching Tier Two Vocabulary Words

In order to incorporate curriculum standards into intervention, many experts today agree that "Tier 2" words should be targeted (Justice, 2012; Moore & Montgomery, 2018; Murza, 2013). Tier 1 words are the basic, common words that students generally pick up automatically during everyday interactions in their environment (e.g. *clock, happy, play*). Tier 3 words are highly specialized, and the frequency of their use is low (*peninsula, isotope, radiation*).

❏ Tier 2 words are high frequency words that are found across a variety of domains; instruction relating to the use of these words is most productive (e.g., *fortunate, coincidence, similar*). There are many online resources to guide professionals to lists of appropriate Tier 2 words.

❏ The Common Core State Standards emphasize use of increasingly abstract vocabulary in the form of Tier 2 words, even in the early grade levels. An example is the following:

Students will distinguish shades of meaning among verbs differing in manner (e.g., look, peek, glance, stare, glare, scowl).

❏ Professionals can increase active engagement with new words and help students learn Tier 2 words by connecting new words with ones that students already know. It is very important to develop knowledge of synonyms.

Example: If a student says "I have to do my homework," the SLP might say, "You are *required* to do your homework."

Tech Tie-In

The website www.flocabulary.com includes resources for teaching words that students are likely to encounter on high-stakes tests. The research team created word lists for grades 2-7 by compiling words from appropriate basal readers and novels, with an emphasis on Tier 2 words. They then analyzed how often these vocabulary words appeared on state tests, and listed those as the ones to teach in The Word Up Project. One can go to the website and print lists of words by grade level for use in intervention.

Table 14.2
Activities For Developing Vocabulary Skills

◆ *Create a Story* - Students use books and pictures of vocabulary words to create stories.

◆ *Category Buckets* - Students put pictures in category "buckets." Each bucket is used for a different word category. Pictures of animals, for example, would be placed in the "animal bucket."

◆ *Guess the Picture* - A student is asked to describe a picture. The other students try to guess which of the pictures on the table is being described.

◆ *Which One Doesn't Belong?* - Five pictures are placed on the table. All but one of the pictures are from the same word category. The student's task is to identify the picture that doesn't belong and to explain why it doesn't belong.

◆ *Memory Games* - Auditory memory games can be created, such as Packing the Suitcase, Grocery Shopping, Catalog Orders, etc. Students are asked to listen to and remember the items named.

◆ *Describe it in Detail* - Students are given points for each attribute mentioned when describing an object or picture of an object. When presented with a picture of an apple, for example, four points would be earned if the student said, "it's shiny, red, juicy, and it's a fruit." Each student receives the same number of turns. The student with the most points at the end of the activity wins.

◆ *Follow the Directions* - Students are asked to manipulate the position of various pictures when presented with verbal directions (e.g., "Put the pencil on the cup before picking up the chair").

◆ *Rhyming Words* - Students think of words that rhyme with vocabulary words presented in pictures. When presented with the word hat, for example, the child might say "cat, mat, and fat." Rhyming should only be used with students whose command of English is strong enough for them to complete this activity without experiencing frustration.

◆ *Word Match* - Students match printed words with pictures of these words.

◆ *Construct a Sentence* - Students construct sentences when presented with a group of words.

◆ *Category Stories* - Students create stories using words from specific categories.

◆ *Drawing Pictures* - Students are asked to draw pictures of new words that they have learned.

◆ *Word Wall* - Students generate the wall list, which contains new words they are learning. Each column can start with a letter, and each list begins with a student's name that starts with that particular letter. For example, the "A" column may start with "Arisbel," the "B" column may start with "Bobby," etc.

◆ *Noun Comparisons* - Students are asked to compare two words/concepts and to discuss what is alike and different about them.

❑ *Fancy Nancy* is an iPad app that I use for teaching synonyms. The app features a girl named Fancy Nancy who likes to use fancy names for common things. Students love learning "sophisticated" synonyms (Tier 2 words) in fun and entertaining ways. For example, Fancy Nancy loves jewelry and shoes; she calls these *accessories*. Fancy Nancy enjoys learning about famous people; she calls them *celebrities*. Kraemer and Bryla (2017) recommend various other iPad apps that can support ELL students with vocabulary deficits.

❑ A free online resource that I have had great success with, especially with teenagers, is freerice. com. This website teaches synonyms (many of which are Tier 2 words) through multiple choice items.

Sample item:
> *Happy* means the same thing as:
> A. Bored
> B. Content
> C. Joyful
> D. Fatigued

If a student answers correctly, 20 grains of rice are literally donated to the United Nations World Food program and given to a hungry person in a developing area of the world. The students I work with love the idea that they are helping those who are less fortunate. If they get the answer wrong, the item is cycled back until they get it right. As the player becomes more knowledgeable and progresses through the levels, the items become more sophisticated.

Tech Tie-In

Visit www.freerice.com for a learning activity from an organization that provides free food to people in developing areas of the world.

Profile

Blanca was a third-grade Spanish-speaking student who had been identified as having LI. Cheryl, the speech-language pathologist who worked with her, had limited Spanish language skills. Cheryl spoke in Spanish to Blanca when possible but conducted her therapy primarily in English. Cheryl frequently sent home assignments for Blanca to do with her parents in Spanish so that Blanca's primary language would be supported.

One of Cheryl's major goals was to increase Blanca's knowledge of the vocabulary used within the classroom curriculum. Stories from Blanca's third-grade classroom language arts book were used in each therapy session. Before Cheryl and Blanca read each story, a "picture walk" was conducted to help Blanca understand the "whole" of the story. Cheryl and Blanca discussed the pictures in the story and talked about what was happening. Next, they read the story together. Cheryl had Blanca write unfamiliar words and their definitions onto index cards. Blanca was also asked to draw a picture of each difficult word. Blanca then recorded the words into her journal and used each word in a sentence. The vocabulary words were reviewed often in subsequent therapy sessions.

Cheryl found that Blanca's classroom performance was greatly enhanced by this method. Blanca's third-grade teacher commented that Blanca appeared to have less difficulty understanding the stories in the language arts book. Her overall grades were also improving.

It is important to teach students vocabulary words that are critical for following directions, completing worksheets, and understanding the content of subject matter emphasized within the classroom. Standardized tests of academic achievement, for example, require understanding of words such as *compare, contrast, define, and describe*. Reproducible Form 14.3 is a list of Tier 2 words that are commonly used in classroom curriculum and on state standardized tests.

BUILDING LITERACY SKILLS

Basic Premise

The acquisition of literacy skills is important for all students who are learning English as an additional language. As students engage in literacy activities, they learn about the world, acquire new vocabulary, and develop a heightened awareness of the structure of language and the ways in which words can be used to communicate information.

Limited literacy skills can lead to negative life outcomes. Two-thirds of students who cannot read proficiently by the end of fourth grade are ending up in jail or on welfare. If a fourth grader has not yet learned to read proficiently, he or she has approximately a 78% chance of never catching up (One World Literacy Foundation, 2017).

❑ ELL students with LI often have limited skills in reading, resulting in poor academic performance. These students often face five barriers:

1. Academic materials are usually in English.
2. Academic learning is intrinsically difficult for these students.
3. Phonological and morphological awareness skills may be limited.
4. Environmental experiences may be limited.
5. Literacy may not be supported at home.

❑ Experiences that provide environmental exposure and build oral language skills are critical in helping students build the conceptual foundations that they need for success in learning to read. This exposure will lead to better oral language skills, enhanced phonological awareness, better morphological awareness, and enhanced narrative skills that are critical for success in acquiring literacy.

❑ A major problem in many school programs is that professionals begin instruction at the "top of the ladder"—they try to teach literacy without the prerequisites of environmental experience and exposure. Oral language skills are taken for granted.

❑ The importance of enhancing environmental exposure and building strong oral communication skills cannot be overemphasized, as oral language is foundational to written language. As Montgomery (2013) stated, the "core of the core" is oral language development.

❑ One way to bridge oral and written language for ELLs with LI is to use curriculum materials from the classroom in intervention activities (Green et al., 2015; Hale, 2017; Ukrainetz, 2017). Materials from the curriculum can be used to improve vocabulary, phonological awareness, morphological awareness, reading comprehension, and other skills.

❑ As has been frequently discussed, it is important, when possible, to build first language literacy skills to support the acquisition of literacy skills in the second language (Goodrich et al., 2013; Simon-Cereijido, 2013).

Reproducible Form 14.3

THE VOCABULARY OF TEST TAKING

Student's Name: _____   **Date:** _____

Place a check mark by each word that has been mastered.

__Circle	***For Math:***
__Underline	__Add
__Fill In	__Put together
__Cross out	__Combine
__Mark	__Subtract
__Find	__Take away
__List	__Borrow
__Name	__Multiply
__Match	__Divide
__Connect	__Estimate
__Check	__Measure
__Label	__Quantify
__Capitalize	__Solve
__Show	__Compute
__Identify	__Evaluate
__Describe	__Category
__Explain	__Term
__Rewrite	__Greater than
__Paraphrase	__Less than
__Summarize	__Equal to
__Compare	__Calculate
__Contrast	
__Imagine	

❏ ELL students with LI may also be in need of activities to stimulate the development of phonological awareness. Activities to build phonological awareness help these students perform more successfully in the classroom.

Strategies for Phonological Awareness Training

Phonological awareness can be defined as the ability to reflect on and consciously manipulate the sound system of a language. Phonological awareness is related to spelling, reading, and writing achievement. Thus, when attempting to develop literacy skills in ELL students with LI, it is important to stimulate the development of phonological awareness in two primary ways: (1) embedded intervention and (2) explicit intervention.

Embedded intervention is indirect and involves "working phonological awareness into the day." For example, during reading and other activities, professionals can informally incorporate such things as rhyming and syllabication. **Explicit intervention** involves focused activities whose specific purpose is to improve phonological awareness.

Research has provided evidence that the development of phonological awareness facilitates the acquisition of literacy.

❏ In a recent study conducted with 104 preschool children in 39 classrooms, children who were exposed to a supplemental phonological awareness curriculum demonstrated significantly greater gains on early literacy measures and were better prepared for kindergarten than students who didn't receive this exposure (Goldstein et al., 2016).

❏ A longitudinal study conducted in Iceland with 267 Icelandic-speaking subjects found that subjects' phonological awareness test scores at 5 years old strongly correlated with math and Icelandic language scores when students were tested in grades 4, 7, and 10. The researchers concluded that early intervention for deficits in phonological awareness is crucial for later academic success (Einarsdottir, Bjornsdottir, & Simonardottir, 2016).

❏ The use of contextualized, language-rich oral narratives was found to be an essential element in increased phonological awareness, increased reading abilities, and increased classroom curriculum participation and engagement among young Hmong ELLs (Pieretti, 2011).

The phonological awareness activities and suggestions below are based on research reported from various sources (Goldstein et al., 2017; Owens, 2016; Pieretti, 2011; Roseberry-McKibbin, 2013b).

1. Ask students to do the following:

   A. Count the number of words in a sentence.
   B. Count the number of syllables in a word.
   C. Count the number of sounds in a word.
   D. Identify rhyming words.
   E. Ask children to blend sounds to create words.
   F. Identify the first sound in a word.
   G. Identify the last sound in a word.
   H. Identify medial sounds in words.
   I. Match words that begin or end with the same sound (Example: "Which pictures show words that begin with /s/?").

2. Use rhythm sticks and clapping to emphasize the number of sounds and/or syllables in words. As you read a rhyme, have students tap the table for each syllable/sound or

use a "shaker" for each syllable/sound.

3. Use alliteration. For example, when working with Spanish speakers, ask students what sound they hear used most at the beginning of words in sentences such as, "Pasa la papa para papá con el papel o pala" (Pass the potato to the father with the paper or shovel.).

4. Use a grab bag. Ask students to pull out objects, name them, and sort them into piles based on their beginning, middle, or ending sounds.

5. Use rhymes. Books such as those written by Dr. Seuss work quite well. Children can recite rhymes, act them out, and view pictures that supplement the rhyme. Singing rhymes facilitates the learning of the rhymes.

6. Use music. For example, the tune to "If you're happy and you know it" may be used by replacing the lyrics with "If your name begins with *b*, raise your hand."

7. Use stories with Rebus-style pictures, and ask students to "read" the pictures.

8. Use word play. For example, the professional might say, "This is a story about Prinderella and the Cince. Prinderella lived with her sticked wepmother and two sistee uglers. What am I really talking about?" The infamous "Pig Latin" is also fun. For example, the professional might say, "I'm so glad that Anuelmay is here today. Who am I really talking about? Right! Manuel!"

9. Ask a student to remove a specific segment from a word. For example, "Say *cowboy* without *boy.*"

10. Tell the student that you are going to play a game that involves making up new words for things. For example, you might say that all things in the room now start with "b." So "desk" becomes "besk," "pencil" becomes "bencil," etc.

11. Use available digital resources to increase phonological awareness skills and build overall literacy and working memory skills (Boudreau & Costanza-Smith, 2010; Kohnert, 2013; Kraemer & Bryla, 2017).

Tech Tie-In

Intervention for Vocabulary and Phonological Awareness Skills
In this video, I use objects buried in kinetic sand to increase this Farsi-speaking student's vocabulary and phonological awareness. His aunt is with him and helps translate into Farsi occasionally to make sure he is understanding the directions. Go to youtube.com and type in Celeste Roseberry (Love Talk Read). Click on the video with the title listed above.

Building Print Awareness

Stimulating the development of print awareness is important, especially for ELL preschoolers who are at-risk or who are diagnosed with LI (Ford, 2017). Many preschoolers need to learn to focus their attention on print. Justice, Pullen, and Pence (2008) examined the extent to which preschoolers attend to print:

❏ During reading, preschoolers only looked directly at print about 5-6% of the time when it was not explicitly referenced.

❏ When adults explicitly referenced print, children looked at print about 12.5 times when the adult read a book verbatim, 17.7 times when the adult made nonverbal reference to print, and 21.2 times when the adult made verbal references to print.

❏ Disadvantaged preschoolers who were exposed to print referencing strategies showed larger literacy gains than children who were not exposed to these strategies.

The incorporation of print referencing strategies into programs for ELL students may facilitate the development of strong foundational preliteracy skills in children with LI. A variety of activities should be included in preschool settings to strengthen print awareness. Table 14.3 includes specific suggestions for building print awareness skills in young ELLs.

Building Morphological Awareness

Morphological awareness is defined as the recognition, understanding, and use of word parts that carry significance. For example, students need to understand that prefixes, suffixes, inflections, and root words are all morphemes that can be taken away from or added to words to change their meaning. Students with strong morphological awareness are able to approach a novel multisyllabic word and break it into parts in order to predict the word's meaning (Apel, Brimo, Diehm, & Apel, 2013).

Many experts have stressed the importance of targeting morphological awareness in instructional programs for at-risk ELLs and those with LI (Crowley, 2012; Kieffer, Biancarosa, & Mancilla-Martinez, 2013; Simon-Cereijido, 2015).

❏ Morphological awareness intervention has been found to lead to gains in morphological awareness itself, phonological awareness, spelling, word reading, and reading comprehension for at-risk readers, including ELLs across grade levels (Zoski & Erickson, 2017). Thus, targeting morphological awareness skills can contribute greatly to improving overall reading skills.

❏ Based on a study of students who spoke English, Mandarin, and/or Spanish. Lam and Sheng (2016) concluded that professionals should explicitly teach morphological rules to bilingual students who are at risk for slow vocabulary development.

❏ Based on research with Spanish-speaking students learning English, Kieffer et al. (2013) concluded that morphological awareness had a significant and unique contribution to reading comprehension and fluency in English.

❏ Schwartz, Taha, Assad, Khamaisi, and Eviatar (2016) found that bilingual children (when compared with monolingual children) had better morphological awareness and increased sensitivity to word structure in both languages. They concluded that being exposed to another language in childhood can result in advantages in linguistic skill in both languages, including morphological awareness skills. Their results were based on data obtained from 93 six-year-old children who had been exposed to Arabic and Hebrew.

❏ Many schools are targeting the development of morphological awareness in the early elementary grades. The Common Core State Standards, for example, include standards at kindergarten level relating to the use of morphological structures in identifying word meanings.

> *Example:* [Students will] use the most frequently-occurring inflections and affixes
> (e.g., -ed, -s, re-, un- pre-, -ful, -less) as a clue to the meaning of an unknown word.

Speech-language pathologists and other professionals can implement simple, inexpensive activities to promote morphological awareness skills as part of overall programs to build oral and literate

Table 14.3

Strategies for Increasing Print Awareness

Children should be taught to do the following:

1. Display interest in reading and sharing books.

2. Hold a book right side up.

3. Identify the front and back of the book.

4. Identify the top and bottom of the page.

5. Look at the book while turning the pages from the left to the right.

6. Identify the title of the story on the book cover.

7. Identify titles of favorite books.

8. Distinguish between pictures and print on a page.

9. Identify where a story begins in the book.

10. Identify letters that occur in their own names.

11. Print the first letter of their name.

12. Recite the first 10 letters of the alphabet.

13. Point to the first letter in a word.

14. Differentiate uppercase from lowercase letters.

15. Use terms such as letter, word, and alphabet.

16. Point to words individually as they are read.

17. Respond to signs in the classroom.

18. Recognize common environmental signs.

language skills. Table 14.4 has a list of activities that speech-language pathologists and other professionals can incorporate to increase morphological awareness skills in ELLs with LI.

Tech Tip

Intervention for English Language Learners: Increasing Preliteracy Skills Through CARE and Wordless Books

Lusine uses CARE (Comment—Ask Questions—Respond—Extend) to discuss a wordless book with these young children as they codeswitch back and forth between English and Armenian. The children are fascinated by the pictures, and no actual reading is necessary as Lusine uses CARE to build pre-literacy skills. An important part of CARE, "extend," occurs when Lusine adds words to the children's utterances.

Go to youtube.com and type in Celeste Roseberry (Love Talk Read). Click on the video with the title listed above.

Strategies for Building Narrative Skills

Skill in narrative production helps to bridge the gap between children's oral and written language (Bitetti & Hammer, 2016). Experts have recommended that to build reading skills, students should be taught specific narrative skills (Catts & Kamhi, 2017). Students who can understand stories that they hear and tell stories in a logical sequence are more likely to experience success when reading and writing stories in the classroom.

❏ Practice in telling stories helps develop children's use of decontextualized language—they learn to talk about abstract objects, ideas, or events that are not immediately present. Thus, oral narrative production has a very important role in fostering young children's literacy development in areas such as narrative writing, reading fluency, and reading comprehension (Bitetti & Hammer, 2016).

❏ When teaching narrative skills, it is important for professionals to be aware of cultural differences in how stories are told. Prath and Palafox (2017) described the narrative elements that are common to most cultures. These elements are presented in Table 14-5. Speech-language pathologists and other professionals can help students to incorporate these elements into their stories.

❏ The use of puppets and other physical props is recommended when working with very young children who are just being introduced to narratives (Karanth, Roseberry-McKibbin, & James, 2017g).

❏ Family members should be encouraged to read stories to their children and to talk about these stories. Talking about wordless picture books can also be effective in improving narrative skills.

Strategies for Increasing Reading Fluency and Comprehension

As students get older, reading fluency and comprehension become increasingly more important for academic success. To foster an interest in reading, the context of the reading materials and learning activities should be relevant to the life experiences of students. Professionals should incorporate students' background knowledge into reading activities (Wallach & Ocampo, 2017).

Professionals should strive to be interactive with students when presenting learning activities. For example, many students like talking with peers and teachers about what they are reading rather than just reading silently without any type of interaction.

Table 14.4

Activities for Increasing Morphological Awareness

✦ Teach the terms *affix, prefix, suffix,* and *root word.* Explicitly teach students that affixes are extra parts that are "fixed on" to root words. Affixes at the beginning of words are called prefixes because "pre" means "before." Suffixes are located at the end of the word.

✦ Have students highlight the root word in words such as *hopeful, carefully, sleepless, workable, unhelpful*

✦ Create flash cards and have students make as many "real words " as they can. Have just one root word or affix on a card:

en-	care
-ous	smile
-ment	over
-ing	approve
-ly	appear
dis-	fulfill
-ful	courage

✦ Ask students to bring in a classroom textbook (e.g., a language arts or social studies book). As a therapy activity, have them write down 10 "big words" that they see. They can highlight root words in yellow, prefixes in green, and suffixes in blue. Have students discuss how affixes change the meaning of the root word.

✦ Have students make 3x5 cards for words and add affixes to change word meanings (Ehren, 2012). For example:

Investigate	Investigator
Investigation	Investigatory
Investigates	Investigated
Investigating	

✦ Make affix and root word card decks. In one bag, put root words; in another bag, put prefixes and suffixes. Provide each student with a sheet of paper. Have them select five root words and five affixes. Set a timer for three minutes, and have the students create as many words as they can with their roots and affixes. These words can then be put into sentences orally, in writing, or both.

Table 14.5
Narrative Elements Common to Most Cultures

Narrative Element	Definition	Example (Cinderella)
Initiating Event	The incident introducing the central conflict in a story	Cinderella's stepsisters and step-mother mistreated her
Attempt	The protagonist's attempt to solve the problem	Cinderella engages the fairy godmother to help her get to the ball to meet the prince
Consequence	The results of the attempt (was the goal attained?)	Cinderella met and danced with the prince, but the clock struck midnight
Resolution	Was the problem solved?	Eventually, the glass slipper fit Cinderella and she married the prince
Setting	The temporal and/or physical context of the story	Cinderella's home; the palace

Adapted from Prath and Palafox, 2017

❑ ***Dialogic Reading.*** For younger children, dialogic reading is very useful. Usually when adults share books with children, they read and the child listens. In dialogic reading, the adult helps the child become the storyteller. The adult plays the role of the audience member, listening and questioning. A key component of dialogic reading is the adult's expansion of the child's utterances. Use of dialogic reading with young ELLs with LI can set the stage for more sophisticated reading such as expository reading, or reading for information.

❑ ***Expository Reading.*** Expository reading (reading for information) is emphasized within the Common Core State Standards. Expository text related to topics that interest students can be highly beneficial in increasing reading fluency. The expository genre, also referred to as language of the curriculum, however, is one of the most difficult for readers to comprehend (Nippold, 2017). Some experts are recommending that professionals expose children to expository reading beginning in preschool (Simon-Cereijido, 2013). The VOLAR program for developing Spanish and English skills in preschoolers with LI, for example, includes a component in which nonfiction books are read (Gutiérrez-Clellen et al., 2013). These books relate to interesting topics such as jellyfish, slugs, and lizards.

1. While narratives/story books are important to development, books that present expository information can be used starting in preschool to prepare children for the greatly increased emphasis on expository reading n the early elementary school grades.

2. When expository reading activities are used, students can be challenged to justify answers to questions with information from the text. Specific Common Core State Standards require that students provide evidence for their answers to questions—they are asked to present arguments justified by the text that they have read (Wells, 2013).

3. Close, attentive, critical reading, referred to as **deep reading**, is crucial if students are to comprehend expository text. ELL students, especially those with LI, often benefit greatly from vocabulary development activities to increase their "deep reading" of expository text.

❑ ***Teaching content-area cognates***. As discussed in an earlier chapter, several researchers have put forth the idea of increasing reading comprehension and fluency by teaching content-area cognates if possible (Kohnert, 2013; Sheng, Lam, Cruz, & Fulton, 2016; Simon-Cereijido, 2013). For example, many words in Spanish are quite similar to their English counterparts. Professionals can use students' Spanish skills to teach new words in English.

> *Example 1:* When teaching geometry to Spanish-speaking students, use cognates such as angle (ángulo), triangle (triángulo), sphere (esfera), and parallel lines (lineas paralelas).

> *Example 2:* When teach geography, use cognates such as gulf (golfo), arid (arido), and volcanic (volcanico).

❑ ***Cloze Activities***. In cloze activities, approximately every fifth, seventh, or ninth word is omitted from a reading passage. Students fill the words in orally, or they can write in the words. Cloze activities help students to predict words and to use context to increase their understanding of what they are reading. A sample cloze reading activity is presented below:

> It was a beautiful day, and the _____ was shining. _____were singing in the trees. Carlita hoped it would not _____, because she wanted to take a walk. She looked up into the sky and saw gray _____ moving in. In Mexico, when it rained, sometimes there was _____ and _____. Everything would be _____ for a long time after it had rained. Carlita decided she had better take an_____ just in case.

❑ ***High Frequency Word Recognition***. Professionals can provide drill activities to help students learn to quickly identify high-frequency words to boost reading fluency. ELL students with LI often struggle when reading even simple high-frequency words such as the following:

the	of	and	a
to	in	you	is
that	it	at	he
for	on	are	as
with	his	they	be

Students who have not mastered high frequency words often find reading activities to be frustrating. I write the words on colorful 3" x 5" index cards (one word per card) and spray them with glitter. Even kindergarten ELLs with LI love reading their "magic words" as quickly as possible. Activities in which students create sentences using these words will increase students' awareness of how these words are used in meaningful contexts.

Tech Tip

How to Improve Reading Fluency Through Sight Word Drill and Sentence Formulation

This Turkish-English speaking 6-year-old child needs to improve her reading skills. In therapy, I work to build her sight word recognition. If children can read the most common sight words in English easily, their reading fluency will increase. Word drills, hands-on activities, etc. are shown in this video.
Go to youtube.com and type in Celeste Roseberry (Love Talk Read). Click on the video title above.

Using Technology to Build Reading Skills

The appropriate use of technology with ELLs can facilitate the development of reading comprehension (Kraemer & Bryla, 2017; Walker, Adams, Restrepo, Fialko, & Glenberg, 2017). Traditional books can be used in conjunction with online videos and interactive resources to present highly motivating activities. For example, reading comprehension can be increased by having students view YouTube videos related to the content of reading passages.

❏ Images and videos from the internet can be used to teach vocabulary and curriculum content. Recently, I was using a story called "Marigolds" with a student who did not know what the title meant. By looking up the word on Google Images, I was able to show the student several examples.

❏ Fun, interactive websites for young children such as www.primarygames.com and www.starfall.com feature music, games, phonological awareness development activities, and curriculum-oriented content in curriculum areas such as science and social studies. The websites include content that is in the public domain.

❏ Other highly-recommended websites include Interesting Things for ESL Students (www.manythings.org) and Repeat After Us: Your Online Library and Language Lab (www.repeatafter-us.com). The latter is a free resource that provides texts, audio clips, and other information to help ELL students increase their English reading fluency and pronunciation skills.

❏ Use of the iPad makes it possible to present special needs students with stories and other reading materials that are accompanied by music, colorful graphics, and interactive opportunities (Kraemer & Bryla, 2017). I use my iPad frequently when working with students who have LI, and find that students are highly motivated by the interactive resources that are available.

The Preview-View-Review Technique

One excellent strategy for increasing students' reading comprehension and overall vocabulary skills is the Preview-View-Review technique, illustrated in Figure 14.2. The adaptation of the Preview-View-Review (PVR) approach described below can help ELLs with LI learn to "read deeply" so that they can comprehend classroom texts and achieve grade level curriculum standards. At every grade level, students need to have the skills necessary to summarize what they have read and to describe themes and details—especially in expository texts.

The PVR technique promotes learning within authentic situations in which an emphasis is placed on meaning. As previously stated, the ideal situation is for professionals to utilize books or other curricular materials from the students' regular education classroom settings. For example, materials from classroom social studies books can be incorporated into speech-language therapy programs.

When working with younger children, professionals can start with a picture walk by talking about pictures before the actual reading takes place. This helps the child comprehend the "big picture" before reading.

Figure 14.2

SUPER POWER READING STRATEGIES

Before I read:

Look at the title, headings, and pictures.

Look at any words in italics or boldface.

Read the introductory and concluding paragraphs.

While I read:

Visualize what I read; make detailed pictures in my brain.

Ask myself questions about what I'm reading.

Predict what will happen next.

Highlight key ideas.

Look up new words that I do not know.

After I have read the whole thing:

Look at the title, headings, and pictures again.

Read over my highlights.

Ask questions about what I have just read.

Summarize what I have just read in my own words.

Suggestions for using the three PVR strategies are listed below:

❏ *Preview*

1. Get an overview of the chapter by doing the following:

    • Read the title.

    • Read the introductory paragraph or section.

    • Look at headings, subdivisions, and illustrations.

    • Make a table-of-contents outline from the information and use it as a study guide.

    • Examine the maps, graphs, charts, and other visuals.

    • Identify words in boldface or italics.

    • Do a "picture walk" by talking about pictures prior to actual reading.

2. Read the main idea sentence of key paragraphs to understand the chapter's general concepts.

3. Read the concluding paragraph or summary.

4. Read the main idea sentence of key paragraphs to understand the chapter's general concepts.

5. Read the concluding paragraph or summary.

❏ *View*

1. Read the text aloud and have the student follow along.

2. At natural stopping points, ask the student to explain what has just been read. If the student is working with a primary-language tutor, then the tutor and the student can discuss the printed text in the primary language.

3. Use the scaffolding technique if the student cannot answer a question. For example, if the student is unable to answer the question "Who was President of the United States during the Civil War?" ask an either/or question. For example, "During the Civil War, was Eisenhower or Lincoln the President of the United States?"

4. Help the student visualize what is being read, especially if there are no pictures accompanying the text. Remind the student to "make pictures in your mind about what we read." For example, if the student is reading about a village in a particular country, you can say, "Tell me what you think the village looks like," or "Make a picture in your mind about that. What does it look like to you?" Students can even draw pictures to illustrate text.

5. Help students look up definitions of unfamiliar terms. Many students need support in learning how to use a glossary. As mentioned previously, students can write new words

---

Tech Tie-In

Another useful site is www.starfall.com. This site targets phonological awareness and literacy skills. I have found that young children love the music and animation; the activities truly hold their interest.

and their definitions on index cards and draw pictures of what these terms depict. They can also use online dictionaries.

6. Have students highlight key words and phrases. If students are not allowed to write in these books, they can use sticky notes to write down questions and ideas that occur during reading. Some digital books permit digital highlighting.

7. Engage students in predicting what might happen next. Ask students, "What do you think will happen next? What made you think so?" This helps students use evidence from the text as mandated by the Common Core State Standards.

❏ *Review*

1. Ask for a brief summary of what was just said.

2. Ask students to express opinions about the material.
    Example:
    "Manuel, what do you think of that?"
    "What was your favorite thing about this adventure?"
    "What didn't you like about this story?"

3. Ask students to speculate about and expand on the information that was presented.
    Example:
    "Sergio, can you think of another example of ...?"
    "How would you have done things differently than...?"
    "What do you think might happen in the end?"

4. Look over chapter headings and subdivisions again to keep the big picture in focus.

5. Review new vocabulary words.

6. Read over highlights.

7. Ask questions about the content.
    1. general comprehension questions
    2. true-false questions
    3. either/or questions

8. Help the student answer the questions at the end of the chapter. Students can respond orally or in writing.

9. Have the student summarize the chapter orally or in writing. If the student types out the main points of the chapter using the computer, additional information can be easily inserted. The final product can be printed out, and the student can keep it for review.

10. Ask the student for his/her opinions about what was read by asking questions such as the following:

    A. What were the most important things in the chapter?

    B. What did you think were the most interesting things in the chapter?

    C. Was there anything you disagreed with? Why?

11. Find out if the student needs questions answered about the chapter.

12. Help the student create possible test questions and then have that student answer these questions. If there is a small group of students, they can exchange questions for practice.

Professionals can use the PVR technique with classroom materials as well as specialized materials. When classroom materials are used, students learn curriculum content as they apply strategies designed to help them learn more efficiently. Ideally, students will learn to use the strategies independently during various learning experiences in the classroom.

Tech Tip   *Intervention for ELLs with Language Impairment: Preview-View-Review for Reading Comprehension*

In this video, I use the Preview-View-Review (PVR) approach to reading with Cameron, a high school freshman. He brings his classroom text to therapy, and I tie therapy to classroom curriculum by using the PVR approach to increase Cameron's comprehension of expository/informational text.

Go to youtube and type in Celeste Roseberry (Love Talk Read). Click on the video with the title above.

CONCLUSION

When working with ELLs who have LI, professionals can use the holistic strategies approach to intervention. It is important to include intervention goals that correspond with classroom curriculum standards. Professionals must also strengthen students' underlying cognitive skills, especially working memory. Educational settings can be modified for optimal learning, and students can be supported as they learn social skills, vocabulary, and literacy skills. Using technology is recommended to enhance intervention efficacy and help students become technologically literate learners who are ready to compete in today's job market.

STUDY QUESTIONS

1. Summarize key components of the holistic-strategies approach.

2. Describe morphological awareness and its relationship to literacy. What are three specific activities professionals can present to increase students' morphological awareness?

3. Summarize the Preview-View-Review approach. How can speech-language pathologists successfully incorporate this approach into their therapy sessions?

MULTIPLE CHOICE

4. Interpersonal communication goals for ELLs with LI may include the following:

    A. The student will maintain appropriate eye contact with others during communication.
    B. The student will request clarification when something is not understood.
    C. The student will listen to others without interrupting.
    D. If a listener shows confusion, the student will repeat exactly what was said.
    E. The student will greet others by smiling and saying "hello" when appropriate.

5. Which one of the following is NOT included in the hierarchy for teaching phonological awareness skills?

    A. Count the number of words in a paragraph.
    B. Count the number of words in a sentence.
    C. Count the number of syllables in a word.
    D. Count the number of sounds in a word.
    E. Use sound-blending skills to identify words.

6. To help ELL students with LI, professionals should do the following:

    A. Use preparatory sets.
    B. Limit clutter in the environment.
    C. Use few visuals to reduce distractions, and rely primarily on the auditory mode of teaching to help students focus on the information being presented.
    D. Seat the learner in the front of the classroom.
    E. Avoid saying the student's name so that he or she does not become self-conscious.

7. You have a number of ELLs with LI on your caseload; they come from numerous language backgrounds. Special education personnel in your school district are making efforts to implement the Common Core State Standards. Which one of the following would NOT help your ELL students achieve the standards?

    A. Work on the vocabulary contained within classroom textbooks.
    B. Include morphological awareness activities in your treatment sessions.
    C. Discourage use of the students' first language at home and school because of the standards' emphasis on correct use of formal English.
    D. Help students learn to "read deeply" with expository text by having them stop occasionally to summarize what they have just read.
    E. Try to increase students' social oral language skills, especially in the areas of turn-taking and listening without interrupting.

8. Assad, a 7-year-old speaker of Pashto from Afghanistan, has LI and is on your caseload. Assad is failing most subjects and has no friends. Based on the teacher's report, Assad has experienced limited success in learning skills emphasized within the Common Core State Standards. He also performed poorly in both English and Pashto when these languages were tested. What will be your top two treatment priorities?

    A. Make sure that Assad is able to produce irregular past tense and plural forms correctly.
    B. Teach Assad how to initiate and continue conversation over 5-6 utterances on the same topic with same-age peers.
    C. Ensure that Assad understands complex Tier 3 vocabulary words from his classroom math book.

   D. Collaborate with the classroom teacher to ensure that classroom supports are in place (e.g., a peer buddy, front row seating, instructions written down).
   E. Work on syllabication of words from Assad's language arts book.

9. Many ELLs with LI that you serve on your caseload have deficits in vocabulary skills. You want to provide multiple exposures to words and to increase the student's active involvement in learning. Which of the following would help you achieve this goal?

   A. Use the internet (e.g., Google Images) to locate and share pictures of the words with students.
   B. Read books that use the words and have students summarize the books' contents using the new words.
   C. Prevent the use of iPad apps because these might be distracting.
   D. Connect with age-appropriate informational websites that contain information about the new words.
   E. Try when possible to play games with actual objects that represent the new words.

10. Juanita Rodriguez is a Spanish-speaking fifth grader with LI. She is struggling in the classroom, especially with more complex English. Juanita has poor auditory memory skills, but she is a gifted artist and draws sophisticated pictures. She enjoys putting together puzzles and enjoys talking about the latest clothing fashions. You want to improve Juanita's comprehension of information presented in the classroom. Select the BEST strategy for achieving this goal.

   A. Focus on key words as the teacher says them and write them down.
   B. Write down information and instructions in a notebook.
   C. Use reauditorization/silent rehearsal.
   D. Use visualization, creating detailed mental pictures as the teacher is speaking.
   E. Rely on the support of a peer buddy who can translate into Spanish so that Juanita's comprehension can be scaffolded throughout the day.

ANSWERS TO STUDY QUESTIONS

   4. A, B, C, and E
   5. A
   6. A, B, and D
   7. C
   8. B and D
   9. A, B, D, E
   10. D

Chapter 15

Working with Special Populations of Students with Disabilities

Outline
- Service Delivery to ELL Students with Hearing Impairment
- Service Delivery to ELL Students with Autism Spectrum Disorder
- Service Delivery to ELL Students with Intellectual Disability
- Students with Augmentative/Alternative Communication Needs
- Providing Services to Internationally Adopted Children
- Conclusion

English Language Learner (ELL) students who have exceptional language needs associated with hearing impairment (HI), neurological problems, and other disabilities present unique challenges for professionals who work with special learners and their families. This chapter addresses the needs of these student populations based on research regarding best practices for service delivery. Current research studies are summarized, and practical implications are described. The populations of ELL students addressed in this chapter include those with autism spectrum disorder (ASD), intellectual disability, hearing impairment, augmentative/alternative communication requirements, and other special learning needs. This chapter also specifically addresses the needs of children who are internationally adopted, and includes practical strategies for service delivery to them and their families. Some of the information reported in previous chapters is reiterated here because of its relevance to the populations being addressed.

As professionals work with culturally and linguistically diverse families who have children with various types of severe disabilities, it is important to be aware of the profound stress that these families may be experiencing. Families often experience shock as well as confusion, anger, anxiety, and a feeling of being overwhelmed. For most parents, the birth of a child with a severe disability creates a family crisis of considerable magnitude. For parents who are also struggling to learn English and survive economically, life can be difficult.

As discussed in previous chapters, parents from many cultures believe that the birth of a child with a disability, especially a severe one, occurs because of bad karma, the wrath of God, sins of parents and ancestors, witchcraft, and various other factors. It is important for professionals to be aware of cultural differences and sensitive to the specific concerns of family members.

❏ Professionals should be aware of the stigma that is associated with severe disabilities in many cultures. Parents can remain in denial for a long time. They may also be reluctant to avail themselves and their children of appropriate services. In many countries, services for children with serious disabilities are practically nonexistent; when these services are available, they are only available in segregated, special schools or institutions. For example, Srinivasan, Mathew, and Lloyd (2011) stated that in India today, only a few schools implement inclusion for children with intellectual disabilities; these children are generally segregated into special schools.

❏ Professionals should convey an attitude of friendship when interacting with families. Families of children with severe disabilities need to work with professionals who are not only knowledgeable and competent, but who also convey compassion and empathy.

❏ Professionals should show an interest in helping families by having resources available to share with them. These resources might include free or reduced cost medical care and other "basics" of life. Working with mediators from the families' cultures of origin is often quite beneficial.

❏ Professionals should encourage family members to speak the first language (L1) at home if they have limited proficiency in English. Children with moderate and severe disabilities often benefit most from exposure to two languages. Fluent, strong L1 skills support English acquisition and keep family members bonded; this is also the case for students with severe disabilities. The development of skills in the first language is an appropriate goal even in homes where a child has a language impairment associated with ASD, profound hearing loss, or another exceptional need.

Immigrant Insight   Vladimir, male speaker of Russian, immigrant from Russia

There were basically three kinds of schools in Russia: private schools, regular schools, and schools for "dummies." Students with disabilities were put in the schools for "dummies." These students were to be kept away from others. In my neighborhood, that school was known as School #22. If someone was sent to that school, they were hidden away and they would be there for life. There were armies of blind people living underground. Even if you only had ADD, you were separated from everyone else and not treated right. They also had separate hospitals for people with disabilities.

SERVICE DELIVERY TO ELL STUDENTS WITH HEARING IMPAIRMENT

In this section, the term hearing impaired (HI) is used to describe children whose hearing difficulties are moderate to profound and whose HI impacts daily communication and general life functions. HI in children can be mild, creating few problems with communication or academics. It can also be severe to profound, causing major communication problems and academic difficulties (Moeller & McCreery, 2017).

The incidence of HI is higher in some cultural groups than in others. Mehra, Eavey, & Keamy (2009) reported, based on their compilation of established studies, that Hispanic Americans had a higher prevalence of HI than children from other ethnic backgrounds. Children of migrant farm workers may be especially vulnerable to childhood-onset moderate-to-severe hearing loss because they work alongside their parents in jobs with high levels of noise exposure. Audiological services for these children are often remote and hard to come by.

Prognosis for the improvement of speech and language skills in children with HI depends on several factors: (1) how early in life these children receive professional help; (2) the scope and quality of the services the children receive; (3) the extent to which parents and other caregivers support these children; and (4) the presence of other disabling conditions (e.g., brain damage, blindness, atypical gross motor development, difficulties with sensory integration). An important consideration in the educational success of HI children is the age at which the hearing loss is identified. The later a hearing loss is identified, the more disruptive it is to the process of language development.

Unfortunately, children with HI who come from culturally and linguistically diverse backgrounds often do not receive the early intervention that they need.

❏ Early identification of hearing impairment often does not occur. Culturally and linguistically diverse families that live in rural areas, for example, may not have access to universal newborn screening, which can detect HI in infancy.

❏ Intervention services that are available may not be utilized. Migrant farm workers who have children with HI, for example, may have difficulty getting time off from work to take children to appointments or may not be able to provide transportation to these appointments. Families that are experiencing poverty may not utilize available services for a variety of reasons. Some parents are not aware of the services available for children with HI or do not understand how these programs will help their children.

Due to cultural differences, some families may view the intervention recommendations made by school professionals as being inappropriate for their children.

❏ Family members may believe that God has given the family a deaf child as a cross that they must bear. In China, some parents hide children with HI from society because of the embarrassment that they feel related to the disability. These parents have a vital role to play in their children's lives—finding a cure for the HI. The goal is to fix what is wrong with the child (Lytle, Johnson, & Hui, 2006).

❏ Some families believe that a faith healer can restore the child's hearing.

❏ Some Chinese parents believe that the use of herbs and acupuncture will "heal" the HI.

❏ Some families believe that a child with HI reflects some fault on the part of one or both parents. They may react to the HI by showing feelings of embarrassment or shame.

❏ In many cultures there are biases against individuals who have HI. Few services and opportunities are available to them, and their educational and vocational opportunities in life may be limited (Lytle et al., 2006; Mason, 2005; Monreal & Hernández, 2005).

❏ Families may be reluctant to seek out aural rehabilitation or to have these children wear a hearing aid. If a hearing aid is desired, professionals should pay attention to the color of the hearing aid selected for the child. Hearing aids will be more acceptable if they closely match children's skin tones.

❏ If the family believes that the HI can be healed by alternative methods, they may postpone seeking intervention and the child may suffer in the classroom. Smiley and Threats (2006) stated that professionals can deal with this problem in either of two ways:

1. Persuade families that the hearing loss is permanent; it cannot be "healed" or improved.

2. Explain that seeking professional services, such as those provided by an audiologist, does not negate the possibility of divine intervention or healing from an alternative means such as acupuncture. As Smiley and Threats (2006, p. 26) stated, "...science is not competing with religion, and they can both co-exist and work together to improve the child's life and possibilities."

Some of the major challenges faced by school professionals in meeting the needs of students with HI are the following:

❏ For many ELL students with HI, identity is a major issue. Does a Hispanic child who is deaf identify first with the Hispanic culture or deaf culture?

❏ The academic underachievement of these children in comparison to their hearing peers is widely documented. Some ELL deaf students start school behind their White peers and fall further behind each year (Parasnis & Fischer, 2005).

❏ Clinically significant oral and written language deficits are common among HI speakers of English and other languages. Tur-Kaspa and Dromi (2001), for example, found that deaf speakers of Hebrew had significantly more grammatical deviations in their written and spoken language samples than matched typically-hearing peers.

Sign Language and ELL Students

American Sign Language (ASL) is used widely with deaf and HI students in the United States. ELL children from other countries, however, may have little or no knowledge of English and may use a sign language system that is considerably different from ASL. Regional differences influence the use of sign language by deaf populations throughout the world. For instance, in China, there are several forms of Chinese sign language (Lytle et al., 2006).

Most Spanish-speaking countries have their own forms of sign language (e.g., Colombian Sign Language, Mexican sign language) (Berke, 2007). In Spain, three major sign languages are used by deaf populations. The first schools for the deaf in Peru were started by immigrants from the United States who brought ASL into the country. Many of these signs have become part of Peruvian Sign Language (Mattes & García-Easterly, 2007).

A variety of issues need to be considered related to the use of sign language with culturally and linguistically diverse populations.

❏ Immigrant parents of students with HI often feel that sign language will hinder the development of spoken language skills. They believe that if children learn to sign, they will not speak.

❏ Deaf children of hearing parents who do not use sign language may struggle more in school than deaf children of deaf parents who use sign language.

❏ ELL students with severe HI who immigrate to the United States may have had no exposure to sign language prior to their arrival. Some do not speak or sign at all, and many have never used a hearing aid. In many developing countries, services for HI students are minimal to nonexistent (Hutchins, 2017).

❏ Families who speak languages other than English at home may face a dilemma because they do not know sign language or English. If they select ASL as an option for their children, it becomes necessary to learn both ASL and English. This may be overwhelming, and the family may indicate that they just want their children to learn spoken English and not ASL.

❏ In some cultures, the sustained eye contact and touching of the head and face that accompany signing are cultural taboos.

❏ If professionals are going to teach sign language to culturally and linguistically diverse children, they may want to speak with a cultural mediator before the teaching begins to ensure that the methods being used are culturally congruent for children and their families.

Intervention for ELL Students with Hearing Impairment

Education of HI children is anchored in two major assumptions: (1) the earlier in life that intervention occurs, the better, and (2) parents play an integral role in the education of deaf children. As mentioned elsewhere in this book, for some families, early independence for children—and thus early intervention—are not priorities. In addition, families from some cultures believe that it is not appropriate for them to be involved in their children's education.

The following options should be considered in intervention programs for ELL students with hearing impairment:

❏ *High quality hearing aids.* Children with HI benefit greatly from hearing aids. Those who wear hearing aids on a regular basis (more than 10 hours a day) show the greatest gains in language and academic skills (Moeller & McCreery, 2017). We can support parents in finding resources to help their children receive and use high quality hearing aids.

❏ *Cochlear implants*. Profoundly deaf children who receive a cochlear implant at a young age develop language skills at a rate comparable to children with normal hearing (National Institutes of Health, 2017). Professionals can help families access insurance, interpreters, and other resources so that they can take advantage of cochlear implants for their young children. Unfortunately, access to cochlear implants is often impacted by socioeconomic status, with diverse families from low-income backgrounds having less access to these implants than White, middle-income children.

❏ *Sign language instruction*. Use of sign language as the medium of instruction facilitates success in learning the classroom curriculum. Communicative proficiency in ASL, for example, can be used to help students acquire knowledge of classroom subject matter (Paul, Norbury, & Gosse, 2018).

Children with HI are increasingly being integrated into general education classrooms with a decrease in the number being taught in self-contained classrooms (Watson, 2017). A possible challenge for diverse families is that in some countries, children with HI are segregated from their hearing peers. In the United States, "culture shock" is common when children with HI are integrated into general education classrooms with "normal" children. Therefore, it is important for teachers to make modifications such as those listed below:

1. Seat the student in a location where full visual access to the teacher is available.

2. Accommodate the student when changes in seating are necessary to maximize visual access.

3. Make sure that teachers and others presenting information have full lighting with no shadows.

4. Face the student when presenting information orally. Try not to speak when writing on the board if you are not facing the student.

5. Select a peer "buddy" to assist the student when problems are experienced understanding information presented orally.

6. Use visual aids as much as possible to supplement what the teacher is saying. For example, when discussing math problems, write the problems on the board or use an overhead projector with transparencies containing the math problems.

7. Ask the student to repeat instructions to verify that the information was heard and understood.

8. Seat the student away from sources of noise such as telephones, pencil sharpeners, and open windows.

It is important to provide the child with appropriate assistive technology. As previously mentioned, FM units can be very helpful. The use of DVDs and computers makes it easy for professionals to use both the auditory and visual modalities to present learning activities. Evidence has been found that the repeated viewing of math expository books on DVDs paired with preteaching of the target vocabulary words was successful in helping subjects learn to sign math vocabulary. The subjects enjoyed the DVDs and did not appear to be bored or fatigued by multiple DVD viewings (Cannon, Fredrick, & Easterbrooks, 2010).

When teaching students with HI, use of both the home language and English can be helpful in facilitating language development in both languages. Bunta and Douglas (2013) studied the effects of dual-language support on the language skills of bilingual Spanish-English children with HI who use listening devices (cochlear implants and hearing aids). They found that both languages (first language and English) can be supported in Spanish-speaking children with HI. Bilingual children who participated in a dual-language Spanish-English program demonstrated language skills on general English language measures that were commensurate with those of their monolingual English-speaking peers. No evidence was found to indicate that either the first language or English should be discouraged.

Based on a literature review, Douglas (2011b, p. 27) stated the following:

> Current literature and examples of today's practicing institutions in North America demonstrate that adequate instruction in both languages can support proficient bilingual acquisition in children with HI. Encouraging minority language development neither impairs children with HI nor prevents them from learning the majority language in the presence of adequate speech perception and an effective immersion process. Furthermore, support of the home language may improve caregivers' ability to maximize benefits from intervention practices and even help them to embrace their children's deafness.

Immigrant Insight

Christine V., university senior,
daughter of Chinese immigrants

I was born with a hearing loss. My dad worked 12 hours a day, six days a week, when I was young. He blamed himself for my hearing loss because he wasn't around to take care of me. Unfortunately, he did not support any type of intervention until my first grade Chinese teacher told him that I might have to repeat a grade and explained how my hearing loss affected my academics and my speech. Because of this, my parents got me hearing aids and let me go see a speech therapist. My dad asked me if I had to wear my hearing aids often, because he preferred that I not wear them. He continued to blame himself for my hearing loss, and took me to a clinic at University of California, Davis to see if the loss was genetic. It turned out that it was, and my father was assured that my hearing loss had nothing to do with his sins. I pointed out that a couple of relatives from both sides of our family had hearing losses. I also assured him that I was doing fine in school. Because of this, he learned to accept my hearing loss even though it took 18 years. I have been accepted into an AuD program, and am excited to start working on my doctorate in audiology!

SERVICE DELIVERY TO ELL STUDENTS WITH AUTISM SPECTRUM DISORDER

An increasing number of children throughout the world are being diagnosed with autism spectrum disorder (ASD) (Karanth, Roseberry-McKibbin, & James, 2017c). In the U.S., approximately 1 in 68 children are diagnosed with ASD (Wright, 2017). Japan, the United Kingdom, China, Denmark, and Russia have also reported an increased number of cases (The Centers for Disease Control & Prevention, 2013). It was reported that in South Korea, the incidence of ASD is 1 in 38 children (Kim et al., 2011). Thus, in the United States, professionals may expect to see an increase in the number of immigrant students with Autism Spectrum Disorder (ASD).

Immigrant Insight   Ngoc, female speaker of Cantonese, immigrant
                           from China and Vietnam

In the Chinese culture, many believe that there are things a woman should not do when she is pregnant. Sharp objects should not be used because that would be clipping off the unborn child's lip which would cause a cleft lip or palate. As parents of an autistic son, we believe that someone in his past life must have done something terribly bad.

❑ Identification of ASD in young children is challenging for professionals who work with monolingual English-speaking children and their families. It is often more complex when ELL students are involved.

❑ ELL students with autism have a triple-layered challenge: they are culturally diverse, linguistically diverse, and have an exceptionality that often involves highly divergent behavior patterns.

❑ Unfortunately, if young children are not speaking, pediatricians may attribute the observed behaviors to the bilingual situation at home and may tell parents that the children will "grow out of it."

❑ In some cultures, there is a greater tolerance for boys who demonstrate delays in learning to speak. These boys are not viewed with alarm or suspicion; they will eventually speak, and no one is worried about their lack of verbalization.

❑ In many countries, there is little or no recognition of the phenomenon of ASD. If there is recognition of ASD, there may be a stigma attached to it. Families may believe that the child's problem is the outcome of witchcraft, punishment for sins, and other causes; this can make them reluctant to seek services.

❑ Some families fear that females with disabilities will have difficulty finding a marriage partner. In other Asian cultures, many believe that even siblings of children with disabilities will experience difficulty finding marriage partners (Chan & Chen, 2011). Thus, the family may not be willing to accept the ASD diagnosis.

❑ It is imperative that educational professionals help educate members of the medical community about early ASD diagnosis in ELL children because early assessment and intervention are critical in helping these children achieve their potential.

In one research study (Zuckerman et al., 2013), a survey was sent to 267 California pediatricians who served Hispanic families. Although 81% of the pediatricians offered some form of developmental screening, only 29% offered Spanish ASD screening per American Academy of Pediatrics guidelines. Only 10% offered both Spanish general developmental and Spanish ASD screening per American Academy of Pediatrics guidelines.

Most pediatricians in this survey thought parents in families who spoke primarily Spanish were less knowledgeable about ASD than White parents. The most frequent barrier to ASD identification in Hispanic children was lack of access to developmental specialists. The study showed that there was an average 2.5 year delay in diagnosis of ASD in Hispanic children compared to Whites.

These results are somewhat shocking in a state such as California where there are more Hispanics than non-Hispanic Whites. Zuckerman et al. (2013) emphasized the point that there needs to be much earlier, more accurate diagnosis for all children so that they can benefit from early intervention.

The extent to which families are able to accept having children with disabilities such as ASD varies from culture to culture. Cho, Singer, and Brenner (2003) interviewed immigrant Korean mothers to the United States and mothers living in Korea; all were mothers of children with ASD. Cho et al. found that mothers living in Korea experienced more difficulties than those living in the United States. Mothers in Korea shared more situations of experiencing negative reactions from others, especially involving shame and humiliation in public when their children misbehaved. They reported feeling demoralized much more often than mothers from the United States.

Cho et al. (2013) recommended that especially upon initial diagnosis of ASD in children, professionals need to listen carefully to Korean mothers and be sensitive to low morale and suicidal ideation. In some traditional Korean families, suicide may be considered an honorable way to remove shame from the larger extended family. Stress levels for Korean mothers of children with ASD in the U.S. were greatly mitigated by support groups, the provision of services for children, and professional support.

Mahendra (2012) conducted an in-depth interview with an Asian Indian mother of a child with ASD. This mother experienced a high level of stress, and stated that she felt sidelined and isolated by some of the accomplished, educated Asian Indian parents in her social network. The mother shared that these parents had very high aspirations for their children's social and academic achievement, and were entirely unaware of ASD and its impact on development. This mother grew to realize that she was not always welcome in select social circles; she and her son were not invited to play dates and parties. Her sense of isolation and sorrow was very great, as her family was back in India.

Professionals should look for specific "red flags" that are common to children across different countries and cultures (Karanth, Roseberry-McKibbin, & James, 2017a; Rubin, 2017):

1. Child does not respond when others smile.

2. Child does not respond when name is called.

3. Child does not respond when others point.

4. Child does not "read" others' faces for information.

5. Child does not join functional play with an adult.

6. Child does not initiate requests.

7. Child shows a clear preference for non-social stimuli and less social engagement.

Some families of students with suspected or diagnosed ASD view disabilities differently than mainstream professionals and thus may not be comfortable with recommended assessment and intervention protocols.

❏ Some Navajos believe that a person with a disability is a teacher for the entire tribe. The person with the disability brings special lessons to the tribe; she has a unique gift to offer. If she receives specialized interventions, this could potentially interfere with the delivery of the message to the tribe (Dyches et al., 2004; Rogers-Adkinson, Ochoa, & Delgado, 2003).

❏ As stated, the provision of services for ASD students may conflict with the cultural values of some culturally and linguistically diverse families. Also, the teaching strategies used in such programs may not "fit" with the expectations of parents. For example, in many cultures, the use of token economies (a popular strategy for the treatment of students with ASD) is a completely unfamiliar concept (Rogers-Atkinson et al., 2003).

❑ Some special education professionals use a play-based approach to treatment for young children with ASD. Asian parents, however, may prefer highly structured learning that involves repeated and systematic practice of new skills (Trembath et al., 2005).

❑ Individuals from some cultures may feel uncomfortable participating in activities involving dolls and plastic toys because they do not have these items at home (Norbury & Sparks, 2012).

❑ Some families will reject intervention that calls for parents to follow a child's lead in play, to engage in pretend play, or to talk about what children are doing. This is because (1) the family's circumstances do not allow for play, and/or (2) adults within the culture typically do not engage in play activities with children. In these circumstances, older siblings and peers can be trained to carry out and generalize therapy goals.

Immigrant Insight   Hafeza, daughter of Moroccan immigrants

My mother is a principal of a Moroccan public school. She told me that there is no special education in the public schools and that they have special centers to work with children with problems. Children with autism are treated like they are possessed, so they chain them, and put them in a cave where supposedly good men used to live, and they leave them there all night long...the government is not doing anything about it.

Working with Parents of Students with Autism Spectrum Disorder

School professionals should interact with parents to determine how the child's disability is impacting their lives. It is important to respect beliefs that parents have relating to the cause of the child's disorder and how it should be treated. Parents often feel isolated and may experience depression related to the child's disability.

❑ Shakir and Roseberry-McKibbin (2014) found that over 70% of caregivers of children with ASD in a culturally diverse support group agreed or strongly agreed that they experienced feelings of isolation; one mother commented "I don't know nobody who got kids with autism." Over 50% of caregivers in the support group agreed that the child with ASD had a negative impact on their marriage.

❑ Ijalba (2016) surveyed Hispanic immigrant mothers of children with ASD. These mothers reported that they experienced frequent social isolation and stigmatization; they were also reluctant to speak Spanish with their children.

❑ Treatment procedures used with students who have ASD in our schools may be very different from those used within the child's home country.
  1. In China, treatment for children with ASD can include acupuncture, music therapy, and herbal remedies (Chan & Chen, 2011). Acupuncture for children with ASD is believed to focus on areas thought to be involved with ASD (e.g., the frontal lobe and cerebellum) (Clark & Zhou, 2005).

2. Qigong, a highly specialized type of Chinese massage has been found to help some children with ASD (Silva & Cignolini, 2005).

3. Some Filipinos believe that faith healers can heal ASD in children (Santos & Chan, 2011).

❑ Professionals should inform parents that instructional approaches used in school can coexist with alternative forms of intervention. For example, if a Chinese family accepts Western intervention for their child with ASD, the use of Qigong massage doesn't necessarily need to be discontinued at home.

❑ It is important to consider parents' feelings related to use of the primary language and English in instructional programs. A survey of parents of children with ASD revealed that many were concerned that a bilingual home environment would be confusing for their children and exacerbate language delays. This was especially true of parents whose children had lower verbal skills. Parents, however, also identified potential benefits of bilingualism, including maintenance of an affectionate and close bond with their children (Hampton, Rabagliai, Sorace, & Fletcher-Watson, 2017).

Immigrant Insight   Diana, female college senior, speaker of Spanish from Mexico

My younger brother Daniel was diagnosed with autism at the age of 2. He went to a speech-language pathologist in California who was a monolingual English speaker. My mom only spoke Spanish at the time. The speech-language pathologist recommended that our family choose just one language for Daniel to speak; she believed that Daniel's exposure to two languages was contributing to his delay. Now Daniel is fluent in English (at 12 years old) and can only say a few basic sentences in Spanish. But we recently went to Mexico for three weeks, and it was astonishing to see the amount of Spanish that Daniel picked up. If we had stayed one month longer, he would have probably become fluent! He would crack jokes in Spanish, tell stories, go to the store by himself and buy candy and chips using Mexican currency…kids with special needs have the potential to learn two languages and we shouldn't be limiting them. I think a second language provides more vocabulary and opportunities and gives an individual more flexibility to communicate.

When working with parents of children who have ASD, it is important to do the following:

1. Set aside time to have conversations with parents to ensure that you understand their concerns.

2. Provide detailed information to parents about ASD and the treatment options that are available.

3. Provide families with information about respite care.

4. Encourage caregiver participation in the treatment program so that caregivers do not feel "sidelined."

5. Emphasize that bilingualism is a desirable goal and that bilingual exposure will not be confusing or deleterious to children with ASD. Research studies have found that bilingualism in children with ASD is attainable, realistic, and desirable (Ijalba, 2016; Kay-Raining

Bird et al., 2012; Reetzke, Zou, Sheng, & Katsos, 2015). Bilingual parents of children with ASD, however, are often discouraged from training their children to speak more than one language (Kay-Raining Bird et al., 2012; Yu, 2013).

6. Provide parents with resources and practical strategies for supporting bilingual development in children with ASD.

Intervention Suggestions for Students with Autism Spectrum Disorder

The following suggestions will he helpful in intervention programs for students with ASD:

1. Use bilingual specialists to provide instruction if at all possible. If bilingual specialists are not available, English as a Second Language and special education personnel can collaborate to design appropriate programs.

2. Encourage the development of proficiency in both the primary language and English. Students with ASD can and do become bilingual; it is important for these students to maintain their home language in addition to learning English so they can interact and communicate at home, school, and in the community.

3. Reinforce the student for following school rules and conforming to classroom expectations. Many children with ASD, for example, are sensitive to food textures. Families often want their children to eat ethnic foods as much as possible. Although efforts should be made to offer "ethnic foods," students should also learn to tolerate the more "mainstream" foods that are commonly offered at school (Rogers-Adkinson et al., 2003).

4. Pair students with peer buddies for increased socialization opportunities. Students with ASD generally need to learn basic social interaction skills (Karanth, Roseberry-McKibbin, & James, 2017b).

Profile

Abdul S. was referred to me by his kindergarten teacher. The teacher was concerned because after two years of kindergarten, Abdul rarely spoke in the classroom setting. He was from a Pakistani Urdu-speaking family, and the teacher had initially told herself to "give him time" to develop. She did not want to refer him unnecessarily for a special education evaluation. However, after two years of kindergarten and "extra" non-special education services, Abdul's progress was very limited.

When I met with his mother, Mrs. S., she said that prenatal testing during her pregnancy with Abdul revealed that he only had one kidney. The hospital personnel strongly urged Mrs. S. to terminate the pregnancy. Mrs. S., being Muslim, would not terminate her pregnancy. Abdul was born at seven months' gestation and spent much of the first year of his life in the neonatal intensive care unit.

Mrs. S. told me that Abdul spoke his first word in Urdu when he was three years old. She said that his brother spoke much better and earlier than Abdul. Abdul often echoed what his brother said and had difficulty remembering directions that were given to him at home in Urdu.

I evaluated Abdul in both English and Urdu (with the help of an interpreter). He was placed into speech-language therapy. He was also evaluated by the school psychologist, using a battery consisting primarily of nonverbal measures, and was diagnosed with an intellectual disability and autistic-like behaviors.

Today, Abdul is a handsome, well-behaved fifth grader who receives speech-language therapy and support from the site resource specialist. In junior high school, he will probably participate in a functional life skills class especially designed to support students with similar learning needs.

We found out after several years of intervention that Abdul's parents were first cousins.

SERVICE DELIVERY TO ELL STUDENTS WITH INTELLECTUAL DISABILITY

The identification of intellectual disability (ID) is often difficult in students who speak two languages. ELL students tend to be over-identified with ID because of biased standardized testing in English. Conversely, they may be under-identified because school personnel attribute signs of ID to typical second language and bilingualism phenomena. The support of bilingual professionals and the use of nonbiased assessment tools is critical.

❏ Some populations of ELL students are vulnerable to ID because of poverty. Pregnant mothers may not be able to access prenatal health care or nutritious food and, therefore, are more likely to have children with ID. Professionals need to help these mothers become aware of free prenatal services.

❏ ELL students may also be exposed to lead pre- or post-natally at a higher rate than mainstream students if they are poor or work with their migrant parents in the fields.

❏ Kay-Raining Bird, Cleave, Trudeau, Thordardottir, Sutton, and Thorpe (2005) compared the language abilities of children with Down syndrome who were being raised bilingually with those of three control groups matched on developmental level. These three control groups consisted of (1) monolingual typically-developing children; (2) monolingual children with Down syndrome; and (3) bilingual typically-developing children. The results indicated that exposure to two languages had no detrimental effects on the language development of children with Down syndrome. Kay-Raining Bird et al. (2005) stated that diverse children with Down syndrome can become functionally bilingual; they should not be restricted to just one language.

❏ Kay-Raining Bird, Genesee, and Verhoeven (2016) argued for the implementation of full inclusion policies, in schools, that provide increased access to dual language programs for children with ID. Bilingual children with ID tend to be placed in restrictive educational settings, and they need access to a complete range of support services.

❏ Gronroos (2003) discussed recommendations for interacting with ELL families who have children with ID. She stated that the services of a cultural mediator should be used, and that this mediator should be provided by the school district, not the parents. Parents might not anticipate a diagnosis of ID, and to have someone from their community give them this news might be humiliating for them.

❏ Checa, Galeote, and Soto (2016) studied the early vocabulary development of Spanish-speaking children with Down syndrome and their typically-developing peers. The children with Down syndrome produced more nouns than their peers. Checa et al. recommended that intervention programs for Spanish speakers with Down syndrome address the development of necessary word classes.

Immigrant Insight   Miriam A., university senior, Yemen and Lebanon

My uncle, who has Down syndrome and is Yemeni, was raised in the U.S. Growing up here, he participated in Special Olympics, learned how to play the guitar, and still goes to school to this day. In contrast, my aunt (Palestinian and Egyptian) was raised in Lebanon in a refugee camp. She is 35 years old now. She started going to school when she was young, but her mother figured "What's the point?" and took her out of school. School was expensive, and the family's resources were limited. My aunt stays at home most of the time with family, and goes out with them every once in a while. Her mother (my grandma) passed away after caring for my aunt, and now my aunt's older siblings take care of her and find things for her to do. They have helped her develop hobbies. I hope that in the future, those in refugee camps will become more aware of persons with disabilities.

Supporting Parents of Students with Intellectual Disability

In many countries, services for children with ID are limited, and these children are neglected by the system (Wang, Hsieh, Heller, Davidson, & Janicki, 2007). Parents are not able to discuss their children's issues openly. They may feel shame and personal responsibility for their children's circumstances. For example, some Chinese parents who have children with ID experience feelings of humiliation and believe that the ID is a result of sins committed by parents or ancestors (Wang et al., 2007).

School professionals need to be sensitive to cultural differences in beliefs about disabilities and attitudes relating to intervention for students with ID.

❑ Some East Indian parents who practice Hinduism and believe in karma view ID as punishment for actions in a past life (Nichols & Keltner, 2005). Even if these parents live in the United States, they may hide the child and not seek out health or educational services.

❑ Some culturally diverse families believe that they need to take on the entire responsibility for the care of children with ID, even after these children become adults (Rueda, Manzo, Blacher, Shapiro, & Gonzalez, 2005). These families should be presented with options for accessing services if they want them. Mothers who spend all of their time caring for children with ID may experience depression if they do not have access to support and services.

❑ Chan and Chen (2011) discussed Asian mothers' beliefs about children with ID; one mother believed that her failure to eat adequate amounts of bone soup during pregnancy had led to her daughter's Down syndrome. A Vietnamese mother attributed her son's intellectual disabilities to the shellfish she ate during pregnancy. Many Asian parents believe that children's disabilities are punishment for sins or moral transgressions of parents or ancestors.

❑ Skinner, Correa, Bailey, and Skinner (2001) conducted interviews with 250 Mexican and Puerto Rican parents of young children with ID who lived in the United States. They found that for the majority of the subjects, faith in God and the church constituted strong foundations of support as they cared for their children. If parents of ELL children with ID refuse support or services from educational or medical institutions, they might be willing to accept support from their churches. Professionals can create ties with local churches to obtain their support.

Immigrant Insight   Alicia, speaker of Chinese, daughter of Chinese immigrants

In Chinese culture, it is normal to believe that things can affect the body in good or bad ways. One of my aunts conducts blood testing for race horses. When she got pregnant with her first child, the doctors found through prenatal testing that the baby had Down syndrome. My aunt decided to abort the baby. My grandma was convinced that the reason the baby had Down syndrome was that my aunt worked with horses' blood; the blood had supernatural properties that affected the baby she was carrying. I told my grandma that as a speech-language pathologist, I would be working with children who had intellectual disabilities. She advised me to stop pursuing the field of speech-language pathology because she feared that working so closely with children with these disabilities would affect my womb and cause my future babies to have disabilities.

STUDENTS WITH AUGMENTATIVE/ALTERNATIVE COMMUNICATION NEEDS

The use of augmentative/alternative communication (AAC) devices is common in programs for students with disabilities that affect oral expression. An AAC system utilizes strategies, aids, symbols, and techniques to augment communication and/or provide alternative ways of communicating (King, 2014). The purpose of intervention using AAC devices is to provide students with skills that will help them become self-reliant, independent, and productive adults. Significant advances in technology have resulted in improvements in the quality of life for many students with severe developmental and intellectual disabilities (Davidoff, 2017).

Profile

Alexi, a student in tenth grade, came to an American school as a second grader. His family immigrated from Russia. Alexi had cerebral palsy and was a quadriplegic. He used an augmentative communication device because he was unable to speak. The speech-language pathologist who assessed him in tenth grade found that he had no history of receiving ESL services. No one even knew he was Russian. The speech-language pathologist arranged for Alexi to have ESL support services as well as speech-language therapy to help him become a more successful communicator at school and at home.

Research documents the fact that today, more and more users of AAC devices are from culturally and linguistically diverse communities (Binger & Light, 2006; Binger, Kent-Walsh, Berens, Del Campo, & Rivera, 2008; Karanth, Roseberry-McKibbin, & James, 2017f; Nakamura, Iwabuchi, & Alm, 2006). In fact, AAC technologies are increasingly being used in other countries (Crowley & Baigorri, 2012; Srivivasan et al., 2011). It is projected that by the year 2020, the largest non-European American population of AAC consumers will be members of the Hispanic community (Soto, Huer, & Taylor, 1997). When the students are from ELL backgrounds, the following questions are important to consider:

❏ *What are the socio-pragmatic rules governing interaction in the child's own culture?* We cannot just superimpose Western notions of what comprises successful and appropriate interactions onto clients from various culturally and linguistically diverse backgrounds. For example, children from traditional African backgrounds are generally not encouraged to question adults or initiate verbal communication with them. However, if an African child uses an AAC device and spends most of her time with an adult caregiver, she will need to learn to do this. Cultural issues are important to consider in determining how AAC devices will be used with students. The environmental context in which assistive technology strategies are to be implemented often influences a family's willingness to use these strategies (Parette, Chang, & Huer, 2004; Parette, Huer, & Peterson-Karlan, 2008).

❏ *To what extent do family members use computers and other "high tech" devices at home?* Some families, especially if they have immigrated from rural areas in developing countries, will be intimidated and overwhelmed by electronic AAC devices and computer-based AAC systems. In cases such as these, professionals may need to introduce low-tech devices or even printed boards that have picture symbols placed on them (Crowley & Baigorri, 2012). Words on communication boards can be arranged alphabetically or grouped into categories.

❏ *Do parents and family members view the use of AAC devices as appropriate for children with disabilities?* If the family views the disability as the "will of God," for example, the use of AAC devices may be considered inappropriate. Families (including members of the extended family) should always be made aware of a range of choices and options with regard to the use of AAC devices by their children (Parette, Huer, & Wyatt, 2003; Vanbiervliet & Parette, 2002).

❏ *Is the development of augmentative communication skills viewed as a high priority by the child's family?* Huer and Soto (2006) stated that for some culturally and linguistically diverse families, issues of survival might take priority over educational and clinical concerns.

❏ *How should parents be taught to use AAC devices?* Kent-Walsh and Rosa-Lugo (2006) reported that ELL families are not provided with sufficient training in the use of AAC devices. The families in their study valued actual demonstrations of facilitative interaction strategies much more than verbal explanations. It is important to show parents how AAC devices can be used to facilitate effective communication and social interactions in a variety of contexts.

Using Picture Symbols with Bilingual Students

Suggestions are listed below for selecting and using picture symbols with ELL students who have AAC needs:

❏ *Make efforts to set up AAC devices that will make it possible to communicate in both the home and school languages.* Picture communication systems with printed text in L1 and English make it possible for the child to interact with speakers of either language. The Bilingual Picture Symbol Communication Resource (Academic Communication Associates, 2007) includes picture communication boards with text in both English and Spanish. These boards can be used to communicate basic needs and to share information in either language.

❏ *Record messages for voice output devices in the family's primary language* (Davidoff, 2017). This will facilitate communication that is culturally relevant.

❏ *Make sure that the picture symbols used in AAC devices are relevant to the cultural experiences of the student.* Students from different cultural backgrounds may assign different meanings to identical symbols. Moreover, multiple symbols may be needed even for high frequency words. A picture symbol for the word "eat," that shows a child eating with a fork, for example, may not be a good choice for children who eat with chopsticks at home.

❏ *Consult with families when selecting vocabulary items. Items should be selected that are used frequently at home and in the child's community.* AAC devices need to provide access to vocabulary that will help the student function effectively in his social environment.

❏ *Make sure to arrange picture symbols in sequences that are appropriate for the structure of the student's language.* Sentences in Spanish, for example, often include more words than their English translations. Moreover, word order often differs in the two languages. Therefore, boards created for use in English may need to be adapted for use in other languages such as Spanish.

❏ *Encourage family members to participate in the actual development of AAC learning materials.* Family members, for example, can record words in the home language for use in AAC devices as mentioned previously.

AAC Research with ELL Students

Limited research has been conducted relating to the use of AAC devices with ELL students.

❏ Huer, Parette, & Saenz (2001) used interview procedures to obtain information about the use of AAC devices with ELLs from Mexican American families. The results indicated that families preferred that their children use speech or sign language over assistive technology. Families were concerned about the cost of AAC equipment, and some family members felt uncomfortable with the responsibility of using expensive equipment. The researchers conjectured that perhaps some of the AAC devices given to these families were not useful at home because they were programmed in English for use at school. All of the families in this study wished for devices that would make Spanish communication possible. They also wanted more training in how to operate their children's AAC devices.

❏ Parette, Chuang, and Huer (2004) interviewed six Chinese families who had immigrated to the United States from Taiwan and Hong Kong. Each family had been in the United States for at least 10 years. In each family, a child had ASD and used an AAC device. Parette et al. found that Chinese families in their sample differed from stereotypical Asian families in several respects. First, these families did not feel personal shame about their children's ASD. They embraced the mainstream American value of independence for their children. In addition, they actively participated in educational decisions for their children and were happy to be included; they did not abdicate responsibility solely to specialists. The researchers concluded that the higher degree of income, educational level, and acculturation of these particular families might have impacted their reactions to service providers and willingness to accept services.

❏ ELLs respond positively to iPad apps that train language skills (Bryla & Roseberry-McKibbin, 2014; Kraemer & Bryla, 2017). The iPad can be used in a variety of ways to facilitate communication. Apps can also be used with iPhones. However, professionals must make sure that play and communication apps do not result in focusing more on technology than on the needs of the child (Davidoff, 2017; Karanth, Roseberry-McKibbin, & James, 2017g).

Profile

Xiu came to the United States from Huangzhow, China to seek help for her son Shing, a student with ASD. In China, when Shing was approaching two years of age, Xiu began to realize that there was something "different" about him. She approached the pediatrician, who told her that everything was fine, emphasizing that children develop on different timelines. After another year had gone by, Xiu knew that Shing wasn't fine. She took him to specialists, who diagnosed him with ASD. After learning about this diagnosis, Xiu's husband divorced her. He disowned Shing and blamed Xiu, saying that it was her fault that Shing had these problems. He and his family decided to try to kill Xiu and Shing, as they were bringing dishonor to the family lineage.

Xiu fled to the United States in search of help and support. She brought Shing to a local center that provided speech-language therapy and academic help. Xiu decided to change her name and that of her child because she was afraid for their safety. She knew that she had shamed her husband's family by giving birth to a child with ASD.

Shing responded well to intervention and continues to make progress. Xiu now expresses gratitude for the help provided to Shing since her arrival in the United States and for the support that she has received.

PROVIDING SERVICES TO INTERNATIONALLY ADOPTED CHILDREN

Immigrant Insight   Jessica, senior college student from Korea
                            adopted by White American parents

I was adopted by American parents when I was 4 months old. I know almost nothing about my birth parents, except that both were tall and they met in a bar. In Korea, it is a great disgrace to have a child out of wedlock. Korean orphanages are high quality; caregivers attend to and play with the children. My adoptive mom is blond and blue-eyed. She and my dad have been very open with me about things, and have taken me to a lot of Korean and international adoption types of events.

I visited Korea several years ago with a friend. She actually got to meet her biological parents. There were five older siblings and a younger brother. My friend's parents stated that they gave her up for adoption because they were farmers and wanted a boy, not another girl, to help them run the farm. When this young lady was born—the sixth girl—they gave her up and tried (successfully) for a boy. My friend's parents were not especially enthusiastic about meeting her, and it was a very tough and awkward interaction.

Background and Statistics

Many American parents adopt children from overseas. The peak of international adoption in the U.S. occurred in 2004 (23,000 children) and dropped down by almost 80% to 5,370 children in 2016 (U.S. Department of State, 2017). In 2012, the most common countries that Americans adopted children from were China, Ethiopia, Russia, South Korea, and Ukraine.

Thousands of Americans have adopted children from Russia over the years. However, on December 28, 2012, Russian president Vladimir Putin signed a new law banning Americans from adopting children from Russia. This law went into effect on New Year's Day in 2013, and it has impacted the number of international adoptions that are occurring in the U.S. today. Reportedly, in Russia, 56% of those surveyed in an opinion poll backed Putin and did not want Americans adopting Russian children (Rapoza, 2013).

In May 2017, the U.S. Department of State put out an alert that Ethiopia may be banning international adoptions of Ethiopian children. American parents in the process of adopting children from Ethiopia were urged to consider adoption from other countries.

Immigrant Insight   Oksana, female speaker of Russian, immigrant from Russia; senior college student

> My husband and I worked numerous times in Russian orphanages, and we both have a passion for adoption. Our experience working with Russian orphans has been nothing but heartbreaking. Yet the situation gets worse with the new law—my husband Andrey and I are devastated. Because we are now U.S. citizens, we hoped to adopt a child—but we can't. Family values are almost nonexistent in Russia, and the number of orphans continues to rise. Today is Mother's Day and it is a difficult day for many children.

There are several reasons for the declining number of IAC in the U.S. First, many countries are developing stronger resources for domestic adoption. An issue for would-be adoptive parents from outside those countries is that generally, in-country adoptive parents want to adopt young, healthy children. Thus, the only children left for international adoption are older and have more entrenched problems in a variety of areas (Elleseff, 2013). Other reasons for the decline in international adoptions in the U.S. include more paperwork and longer wait times (Rapoza, 2013).

❏ In some countries, children are placed in foster care. These children are generally seen to have stronger health and cognitive outcomes relative to peers adopted from institutions in the same country (Wilson, 2012). However, one variable that must be taken into account is that many children have experienced multiple foster care placements with resulting negative sequelae.

❏ The reasons that children become available for adoption vary from country to country. For example, families in China, India, Vietnam, and other countries tend to prefer male children over female children. As a result, more girls than boys are available for adoption. China's "one child" policy and the larger value placed on male children has led to greater numbers of Americans adopting Chinese girls in particular (Chan & Chen, 2011; Roberts & Scott, 2011).

❏ In 2016, China changed its policy to allow two children per family. It remains to be seen whether or not this change in Chinese family policy impacts the number of Chinese girls adopted by American families.

❏ In many countries, poverty is an issue that causes children to be placed in orphanages. In some countries, there is a stigma attached to being a single mother, and babies are abandoned for this reason (Wilson, 2012). Children may also be removed from homes in which abuse or neglect has occurred (Rimashevskaia, 2007).

❏ For many children previously adopted from Russia, the paperwork documenting their parents' termination of rights refers to alcoholism (Landry, 2007). Many Russian women drink alcohol during pregnancy. Parents often do not know that alcohol consumption is deleterious to their babies' development (Aronson, 2007). The presence of Fetal Alcohol Syndrome has been documented in children from Ukraine, Russia, and other parts of Eastern Europe (Elleseff, 2013; Ladage & Harris, 2012).

❏ During pregnancy, expectant mothers may experience other factors that impact their developing fetuses. These factors include malnutrition, mental health disorders, infectious diseases, environmental exposure to heavy metals, radiation, and other toxins, and intake of tobacco, alcohol, and illicit as well as legal drugs. Some mothers have engaged in prostitution and may have sexually transmitted diseases. Maternal malnutrition is common (Ladage & Harris, 2012).

❏ Conditions in orphanages vary from country to country. Experts have frequently pointed out that there are often great differences in the quality of orphanages in Asia as compared to Eastern Europe (Hwa-Froelich, 2012; Turnbull & Justice, 2012). For example, Hwa-Froelich (2012) stated that current evidence indicates that there have been positive language development outcomes for school-age Asian children who had been adopted. On the other hand, children adopted from Eastern European countries appear to be at increased risk of communication difficulties during school age. These students are at risk for learning problems in the areas of reading, overall language skills, and phonological processing.

❏ Children in Romanian orphanages have often experienced severe neglect, deprivation, and sometimes even abuse (Hwa-Froelich, 2012; Roberts & Scott, 2011). Media coverage in the early 1990s documented shocking conditions in some orphanages, including a ratio of one adult per 60 children in some cases.

Immigrant Insight   Ioana, female speaker of Romanian, orphanage worker
(guest speaker in my multicultural class)

Our children in Romania often come to the orphanage because of birth control and abortion laws and policies. Parents may end up having too many children to feed, so they keep some and give the others to orphanages. Sometimes if there is an autistic child in the family, the parents give him or her to an orphanage because due to the child's behaviors, the siblings are being sacrificed. The family can't go anywhere because they will be stared at with pity. Having a child with autism is a sign of God's wrath—it is a punishment and a curse.

I saw a lot of things during my years working in Romanian orphanages. Many children never leave the same room in their entire lives. Food is thrown in to them. I worked with one 20-year-old who weighed 45 lbs. The children live like animals, and some are crippled from being tied up. As punishment, some teen boys are tied up and beaten and then medicated. Often they die young due to being overmedicated—their hearts give out. Some children live in a crib 24/7 for years; some 5-year-old children don't know how to walk. We have 16-year-old children who drink from bottles because they don't know how to chew or swallow.

Approximately 85% of the children have no speech. Children are not allowed to initiate; if they do, they are told "no." Many of the children are aggressive—biting, hitting, and scratching are common. I have successfully used PECS (Picture Exchange Communication Symbols) with some of these children; chocolate helps too!

❑ Many orphanage workers, especially in Romania, are trained in health care but not in child development (Hwa-Froelich, 2012).

❑ Although conditions have improved in some Romanian orphanages, recent media coverage (ABC News 20/20, 2013) revealed that there are still many children living in squalid environments without adequate attention. Many babies lie in cribs sucking on bottles with very little human contact.

❑ In Romania, some children are confined to straitjackets or tied to their chairs with their own shirtsleeves; toddlers sit in their own urine, banging their heads against their steel cribs. Some children starve to death. When children leave orphanages at 18 years old, they often live on the streets, begging or selling their bodies to survive (ABC News 20/20, 2013).

❑ In many orphanages, infants and toddlers are put into cribs twice a day for three-hour naps. Thus, much time is spent in an isolated, physically restricted space (Morris, 2011). Infants and young children are often expected to feed themselves from bottles propped up in their cribs.

❑ Often in orphanages, children are served soft/pureed food. Thus, these children have limited opportunities to chew and develop lateral tongue movements and overall oral muscle tone. They may eventually manifest with underdeveloped chewing skills and an aversion to oral textures (Ladage & Harris, 2012).

❑ Researchers in Europe have stated that some IAC may exhibit Post-Institutional Autistic Syndrome (also called quasi-autism), a condition in which they have experienced such neglect and trauma that they exhibit autistic-like behaviors such as rocking, hair pulling, stereotyped repetitive behaviors, and others (Fensbo, 2004; Kaland, Moller-Nielsen, Smith, Mortensen, Callesen, & Gottlieb, 2005).

❑ Children who have craniofacial anomalies such as cleft palate may be severely neglected. They may be confined to 'lying down' rooms where they receive no medical care and limited staff attention.

Immigrant Insight   Yuliya, university senior, speaker of Russian,
                                        daughter of Russian immigrants

In former Soviet Union countries, it is a stigma to be an orphan. When an orphan grows up, it is hard to find a job or get into a good school.

Life conditions in orphanages are horrible. There are never enough workers because the pay is so low. Usually the workers hate their jobs but have no other choice. They steal food and supplies. The children are abused and neglected. The workers don't want the babies to walk so that they won't run around and get into trouble. Sometimes they even tie the babies up, which is one reason that the babies are malnourished and often require physical therapy later on.

Physical and Emotional Issues Impacting Internationally Adopted Children

Immediate physical concerns that parents of IAC need to pay attention to are (1) the possible presence of diseases (especially HIV and tuberculosis), (2) immunization status, and (3) short physical stature (Ladage & Harris, 2012).

❏ A problem for adoptive parents is that immunization records from other countries may be inaccurate, incomplete, or nonexistent. The American Academy of Pediatrics (2013) stated that most vaccines may be administered more than once safely.

❏ It is often difficult to determine the exact ages of children within the IAC population. Some nations do not commemorate birthdays as we do in the U.S. Families adopting from Ethiopia have reported that children who are processed by courts at the same time may all be given the same birth date (Ladage & Harris, 2012).

❏ For IAC who have lived in stressful conditions in institutions, persistently elevated levels of cortisol (stress hormone) can attenuate production of the growth hormone. Many IAC are physically small for their ages; elevated levels of cortisol, malnutrition, and other factors contribute to this.

❏ Motor abilities may be delayed. Because many IAC have been physically restricted, they have poorly developed gross and fine motor skills. As part of a team interdisciplinary evaluation, occupational and physical therapists may evaluate motor skills. These children may need sensory motor intervention as well as other treatments to increase motor skills.

❏ Some IAC have difficulty with feeding. As mentioned earlier, they may only eat soft or pureed foods. Swallowing and overall oral muscle tone should be evaluated, and intervention should be provided if necessary. Speech sound disorders may be present.

❏ Hearing development may be affected. If IAC have undergone neglect and/or abuse, they may have experienced many episodes of untreated otitis media. Audiological evaluation is frequently warranted, as recurrent ear infections can lead to poorer auditory perception.

❏ Pediatricians sometimes fail to refer IAC for needed services in a timely fashion. They may take a "wait and see" approach, depriving these children of early intervention services that they greatly need (Krakow, Mastriano, & Reese, 2005). Interdisciplinary collaboration is highly recommended because of their complex needs (Hwa-Froelich, 2012).

❏ Professionals must remember that IAC often experience culture shock. Within a 24- to 48-hour period, these children have been abruptly removed from their familiar environments and all ties to their cultures and languages have been terminated (Hwa-Froelich, Pettinelli & Jones, 2006). Thus, these children may need psychological services to help them deal with issues resulting from the change in environment (Gindis, 2005).

❏ In addition to experiencing a change in environment, IAC must also deal with learning a new language. This can lead to frustration that may result in anger, acting out, and temper tantrums (Gindis, 2013). Research has consistently documented behavior problems with IAC from Eastern European orphanages especially (Elleseff, 2013). Institutionalized care can have negative effects on IACs' social-emotional development, behavior, and attachment patterns. Therefore, therapy and support groups can be very helpful (Pronchenko-Jain & Fernando, 2013).

❏ Prospective parents may not be aware of the specific problems that their recently adopted children have experienced or are experiencing. If these children demonstrate severe problems, the strain can affect the parents' marriage and overall family dynamics. Professionals may find it appropriate to refer these parents to support groups or counseling in some cases.

Tech Tie-In

Go to www.asha.org and type "Internationally Adopted Children" into the search bar. You will find articles, presentations, and informational resources about internationally adopted children and best practices for service delivery to these children and their families.

Cognitive and Linguistic Characteristics of IAC: Implications For Assessment and Intervention

❏ Research clearly indicates that IAC who are adopted at younger ages generally fare better in almost all areas of development, including language (Hwa-Froelich, 2012; Scott, Pollock, Roberts, & Krakow, 2013; Turnbull & Justice, 2012).

❏ The level of deprivation that children have experienced prior to being adopted is likely to influence their success in acquiring language skills.

❏ IAC who have received adequate care generally show cognitive skills within normal range. However, those who have experienced more extreme deprivation may show lower cognitive skills, with deficits in attention, working memory, and visual-spatial memory and overall skills (Wilson, 2012a).

❏ Overall executive functioning skills may be impacted, especially in the areas of inhibition and self-regulation (Hwa-Froelich, 2012). Children may also show deficits in symbolic play. Because of this, when IAC are evaluated, it will usually be necessary for them to undergo a psychological evaluation as well as assessments in other areas.

❏ Children in orphanages often miss the building blocks or precursors to language. They may not receive adequate modeling, positive feedback, or the reciprocal interaction needed to develop fluent first language skills.

❏ IAC experience interrupted language acquisition. They abruptly switch from listening to and speaking their birth language to learning a new language at an older age (Hwa-Froelich, Matsuo, & Jacobs, 2017).

❏ Adoptive families rarely speak the child's first language. Thus, at the time of adoption, there is arrested development of the first language; proficiency in the first language rapidly decreases as the child gains proficiency in the language used by his adoptive family.

❏ Many IAC have been observed to lose the bulk of their expressive first language skills within the first six months in the U.S. (Gindis, 2013). IAC who learn English in this situation have often been described as "second first language learners" (Hwa-Froelich, 2012; Paradis et al., 2011). During this time period, children often demonstrate limited abilities in both languages and thus it is difficult for professionals to determine if the observed "problems" will be overcome without the services of a speech-language pathologist. Some experts believe that time alone cannot remedy this situation and that intensive, focused intervention by a speech-language pathologist is necessary (Scott & Roberts, 2011; Taddonio, 2003; Tan, 2006). IAC who are not making adequate progress in learning English vocabulary are appropriate referrals for early intervention (Glennen, 2006).

❏ When they first arrive in the United States, many IAC make rapid gains in oral language skills as stated earlier. However, over time (especially as they progress through elementary school), linguistic and cognitive deficits may become evident (Elleseff, 2013; Gindis, 2013).

❏ The development of BICS (Basic Interpersonal Communication Skills) was described in a previous chapter. Gindis (2004) reported that IAC may acquire BICS even more quickly than "typical" English language learners because they are totally immersed in English with no support for the first language. A common observation among IAC is that within 6-12 months of arrival in the U.S., they have adequate conversational communication skills and the ability to make their needs known (Elleseff, 2013). This can lull parents into a false sense of security regarding their children's linguistic abilities. These parents frequently believe that their children will just as easily and automatically acquire the academic language skills necessary for success in the classroom curriculum (i.e., CALP).

❏ However, rapid BICS development does not necessarily result in rapid or completely successful CALP (Cognitive Academic Language Proficiency) development. Often, parents are unpleasantly surprised to learn that their adopted children experience delays in the development of the language skills necessary to function effectively in the classroom. After all, BICS developed within a 6- to 12-month period for many of these children (Gindis, 2005).

❏ IAC who are placed in a grade that is too high can experience tremendous frustration; placing a child in a grade that is too low causes fewer problems (Gindis, 2013).

❏ Assessment of the language skills of IAC is most challenging because they often have first language delays, lose proficiency in the first language rapidly after coming to the United States, and have not yet had sufficient exposure to English to fully master the language. Dynamic assessment is appropriate for these students.

❏ Prelinguistic measures that assess the presence of joint attention, prespeech vocalization, symbolic play, object permanence, social interaction skills, and other language precursors may be helpful in identifying IAC with possible language impairment. Language impairment is common among children who have problems in these areas (Glennen, 2007).

❏ The Communication and Symbolic Behavior Skills—Developmental Profile (CSBS-DP; Wetherby & Prizant, 2002) and the MacArthur Communicative Development Inventory—Words and Gestures (MCDI-WG; Fenson et al., 1993) have been found to be useful in the early identification of IAC with language impairment (Glennen, 2007; Paradis et al., 2011; Roberts & Scott, 2011).

❏ The use of standard measures of prelinguistic abilities that are not language- or culture-specific is a good way to predict eventual language outcomes in newly-arrived internationally adopted infants and toddlers (Glennen, 2007).

❏ Parent reports provide information that can be helpful in identifying IAC who may be in need of language intervention. Hwa-Froelich and Matsuo (2010) examined the communication development of children adopted from Eastern Europe and China. Parent-reported vocabulary comprehension and expression as well as behavioral communication assessments were administered. Early prelinguistic measures (that utilized parent report) were found to be reliable prognostic indicators for later English language development.

Research has provided evidence that parent reports of language development are useful, reliable, and valid in assessing language skills of IAC as well as progress in language learning over time. The use of information-processing measures that are not knowledge-based (e.g., repetition of digits and nonwords) is recommended when assessing older children who are experiencing first language attrition while learning English skills. Psychologists and various other professionals might also consider using nonverbal measures to assess development in specific areas.

Although many IAC eventually achieve age-appropriate language outcomes, there appears to be a higher prevalence of language and academic difficulties among IAC than among children who were not adopted (Paradis et al., 2011). Thus, these children need to be closely monitored over the school years. Moreover, many IAC have social-emotional problems, including difficulty with attachment (Hwa-Froelich, 2012; Wilson, 2012). Children who lack warm early relationships may relate to others with indifference, apprehension, or ignorance. Often, social deprivation within orphanages is profound.

The specific "problems" observed with IAC populations will vary depending on variables such as the amount of time spent in orphanages and the type of care they received. Critical research findings and concerns expressed by researchers are summarized below.

❑ Delcenserie, Genesee, & Gauthier (2013) found that adoptees from China scored significantly lower than typically-developing children on measures of sentence recall, receptive grammar, expressive vocabulary, and word definition skills. No significant differences between the groups were found on measures of cognitive and socioemotional development.

❑ Desmarais, Roeber, Smith, and Pollak (2012) studied the sentence comprehension and spatial working memory abilities of IAC who had been institutionalized. The IAC scored lower than typically-developing peers on some spatial working memory skills and oral sentence comprehension skills. Poor spatial working memory performance partially explained the sentence comprehension difficulties. It was recommended that early intervention take into account the possible need for work on spatial working memory as it relates to oral sentence comprehension.

❑ Glennen (2015) studied IAC who were adopted between one and four years of age by college-educated parents whose incomes were 300% above poverty level. Although these children performed adequately in most areas, weaknesses were identified in expressive syntax and verbal short term memory. Possibly these weaknesses resulted from early environmental deprivation and the learning of a new language (English) after the critical early language learning period had passed.

❑ A meta-analysis of the language outcomes of IAC conducted by Scott, Roberts, and Glennen (2011) revealed that (1) assessment should utilize multiple sources of information, (2) children adopted at younger ages had better outcomes than children adopted at older ages, and (3) for some IAC, increasing the amount of time spent in institutional living situations may increase the likelihood of various health and developmental concerns.

❑ Wilson (2012) stated that children who are removed from a context of early adversity are still at risk for later mental health concerns due to brain adaptations that occur following adversity. These adaptations may include synaptic reduction in areas responsible for problem-solving and planning, a smaller hippocampus resulting in long term memory difficulties, and brain wave abnormalities. The older a child is at the time of adoption, the greater the risk for later poor social adjustment.

When assessing IAC populations, both the structural and functional aspects of communication should be assessed. Elleseff (2012) pointed out that sometimes IAC score appropriately for their age on standardized language tests but demonstrate a variety of social/pragmatic problems when observed during interactions with their peers. These difficulties might include the following:

- Profoundly reduced theory of mind, or ability to take another person's perspective
- Poor ability to convey messages appropriately to different audiences
- Poor ability to interpret body language, gestures, and facial expressions
- Poor initiation of social interaction
- Poor comprehension of inferential and abstract information
- Difficulty seeing the "big picture"
- Difficulty regulating emotions and behaviors

Some IAC demonstrate indiscriminate friendliness, or affection for and over-friendliness to strangers (Hwa-Froelich, 2012). Professionals must help these students learn to interact in ways that are safe.

Issues related to "theory of mind" are often a concern in the IAC population. Learning to see things from another person's viewpoint is important for effective social interactions. Hwa-Froelich et al. (2017) studied the language skills of children between 4 and 5 years of age who were adopted from Asian and Eastern European countries before 2 years of age. These children were found to have difficulty with social communication, including theory of mind. Hwa-Froelich et al. suggested that these children be provided with increased exposure to social interactions involving older children or older children and their parents.

Many students in the IAC population overcome difficulties that affect communication, motor skills, social interaction skills, behavior, and other skills so that they can live full lives (Hwa-Froelich, 2012). Professionals must always bear this in mind and not stereotype these children as being doomed to lifetimes of hardship and disability.

Profile

Julianne, university senior, adopted from South Korea

My brother and I were adopted from South Korea. My U.S. parents are Chinese and they got me and my brother when we were around 2-3 years old. My parents have provided my brother and me with a wonderful life, and I wouldn't change it for the world. One issue I am very sensitive about is when people are ignorant and make comments like "Those aren't your real parents" and "Are you going to find your real parents?"

My parents know that my brother was placed in an orphanage. His birth parents were married, but they could not afford to keep him. My birth mother was young and left me at the hospital, but I was taken care of by a foster family. I was afforded the cuddling and bonding that most babies need at that early age. My brother, on the other hand, did not receive the same kind of nurturing attention in the orphanage. Even though my parents got my brother when he was around 2.5 years old, he still lacks some of the bonding connections with my parents. His theory of mind is under developed and it is hard for him to see other people's viewpoints. He is close with my parents, but he doesn't verbally express his emotions towards them. My mom told me that my brother has "attachment disorder" and it takes him a little longer to adjust to change. A family psychologist told my parents that my brother's attachment disorder stems from the deprivation of attachment and bonding in his orphanage.

Because students in the IAC population appear to be vulnerable to speech and language delays, early speech and language intervention is highly recommended. Parents can learn to interact with these children in ways that facilitate the development of language skills (Gauthier, Genesee, Dubois, & Kasparian, 2011). Speech-language pathologists and other professionals can provide assistance to parents in a variety of ways:

1. Provide parents with information about local services and support groups that may be of help to them. Parents of IAC can especially benefit from support groups that allow them to interact with others who have shared similar experiences.

2. Help parents establish a bond with their children by recommending activities such as playing games, reading, and doing turn-taking tasks. Encouraging parents to hug the children and to provide frequent social reinforcement may also be appropriate.

3. Encourage the use of games that promote mobility and action when working with children who have sensory processing problems and motor delays (e.g., playing Simon Says with instructions that require students to follow simple classroom directions).

4. Present sensory stimulation activities using a box of sand and small toys. Ask children to feel the toys inside the box, draw out a toy, and label it.

5. Demonstrate appropriate ways of expressing both positive and negative feelings. Parents and professionals can model acceptable outlets for anger or aggressive impulses.

6. Provide a well-structured learning environment with daily routines. Overstimulating environments need to be avoided because some children have difficulty with sensory integration. New stimuli should be introduced gradually.

7. Consider using sign language when working with children who have significant language delays. Sign language can facilitate the learning of critical language skills (Dyer, 2004).

8. Make it easy for students to watch lip movements when speaking to them. Mason and Narad (2004) stated that parents should get down to children's eye level so that the children can watch the movement of their lips. They also reported that the use of games involving singing and other vocalizations is helpful when working with children who are not talking.

9. Individualize therapy for each child based upon his or her specific needs.

10. Provide parents with direction so that they can relate optimally with these children. One study showed that two thirds of parents surveyed did not believe that young infants would be impacted by caregiver mood or be able to experience fear or sadness (Lerner & Ciervo, 2010). A reality that many adoptive parents may not be ready for is the fact that children from institutions are accustomed to interacting with other children rather than adults.

11. Provide language stimulation activities that include focused stimulation, conversational recasts, and shared book reading. Specifically, with focused stimulation, parents can provide auditory bombardment of language targets during play activities. Conversational recasts and expansions do not require the child to respond verbally (e.g. Child "I want red." Parent: "Yes, you want the red ball."). Shared book reading activities support emergent literacy (Roberts & Scott, 2011).

12. Use parenting programs such as the Video-Feedback Intervention to Promote Positive Parenting program (VIPP; Juffer, Bakermans-Kranenburg, & Van IJzendoorn, 2008). In

this program, parents are videotaped as they interact with their children on several occasions and are provided with coaching to help them become more effective communication partners. VIPP is becoming more widely used with IAC children and their parents (Hwa-Froelich, 2012). Another program proven to be successful in improving executive skills in preschool children is called the Tools Curriculum (Bodrove & Leong, 2007; Diamond, Barnett, Thomas, & Munro, 2007).

Profile

At an outpatient rehabilitation center, I met Sharon, who brought her 7-year-old son Gregor for his weekly physical therapy session. Sharon and Gregor were in tears; clearly they had a rough day. After Gregor went in for his physical therapy appointment, I asked Sharon if she would like to talk. She poured out her story.

Gregor was residing in a Bulgarian orphanage when he was adopted by Sharon and her husband at three years of age. When they arrived at the orphanage to bring him to their home in California, he was living in conditions of filth and squalor. Gregor had been beaten, sexually abused, kicked in the head, and locked in small closets. There were scars on his head from the abuse.

When Gregor arrived in the United States, he would not let Sharon out of his sight. She could not let him hear the sound of a door shutting; if he heard this, he would scream and cry inconsolably. She could not even spend a few minutes a day away from the child; Gregor had to have her within his range of vision at all times.

Gregor was diagnosed as having significant emotional and behavioral problems, gross and fine motor delays, intellectual disability, and significant post-traumatic stress syndrome. He also had a profound language delay.

Gregor's speech was highly unintelligible, and his utterances were generally between three and four words in length. I wanted to recommend speech-language therapy, but Sharon was exhausted, depleted, and depressed. Her financial resources were stretched to the breaking point because she was paying for so many services for Gregor.

CONCLUSION

ELL students who have language impairments associated with exceptional needs can present a particular challenge to professionals. Some research has been conducted to address best service delivery practices for these students, but much more research needs to be done. In the meantime, professionals can work as part of multidisciplinary teams to support students and their families, using the services of cultural mediators to bridge the gap between the families and the professionals who serve them.

STUDY QUESTIONS

1. Many culturally and linguistically diverse parents of children with special needs do not believe that early intervention is necessary or desirable. How can professionals work with these parents in a manner that is culturally sensitive but that encourages parents to seek out this intervention?

2. If an ELL student has a severe disability such as intellectual disability, should school professionals encourage the use of only one language? Why or why not? What advice should professionals give to parents of these children when the language of the home is something other than English?

3. Describe some of the challenges experienced by internationally adopted children and their families. What particular areas of concern might professionals watch for when assessing these children?

MULTIPLE CHOICE

4. Challenges experienced by some Internationally Adopted Children (IAC) may include:

   A. Attention deficit disorder
   B. Indiscriminate attachment to strangers
   C. Hearing loss
   D. Refusal to chew
   E. Aggression and tantrums

5. Research with some culturally and linguistically diverse families of children who used AAC devices has shown that:

   A. Parents' reactions can be influenced by factors such as a higher degree of acculturation and educational level.
   B. Over 80% of these parents believed that institutionalized would be the best choice for their children.
   C. Some families felt uncomfortable with "high tech" devices, preferring that their children use speech or sign language.
   D. Most families did not want AAC devices that were "bilingual"; they desired devices that were only programmed in English.
   E. It is best not to provide first language support for children who use AAC devices; restricting them to just English will better support their academic development in American schools.

6. When providing support for ELL children with intellectual disability and their families, professionals should remember that:

   A. ELL students are underrepresented in the category of "intellectual disability," so professionals must be especially careful not to miss these students in screenings and assessments.
   B. Children with intellectual disability should not be asked to learn a language that is not critical for success in their everyday social interactions (e.g., learning a foreign language in high school).
   C. Some ELL mothers of children with intellectual disability experience depression because they spend all of their time caring for these children.
   D. ELL parents of children with intellectual disability may accept support from their churches, even if they do not want help from schools or medical institutions.

7. Lia X. is a Chinese immigrant mother whose 3-year-old son, Fong, has ASD. The speech-language pathologist must remember which of the following when working with Mrs. X and Fong?

   A. Mrs. X. will probably appreciate a play-based approach to treatment.
   B. Use of a token economy, so popular in the treatment of children with ASD, will probably be highly successful.
   C. Mrs. X. may believe that acupuncture and herbal remedies will be helpful in treating Fong's ASD.
   D. It is important to stress to her that acupuncture and herbal remedies will not be helpful. Emphasize that Fong needs traditional, research-based intervention.
   E. It would be ideal to find a bilingual specialist to provide Fong with intervention.

8. Many professionals believe that if students have severe impairments such as ASD, intellectual disability, or HI, they should only use one language. However, we know that according to research:

   A. Studies have shown that children with Down syndrome can become bilingual.
   B. Research is conclusive that children with HI should "stick to one language" because of the difficulties inherent in being exposed to two languages.
   C. Children on the autism spectrum can and do become bilingual.
   D. A, C
   E. A, B, C

9. You are presenting an inservice program for parents of internationally adopted children. During this program, you plan to talk about the challenges experienced by internationally adopted children and to present strategies that parents can use with these children to strengthen linguistic and cognitive skills. Based on research, you can confidently say the following:

   A. Children who have experienced maltreatment in orphanages will not be overly friendly when interacting with strangers.
   B. Internationally adopted children may be especially vulnerable to difficulties with theory of mind, or viewing things from another's perspective. Therefore, social skills therapy may be necessary.
   C. It is possible that there may be delays in motor skill development, so evaluations by an occupational and physical therapist are often necessary.
   D. Most students in the IAC population have intact cognitive skills and, therefore, there should be no need for a psychological assessment.
   E. Parents can often benefit from support groups that help them determine optimal ways of providing emotional, cognitive, and linguistic stimulation and support.

10. Specific assessment and treatment programs that are supported by research as being successful for use with IAC include:

    A. Communication and Symbolic Behavior Skills—Developmental Profile
    B. Test of Auditory Comprehension of Language
    C. Test of Language Development
    D. MacArthur Communicative Development Inventory—Words and Gestures
    E. Video-Feedback Intervention to Promote Positive Parenting program

ANSWERS TO STUDY QUESTIONS

    4. All of the above
    5. A, C
    6. B, C, D
    7. C, E
    8. D
    9. B, C, E
    10. A, D, E

Appendix
Sample Case History Form

Developed by LiRong Lilly Cheng

Instructions: We are going to ask you some questions about your child's medical history, educational history, and related areas. Please be as thorough as you can in your remarks. If I am not clear, please stop me and ask me to say it again. If you don't feel comfortable in answering the question, please let me know. All we want to do here is to obtain as much background information as possible, and, since you are the child's parent, we feel that you have much to contribute.

1. Where was your child born?

2. Was this a hospital?

3. How was the pregnancy?

4. How was your health during pregnancy?

4. How was the delivery?

5. Were any instruments used?

6. Were there any postnatal complications?

7. How was your child's physical development? Were there any handicapping conditions? If yes, who made the diagnosis? When? How did you feel about it?

8. Was your child ever hospitalized? If yes, where? When? Why? How long? Who was the physician?

9. Were there problems in feeding?

10. Were there any prolonged illnesses? High fever? Accidents?

11. Has his/her hearing been checked?

12. Has his/her vision been checked?

13. Has he/she seen a dentist? What is the condition of his/her teeth?

14. What is his/her diet history?

15. How is his/her diet now?

16. Does he/she have a pediatrician? Who? Has your child seen any other medical specialist? If yes, Who? When? Where? Why?

17. When did you come to the United States? Why did you come?

    For refugees: Was he/she ever in a refugee camp? How long? Tell us about it.

18. Was he/she ever on a boat? How long? Tell us about it.

19. How many brothers and sisters does he/she have? Are they all here?

20. Are there any family members who had or have difficulty in speaking or hearing, or problems such as mental retardation, cerebral palsy, cleft palate, or stuttering? If yes, please explain.

21. Was your child ever in school? Where? How long?

22. How was his/her performance in school? Grade?

Source: Cheng., L. L. (1991). *Assessing Asian Language Performance: Guidelines for Evaluating Limited-English Proficient Students.* (2nd edition) Oceanside, CA. Academic Communication Associates. Reprinted with permission.

23. Do you have a report from the school? Any comments from the teacher?

24. Was he/she involved in special programs? How did he/she do?

25. Was he/she in a day-care or child care program? If yes, how did he/she do?

26. Did he/she repeat a grade? If yes, why?

27. How was the program similar to his/her program now? How was the program different from his/her program now?

28. How many are living in your home?

29. Who takes care of your child after school?

30. Who makes the decisions at home?

31. Does your child have his/her own room? If no, who does your child share the room with? Where does he/she study?

32. Does your child mostly play inside the house? Outside? By himself/herself? With a sibling?

33. Who does he/she play with? Are they older or younger? How does he/she play?

34. What does he/she like to play? What toys do you have? Does he/she read? What books and magazines do you have?

35. Do you work? If yes, what do you do? When are you home?

36. Does your spouse work? If yes, what does he/she do? When is he/she home?

37. What is your educational background? Your spouse's educational background?

38. What language(s) is used at home?

39. When did your child say his/her first word? How do you feel about his/her speech now?

40. Do you feel that your child understands everything you say? Explain.

41. What language does he/she speak when he/she responds to you?

42. Does your child speak your native language with his siblings? Friends?

43. Do your children speak your native language or English among themselves?

44. Do you help your child with homework?

45. How do you feel about his/her maintenance of your native language? Do you send him/her to language school during the weekend?

46. What do you expect the school to do for your child?

47. Do you attend any social function? Where? With whom? What are your leisure activities?

48. Do you have difficulty disciplining your child? His/her siblings?

49. What responsibilities are placed on your child? On his/her siblings?

50. Does he/she dress himself/herself?

51. Does he/she know your telephone number and address?

52. Do you read to him/her? What are his/her favorite stories? Can he/she tell the story back to you?

53. Does he/she watch TV? What is his/her favorite program?

References

Abboud, S. K., & Kim, J. (2007). *How do Asian students get to the top of the class?* Retrieved from http://www.greatschools. net/cgi-bin/showarticle/ca/933?cpn=20070404pal

ABC News 20/20 (2013). *Inhumane conditions for Romania's lost generation.* Retrieved from http://abcnews.go.com/2020/ story?id=124078&page=1&singlePage=true

Academic Communication Associates (2007). *Bilingual picture symbol communication resource.* Oceanside, CA: Author.

Accredited Language Services (2017). *The 10 most popular languages in the U.S.* Retrieved from https://www.accreditedlan-guage.com/2016/09/13/the-10-most-popular-languages-in-the-us/

Ahmad, N. M. (2004). *Arab-American culture and health care.* Retrieved from http://www.case.edu/med/epidbio/mphp439/ Arab-Americans.htm

Akella, D., & Elimimian, J. (2012). Can there be an African American pedagogy? *The Journal of Multiculturalism in Education, 8*(1), 1-25.

Al-Jafar, A., & Buzzelli, C. A. (2004). The art of storytelling for cross cultural understanding. *International Journal of Early Childhood, 36,* 35-48.

Al Khatib, J. M. (2017). *Arab American children with disabilities: Considerations for teachers and service providers.* New York: Routledge.

Allison, S. R., & Vining, C. (1999). Native American culture and language: Considerations in service delivery. *Bilingual Review, 24,* 193-205.

Al Thani, H. (2009). *United Nations special rapporteur on disability, 2009.* Retrieved from http://www.srdisability.org/arti-cles/disability-arab

Al Zidjaly, N. (2012). What has happened to Arabs? Identity and face management online. *Multilingua-Journal of Cross-Cultural and Interlanguage Communication, 31*(4), 413-439.

American Academy of Pediatrics (2013). *A healthy beginning: Important information for parents of internationally adopted chil-dren.* Retrieved from http://www.healthychildren.org

American Academy of Pediatrics (2017). *Handheld screen time linked with speech delays in young children.* Retrieved from http://www.aappublications.org/news/2017/05/04/PASScreenTime050417

American-Arab Anti-Discrimination Committee (2013). *Thirty years of advocacy and achievement.* Retrieved from http:// www.adc.org/

American Civil Liberties Union (2017). *Facts about the over-incarceration of women in the United States.* Retrieved from https://www.aclu.org/other/facts-about-over-incarceration-women-united-states

American Institutes for Research (2017a). *Content and technical expertise in refugee and migrant initiatives.* Retrieved from http://www.air.org/resource/content-and-technical-expertise-refugee-and-migrant-initiatives

American Institutes for Research (2017b). *AIR study finds California's transitional kindergarten gives English Language Learner students advantage for kindergarten.* Retrieved from http://www.air.org/news/press-release/air-study-finds-california-s-tra-ditional-kindergarten-gives-english-learner

American Speech-Language-Hearing Association. (2011). *Cultural competence in professional service delivery* [Position statement]. Retrieved from www.asha.org/policy

American Speech-Language-Hearing Association (2017). Too much TV linked to decreased school readiness, particularly in low-income children. *The ASHA Leader, 22*(5), 13.

Apel, K., Brimo, D., Diehm, E., & Apel, L. (2013). Morphological awareness intervention with kindergarteners and first- and second-grade students from low socioeconomic status homes: A feasibility study. *Language, Speech, and Hearing Services in Schools, 44,* 161-173.

Arab American Institute (2017). *Demographics.* Retrieved from http://www.aaiusa.org/demographics

Arias, G., & Friberg, J. (2017). Bilingual language assessment: Contemporary versus recommended practice in American schools. *Language, Speech, and Hearing Services in Schools, 48*(1), 1-15.

Asher, J. J. (2007). *TPR: After 40 years, still a very good idea.* Retrieved from http://www.tpr-world.com/JapanArticle.pdf

Asian and Pacific Islander American Health Forum (2017). *Health facts.* Retrieved from http://www.apiahf.org

Banks, J. (2013). *An introduction to multicultural education* (5th ed.). New York: Wiley.

Barrueco, S., Lopez, M., Ong, C., & Lozano, P. (2012). *Assessing Spanish-English bilingual preschoolers.* Baltimore: Paul H. Brookes Publishing.

Battle, D. E. (Ed.) (2012). The cultures of African American and other Blacks around the world. In D. E. Battle (Ed.), *Communication disorders in multicultural and international populations* (4th ed.) (pp. 20-36). St. Louis, MO: Elsevier Mosby.

Battle, E. D. (2015). Persons with communication disabilities in natural disasters, war, or conflict. *Communication Disorders Quarterly, 36*(4), 231-240.

Beck, I. L., McKeown, M. G., & Kucan, L. (2013). *Bringing words to life: Robust vocabulary instruction* (2nd ed.). New York: The Guilford Press.

Bedore, L. M., Peña, E. D., Joyner, D., & Macken, C. (2011). Parent and teacher rating of bilingual language proficiency and language development concerns. *International Journal of Bilingual Education and Bilingualism, 14*, 489-511.

Bell, N. (1991). *Visualizing and verbalizing for language comprehension and thinking*: Paso Robles, CA: Academy of Reading Publications.

Benally, H., & Carey, H. (2013). *Navajo people.* Retrieved from http://navajopeople.org

Berke, J. (2007). *Sign language—Spanish sign language: Your guide to deafness.* Retrieved from www.deafness.about.com

Bialystok, E., Craik, F. I. M., & Luk, G. (2012). Bilingualism: Consequences for mind and brain. *Trends in Cognitive Science, 16*(4), 240-250.

Bilinguistics (2014). Difference or disorder? *Understanding speech and language patterns in culturally and linguistically diverse students.* Bilinguistics, Inc.: Austin, TX.

Binger, C., Kent-Walsh, J., Berens, J., Del Campo, S., & Rivera, D. (2008). Teaching Latino parents to support the multi-symbol message productions of their children who require AAC. *Augmentative and Alternative Communication, 24*(4), 323-338.

Binger, C., & Light, J. (2006). Demographics of preschoolers who require AAC. *Language, Speech, and Hearing Services in Schools, 37*, 200-208.

Bitetti, D., & Hammer, C. S. (2016). The home literacy environment and the English narrative development of Spanish-English bilingual children. *Journal of Speech, Language, and Hearing Research, 59*, 1159-1171.

Blom, E., Paradis, J., & Sorenson Duncan, T. (2012). Effects of input properties, vocabulary size, and L1 on the development of third person singular –"s" in child L2 English. *Language Learning, 62*, 965-994.

Blom, E., & Paradis, J. (2013). Past tense production by English second language learners with and without language impairment. *Journal of Speech, Language, and Hearing Research, 56*, 281-294.

Bloom, L., & Lahey, M. (1978). *Language development and language disorders.* New York: John Wiley & Sons.

Bodrova, A. E. & Leong, D. J. (2007). *Tools of the mind: The Vygotskian approach to early childhood education* (2nd ed.). Columbus, OH: Merrill/Prentice Hall.

Boudreau, D., & Costanza-Smith, A. (2011). Assessment and treatment of working memory deficits in school-age children: The role of the speech-language pathologist. *Language, Speech, and Hearing Services in Schools, 42*, 152-166.

Brandeker, M., & Thordardottir, E. (2015). Language exposure in bilingual toddlers: Performance on nonword repetition and lexical tasks. *American Journal of Speech-Language Pathology, 24*, 126-138.

Brea-Spahn, M. R., & Davison, M. D. (2013). Writing intervention for Spanish-speaking English language learners: A review of research. *EBP Briefs, 7*, 7-20.

Brice, A. E. (2013). *Hispanic childhoods: Introduction.* Oxford Bibliographies Online: Childhood Studies. Retrieved from http://www.oxfordbibliographies.com/view/document/obo-970199791231/obo-9780199791231-0101.xml

Brice, A. E. (2015). Multilingual language development. In J. D. Wright (Ed.), International encyclopedia of social and behavioral sciences, 2nd ed., vol. 16, pp. 55-64. Cambridge, MA: Elsevier.

Brice, A. E., Brice, R., & Kester, E. (2010). *Language loss in English language learners (ELLs).* Pedia Staff newsletter. Retrieved from http://www.pediastaff.com/resources-language-loss-in-english-language-learners-ells-february-2010

Brice, A. E., Gorman, B. K., & Leung, C. B. (2013). Spanish-English speech perception in children and adults: Developmental trends. *Clinical Linguistics and Phonetics, 27*(3).

Brice, A. E., Leung, C. L., & Gorman, B. K. (2014). Vocabulary skills of Spanish-English speaking elementary students: A pilot study article. *Perspectives in Communication Disorders and Sciences in Culturally and Linguistically Diverse Populations, 22*(3).

Britto, P., Brooks-Gunn, J., & Griffin, T. M. (2006). Maternal reading and teaching patterns: Associations with school readiness in low-income African American families. *Reading Research Quarterly, 41*, 68-89.

Bryla, J., & Roseberry-McKibbin, C. (2014). *iPad technology in the classroom: Practical applications for SLPs.* Paper presented at the annual convention of the California Speech-Language-Hearing Association, San Francisco, CA.

Buenconsejo-Lum, L. (2011). *How data, policies and culture impact cancer in Native Hawaiians and Pacific Islanders.* Asian and Pacific Islander American Health Forum. Retrieved from http://www.apiahf.org

Bunta, F., & Douglas, M. (2013). The effects of dual-language support on the language skills of bilingual children with hearing loss who use listening devices relative to their monolingual peers. *Language, Speech, and Hearing Services in Schools, 44*, 281-290.

Caesar, L. G., & Kohler, P. D. (2007). The state of school-based bilingual assessment: Actual practice versus recommended guidelines. *Language, Speech, and Hearing Services in Schools, 38,* 190-200.

Caesar, L. G., & Nelson, N. W. (2013, February 01). Picturing literacy success. *The ASHA Leader.*

Caesar, L. G., & Nelson, N. W. (2014). Parental involvement in language and literacy acquisition: A bilingual journaling approach. *Child Language Teaching and Therapy, 30*(3), 317-336.

Campbell, T., Dollaghan, C., Needleman, H., & Janosky, J. (1997). Reducing bias in language assessment: Processing-dependent measures. *Journal of Speech, Language, and Hearing Research, 40,* 519-525.

Campbell-Wilson, F. (2012). Middle East and Arab American cultures. In D. E. Battle (Ed.), *Communication disorders in multicultural and international populations* (4th ed.) (pp. 61-75). St. Louis, MO: Elsevier Mosby.

Cannon, J. E., Fredrick, L. D., & Easterbrooks, S. R. (2010). Vocabulary instruction through books read in American Sign Language for English-Language-Learners with hearing loss. *Communication Disorders Quarterly, 31*(2), 98-112.

Catts, H. W., & Kamhi, A. (2017). Prologue: Reading comprehension is not a single ability. *Language, Speech, and Hearing Services in Schools, 48,* 73-76.

Centeno, J. G. (2007). From theory to realistic praxis: Service-Learning as a teaching method to enhance speech-language services with minority populations. In A. J. Wurr & J. Hellenbrandt (Eds.), *Learning the language of global citizenship: Service-learning in applied linguistics* (pp. 190-218). Boston: Anker Publishing Company, Inc.

Center for American Progress (2017). *The facts on immigration today: 2017 edition.* Retrieved from https://www.americanprogress.org/issues/immigration/reports/2017/04/20/430736/facts-immigration-today-2017-edition/

Center for Universal Design for Learning (2015). *UDL implementation: A process of change.* Retrieved from http://www.udl-center.org/implementation

Centers for Disease Control and Prevention (2011). *CDC Health Disparities & Inequalities Report (CHDIR).* Retrieved from http://www.cdc.gov/minorityhealth

Centers for Disease Control and Prevention (2013). *Minority health.* Retrieved from http://www.cdc.gov/minorityhealth

Centers for Disease Control and Prevention (2013). *Autism spectrum disorders.* Retrieved from http://www.cdc.gov/ncbddd/autism/data.html

Centers for Disease Control and Prevention (2017a). *Autism spectrum disorder.* Retrieved from http://www.cdc.gov/ncbddd/autism/data.html

Centers for Disease Control and Prevention (2017b). *Health of American Indian or Alaska Native populations.* Retrieved from http://www.cd.gov/nchs/fastats/american-Indian-health.htm

Centers for Disease Control and Prevention (2017c). *Health insurance coverage for Asian population.* Retrieved from http://www.cdc.gov/nchs/fastats/asian-health.htm/

Centers for Disease Control and Prevention (2017d). *Health of Black or African American non-Hispanic population.* Retrieved from http://www.cdc.gov/nchs/fastats/black-health.htm

Champion, T., & Mainess, K. (2003). Typical and disordered narration in African American children. In A. McCabe & L. S. Bliss, *Patterns of narrative discourse: A multicultural lifespan approach* (pp. 55-70). Boston: Allyn & Bacon.

Chan, F., & Chen, D. (2011). Families with Asian roots. In E. W. Lynch & M. J. Hanson (Eds.), *Developing cross-cultural competence: A guide for working with children and their families* (4th ed.) (pp. 234-318). Baltimore: Paul H. Brookes Publishing Co.

Checa, E., Galeote, M., & Soto, P. (2016). The composition of early vocabulary in Spanish children with Down Syndrome and their peers with typical development. *American Journal of Speech-Language Pathology, 25,* 605-610.

Cheng., L. L. (1991). *Assessing Asian language performance: Guidelines for evaluating limited-English proficient students.* (2nd ed.) Oceanside, CA. Academic Communication Associates.

Cheng, L. L. (2012). Asian and Pacific American languages and cultures. In D. E. Battle (Ed.), *Communication disorders in multicultural and international populations* (4th ed.) (pp. 37-60). St. Louis, MO: Elsevier.

Chhuon, V, & Sullivan, A. (2013). Racialization of abilities and disabilities in U.S. schools: Asian American students in gifted and special education. *Perspectives on Communication Disorders and Sciences in Culturally and Linguistically Diverse (CLD) Populations, 20*(2), 49-59. Retrieved from http://journals.asha.org/perspectives/terms.dtl

Cho, S. J., Singer, G. H. S., & Brenner, M. B. (2003). A comparison of adaptation to childhood disability in Korean immigrants and Korean mothers. *Focus on Autism and other Developmental Disabilities, 18,* 9-19.

Christensen, R. V, & Hansson, K. (2012). The use and productivity of past tense morphology in specific language impairment: An examination of Danish. *Journal of Speech, Language, and Hearing Research, 55,* 1671-1689.

Clark, E., & Zhou, Z. (2005). Autism in China: From acupuncture to applied behavioral analysis. *Psychology in the Schools, 42,* 285-295.

Coelho, E. (2012). *Language and learning in multilingual classrooms: A practical approach.* New York: Multilingual Matters.

Cohen-Mimran, R., Reznik-Nevet, L., & Korona-Gaon, S. (2016). An activity-based language intervention program for kindergarten children: A retrospective evaluation. *Early Childhood Education, 44,* 69-78.

Colby, S. L., & Ortman, J. M. (2015). Projections of the size and composition of the U.S. population: 2014 to 2060. *U.S. Department of Commerce.* Retrieved from http://census.gov/content/dam/Census/library/publications/2015/demo/p25-1143.pdf

Common Core State Standards Initiative (2017). *Preparing America's students for success.* Retrieved from http://www.corestandards.org/

Connor, C. M., & Craig, H. K. (2006). African American preschoolers' language, emergent literacy skills, and use of African American English: A complex relation. *Journal of Speech, Language, and Hearing Research, 49,* 771-792.

Costa-Guerra, L., & Rhein, D. (2011). *Diversity in the Tewa and Dineh populations.* Paper presented at the national convention of the American Speech-Language-Hearing Association, San Diego, CA.

Cox, P. (2006). *Samoan Americans.* Retrieved from http://www.everyculture.com/multi/Pa-Sp/Samoan-Americans.html

Coyne, R. T. (2012). Teacher responses to participation in Hawaii's Kahua induction program. *The Journal of Multiculturalism in Education, 8,* 1-30.

Craig, H. K., & Crogger, J. T. (2012). Influences of social and style variables on adult usage of African American English features. *Journal of Speech, Language, and Hearing Research, 55,* 1274-1288.

Craig, K. K., & Washington, J. A. (2004a). A language screening protocol for use with young African American children in urban settings. *American Journal of Speech-Language Pathology, 13,* 329-340.

Craig, H. K., & Washington, J. A. (2004b). Grade-related changes in the production of African American English. *Journal of Speech, Language, and Hearing Research, 47,* 450-463.

Crowley, C. J. (2003, October). Diagnosing communication disorders in culturally and linguistically diverse students. *ERIC Digest E650.*

Crowley, C. J. (2012). *Reading comprehension, vocabulary skills, and multicultural populations.* Paper presented at the annual convention of the American Speech-Language-Hearing Association Schools Conference, Milwaukee, WI.

Crowley, C. J., & Baigorri, M. (2012, October 30). International service that really serves. *The ASHA Leader.* Retrieved from http://www.asha.org/Publications/leader/2012/121030/International-Service-That-Really-Serves/

Crowley, C. J., Guest, K., & Sudler, K. (2015). Cultural competence needed to distinguish disorder from difference: Beyond Kumbaya. *Perspectives on Communication Disorders and Sciences in Culturally and Linguistically Diverse Populations, 22,* 64-76.

Cummins, J. (1992a). Bilingual education and English immersion: The Ramírez report in theoretical perspective. *Bilingual Research Journal, 16* (1,2), 91-104.

Cummins, J. (1992b). Empowerment through biliteracy. In J. R. Tinajero & A. F. Ada (Eds.), *The power of two languages: Literacy and biliteracy for Spanish-speaking students.* New York: MacMillan/McGraw Hill.

Cummins, J. (1992c). The role of primary language development in promoting educational success for language minority students. In C. Leyba (Ed.), *Schooling and language minority students: A theoretical framework.* California State University, Los Angeles, CA.

Cummins, J. (2012). *Dr. James Cummins explains the differences between BICS and CALP.* YouTube video Retrieved from http://vimeo.com/56112120

Cummins, J. (2017). Teaching for transfer in multilingual school contexts. In O. Garcia, A. Lin and S. May (Eds.), *Bilingual and multilingual education* (pp. 103-115). New York: Springer International Publishing.

Dapice, A. N. (2006). The medicine wheel. *Journal of Transcultural Nursing, 17,* 251-260.

Davidoff, B. E. (2017, January). AAC with energy—earlier. *The ASHA Leader,* 49-53.

Davis, P. N., & Banks, T. (2012). Intervention for multicultural and international clients with communication disorders. In D. E. Battle (Ed.), *Communication disorders in multicultural and international populations* (4th ed.) (pp. 279-295). St. Louis, MO: Elsevier Mosby.

De Groot, B. J. A., Van den Bos, K. P., Van der Meulen, B. F., & Minnaert, A. E. (2015). Rapid naming and phonemic awareness in children with reading disabilities and/or specific language impairment: Differentiating processes? *Journal of Speech-Language-Hearing Research, 58,* 1538-1548.

Delcenserie, A., Genesee, F., & Gauthier, K. (2013). Language abilities of internationally adopted children from China during the early school years: Evidence for early age effects? *Applied Psycholinguistics, 34*(3), 541-568.

Deiner, M. L., Hobson-Rohrer, W., & Byington, C. L. (2012). Kindergarten readiness and performance of Latino children participating in Reach Out and Read. *Journal of Community Medicine & Health Education, 2*(3), 1-7.

Desmarais, C., Roeber, B. J., Smith, M. E., & Pollak, S. (2012). Sentence comprehension in postinstitutionalized school-age children. *Journal of Speech, Language, and Hearing Research, 55,* 45-54.

Diamond, A., Barnett, W., Thomas, J., & Munro, S. (2007). Preschool program improves cognitive control. *Science, 318,* 1387-1388.

Dispaldro, M., Leonard, L. B., & Deevy, P. (2013). Real-word and nonword repetition in Italian-speaking children with specific language impairment: A study of diagnostic accuracy. *Journal of Speech, Language, and Hearing Research, 56,* 232-336.

Dixon, L. Q., & Zhao, J. (2017). Bilingual language development. In J. B. Gleason & N.B. Ratner, *The development of language* (pp. 285-307). Boston: Pearson.

D'Oro, R. (2011). *Suicide rate remains high in Alaska, especially among Natives.* Retrieved from http://www.adn.com/2011/01/12/1645956/report-says-suicide-remains-an.html

Dodge, E. (2010). *Kimochis: Toys with feelings inside.* Retrieved from http://www.kimochis.com/

Dollaghan, C. A., & Campbell, T. F. (1998). Nonword repetition and child language impairment. *Journal of Speech, Language, and Hearing Research, 41,* 1136-1146.

Dollaghan, C. A., & Horner, E. A. (2011). Bilingual language assessment: A meta-analysis of diagnostic accuracy. *Journal of Speech, Language, and Hearing Research, 54,* 1077-1088.

Douglas, M. (2011a). Spoken language assessment considerations for children with hearing impairment when the home language is not English. *Perspectives on Hearing and Hearing Disorders in Children, 21*(1), 4-19.

Douglas, M. (2011b). Teaching children with hearing impairment to listen and speak when the home language is not English. *Perspectives on Hearing and Hearing Disorders in Children, 21*(1), 20-30.

Dunn, L. M., & Dunn, L. M. (1997). *Peabody Picture Vocabulary Test—3rd edition.* Circle Pines, MN: American Guidance Service.

Duran, L. K., Hartzheim, D., Lund, E. M., Simonsmeier, V., & Kohlmeier, T. L. (2016). Bilingual and home language interventions with young dual language learners: A research synthesis. *Language, Speech, and Hearing Services in Schools, 47,* 347-371.

Dyches, T. T., Wilder, L. K., Sudweeks, R. R., Obiakor, F. E., & Algozzine, B. (2004). Multicultural issues in autism. *Journal of Autism and Developmental Disabilities, 34,* 211-222.

Ebert, K. (2016, November*). Eliciting accurate parent reports in the assessment of school-age children from Hispanic families.* Paper presented at the annual convention of the American Speech-Language-Hearing Association, Philadelphia, PA.

Ebert, K. D., & Kohnert, K. (2009). Nonlinguistic cognitive treatment for primary language impairment. *Clinical Linguistics and Phonetics, 23,* 647-664.

Ebert, K., Kohnert, K., Pham, G., Disher, J. R., & Payesteh, B. (2014). Three treatments for bilingual children with primary language impairment: Examining cross-linguistic and cross-domain effects. *Journal of Speech, Language, and Hearing Research, 57*(1), 172-186.

Ebert, K., & Pham, G. (2017). Synthesizing information from language samples and standardized tests in school-age bilingual assessment. *Language, Speech, and Hearing Services in Schools, 48,* 42-65.

Ebert, K. D., Rentmeester-Disher, J., & Kohnert, K. (2012). Nonlinguistic cognitive treatment for bilingual children with primary language impairment. *Clinical Linguistics and Phonetics, 26,* 485-501.

Editorial Projects in Education Research Center (2016, March 31). Issues A-Z: The Every Student Succeeds Act: An ESSA Overview. *Education Week.* Retrieved from http://www.edweek.org/ew/issues/every-student-succeeds-act/

Edwards, J. (2010). *Language diversity in the classroom.* New York: Multilingual Matters.

Edwards J., Rosin M., Gross M., & Chen J. (2013). *Dialect mismatch and its implications for academic achievement.* Seminar presented at the Annual Conference of the American Speech-Language-Hearing Association, Chicago, IL.

Einarsdottir, J. T., Bjornsdottir, A., & Simonardottir, I. (2016). The predictive value of preschool language assessments on academic achievement: A 10-year longitudinal study of Icelandic children. *American Journal of Speech-Language Pathology, 25,* 67-79.

Elleseff, T. (2012). Adoption and pragmatic problems. *ADVANCE for Speech-Language Pathologists and Audiologists, 22*(12), 6-9.

Elleseff, T. (2013, October). Changing trends in international adoption: Implications for speech-language pathologists. *Perspectives on Global Issues in Communication Sciences and Disorders, 3,* 45-53.

Enchautegui, M. E. (2013). *Broken immigration policy: Broken families.* Urban Institute, Retrieved from http://www.urban.org/publications/412806.html

Engel de Abreu, P. M. J., Baldassi, M., Puglisi, M. L., & Befi-Lopes, D. M. (2013). Cross-linguistic and cross-cultural effects on verbal working memory and vocabulary: Testing language-minority children with an immigrant background. *Journal of Speech, Language, and Hearing Research, 56*(2), 630-642.

Engle, P. M., Santos, F. H., & Gathercole, S. E. (2008). Are working memory measures free of socioeconomic influence? *Journal of Speech, Language, and Hearing Research, 51,* 1580-1587.

Eriks-Brophy, A. & Ayukawa, H. (2000). The benefits of sound-field amplification in classrooms of Inuit students of Nunavik: A pilot project. *Language, Speech, and Hearing Services in Schools, 31,* 324-335.

Estes, K. G., Evans, J. L., & Else-Quest, N. M. (2007). Differences in the nonword repetition performance of children with and without specific language impairment: A meta-analysis. *Journal of Speech, Language, and Hearing Research, 50,* 177-195.

Faamanatu-Eteuati, N. (2011). Se'itatou 'aleaga: Samoan educators' insights into inclusive education development. *The Journal of the Pacific Circle Consortium for Education, 23*(2), 65-76.

Fazio, B. B. (1998). Serial memory in children with specific language impairment: Examining specific content areas for assessment and intervention. In R. B. Gillam (Ed.), *Memory and language impairment in children and adults: New perspectives* (pp. 64-82). Gaithersburg, MD: Aspen Publishers, Inc.

Fensbo, C. (2004). Mental and behavioral outcome of inter-ethnic adoptees: A review of the literature. *European Child and Adolescent Psychiatry, 13,* 55-63.

Fenson, L., Dale, P., Reznick, J., Bates, E., Thal, D. J., & Pethick, S. J. (1993). *McArthur Communicative Developmental Inventories: User's guide and technical manual.* San Diego, CA: Singular.

Fiestas, C. E. (2017, March). *Assessing language impairment in bilingual children: Utility of the dynamic assessment of narratives.* Paper presented at the annual convention of the California Speech and Hearing Association, Pasadena, CA.

Fiestas, C. E., & Peña, E. D. (2004). Narrative discourse in bilingual children: Language and task effects. *Language, Speech, and Hearing Services in Schools, 35,* 155-168.

Ford, K. (2017). *8 strategies for preschool ELLs' language and literacy development.* Retrieved from http://www.colorincolorado. org/article/8-strategies-preschool-ells-language-and-literacy-d....

Fortunato-Tavares, T., de Andrade, C. R. F., Befi-Lopes, D. M., Hestvik, A., Epstein, B., Tornyova, L., & Schwartz, R. G. (2012). Syntactic structural assignment in Brazilian Portuguese-speaking children with specific language impairment. *Journal of Speech, Language, and Hearing Research, 55,* 1097-1111.

Gatlin, B., & Wanzek, J. (2015). Relations among children's use of dialect and literacy skills: A meta-analysis. *Journal of Speech, Language, and Hearing Research, 58,* 1306-1318.

Gallaudet Research Institute (April, 2011). *Regional and National Summary Report of Data from the 2009-2010 Annual Survey of Deaf and Hard of Hearing Children and Youth.* Washington, DC: GRI, Gallaudet University.

Gallo, S. L., & Wortham, S. (2012). Sobresalir: Latino parent perspectives on new Latino diaspora schools. *International Journal of Multicultural Education, 14*(2), 1-17.

Garcia, O., & Lin, A. M. Y. (2017). Extending understandings of bilingual and multicultural education. In O. Garcia, A. M. Y. Lin, & S. May (Eds.), *Bilingual and Multilingual Education* (pp. 1-20). New York: Springer International Publishing.

Gardner-Neblett, N., Pungello, E. P., & Iruka, I. U. (2012). Oral narrative skills: Implications for the reading development of African American children. *Child Development Perspectives, 6,* 218-224.

Gaskell, S. (2012). Speech-language pathologists supporting indigenous language American Indian credentialed teachers. *The CSHA Newsletter,* Retrieved from http://www.csha.org/diversity.cfm

Gatlin, B., & Wanzek, J. (2015). Relations among children's use of dialect and literacy skills: A meta-analysis. *Journal of Speech, Language, and Hearing Research, 58,* 1306-1318.

Gauthier, K., Genesee, F., Dubois, M. E., & Kasparian, K. (2011). Communication patterns between internationally adopted children and their mothers: Implications for language. *Developmental Applied Psycholinguistics, 34*(2), 337-359.

Genesee, F. (2016). *At-risk learners and bilingualism: Is it a good idea?* Retrieved from http://www.colorincolorado.org/article/risk-learners-and-bilingualism-it-good-idea

Gillam, S. L., & Gillam, R. B. (2014). The development of morphology and syntax. In N. C. Singleton and B. B. Shulman, *Language development: Foundations, processes, and clinical applications* (2nd ed.), pp. 165-184.

Gillispie, M. (2016, August). Need for Culturally Responsive Literacy Instruction in Native American Communities. *Perspectives of the ASHA Special Interest Groups,* Vol. 1 (SIG 14), 56-68.

Gindis, B. (2004). Language development in internationally adopted children. *China Connection, 10,* 34-37.

Gindis, B. (2005). Cognitive, language, and educational issues of children adopted from overseas orphanages. *Journal of Cognitive Education and Psychology, 4,* 291-311.

Gindis, B. (2013). *Language-related issues for international adoptees and adoptive families.* Retrieved from http://www.bgcenter.com/languages/htm

Gleason, J. B., & Ratner, N. B. (2017). *The development of language* (9th ed.). Boston: Pearson.

Glennen, S. (2007). Predicting language outcomes for internationally adopted children. *Journal of Speech, Language, and Hearing Research, 50,* 529-548.

Glennen, S. (2015). Internationally adopted children in the early school years: Relative strengths and weaknesses in language abilities. *Language, Speech, and Hearing Services in Schools, 46,* 1-13.

Global Mapping International (2013). *The "Ten commandments" of American culture.* Retrieved from http://www.gmi.org/products/books/american-cultural-baggage/ten-commandments/

Goldstein, B. A., Bunta, F., Lange, J., Rodriguez, J., & Burrows, L. (2010). The effects of measures of language experience and language ability on segmental accuracy in bilingual children. *American Journal of Speech-Language Pathology, 19,* 238-247.

Goldstein, B. A., & Guildersleeve-Neumann, C. (2012). Phonological development and disorders. In B. A. Goldstein (Ed.), *Bilingual language development and disorders in Spanish-English speakers* (2nd ed.) (pp. 285-310). Baltimore: Paul H. Brookes Publishing Co.

Goldstein, B. A., & Iglesias, A. (1996). Phonological patterns in normally developing Spanish-speaking 3- and 4-year olds. *Language, Speech, and Hearing Services in Schools, 27*(1), 82-90.

Goldstein, H. et al. (2017). Efficacy of a supplemental phonemic awareness curriculum to instruct preschoolers with delays in early literacy development. *Journal of Speech, Language, and Hearing Research, 60,* 89-103.

Goode, T. D., Jones, W., & Jackson, V. (2011). Families with African American roots. In E. W. Lynch & M. J. Hanson (Eds.), *Developing cross-cultural competence: A guide for working with children and their families* (4th ed.) (pp. 140-189). Baltimore: Paul H. Brookes Publishing Co.

Goodrich, J. M., Lonigan, C. J., & Farver, J. M. (2013). Do early literacy skills in children's first language promote development of skills in their second language? An experimental evaluation of transfer. *Journal of Educational Psychology, 105,* 414-426.

Gorman, B. K. (2012). Relationships between vocabulary size, working memory, and phonological awareness in Spanish-speaking English language learners. *American Journal of Speech-Language Pathology, 21*, 109-123.

Gorman, B. K., Fiestas, C. E., Peña, E. D., & Clark, M. R. (2011). Creative and stylistic devices employed by children during a storybook narrative task: A cross-cultural study. *Language, Speech, and Hearing Services in Schools, 42*, 167-181.

Grech, H., & McLeod, S. (2012). Multilingual speech and language development and disorders. In D. E. Battle (Ed.), *Communication disorders in multicultural and international populations* (4th ed.) (120-147). St. Louis, MO: Mosby.

Green, L., Stockholm, M., Cearley, J., & Sheffield-Anderson, L. (2015). Direct vocabulary instruction with two 5th-grade English-language-learners with language-learning disabilities: A treatment study. *Contemporary Issues in Communication Science and Disorders, 42,* 191-201.

Grinstead, J., Baron, A., Vega-Mendoza, M., De La Mora, J., Canti-Sanchez, M., & Flores, B. (2013). Tense marking and spontaneous speech measures in Spanish specific language impairment: A discriminant function analysis. *Journal of Speech, Language, and Hearing Research, 56,* 352-363.

Guiberson, M. M. (2016). Gesture, play, and language development of Spanish-speaking toddlers with developmental language disorders: A preliminary study. *Communication Disorders Quarterly, 37*(2), 88-99.

Guiberson, M. M., & Rodriguez, B. L. (2013). Classification accuracy of nonword repetition when used with preschool-age Spanish-speaking children. *Language, Speech, and Hearing Services in Schools, 44*, 121-132.

Guiberson, M. M., Rodriguez, B. L., & Dale, P. S. (2011). Classification accuracy of brief parent report measures of language development in Spanish-speaking toddlers. *Language, Speech, and Hearing Services in Schools, 42*, 536-549.

Gutiérrez-Clellen, V. F. (2012). Narrative development and disorders in bilingual children. In B. A. Goldstein (Ed.), *Bilingual language development and disorders in Spanish-English speakers* (2nd ed.) (pp. 233-250). Baltimore: Paul H. Brookes Publishing Co.

Gutiérrez-Clellen, V. F., Calderon, J., & Ellis Weismer, S. (2004). Verbal working memory in bilingual children. *Journal of Speech, Language, and Hearing Research, 47*, 863-877.

Gutiérrez-Clellen, V. F., & Peña, E. (2008). Dynamic assessment of diverse children: A tutorial. *Language, Speech, and Hearing Services in Schools, 32*, 212-224.

Gutiérrez-Clellen, V. F., & Quinn, R. (1993). Assessing narratives of children from diverse cultural/linguistic groups. *Language, Speech, and Hearing Services in Schools, 24*(1), 2-9.

Gutiérrez-Clellen, V., Simon-Cereijido, G., & Restrepo, M. (2013). *Improving the vocabulary and oral language of bilingual Latino preschoolers: An intervention for speech-language pathologists*. San Diego: Plural Publishing.

Gutiérrez-Clellen, V., Simon-Cereijido, G., & Sweet, M. (2012). Predictors of second language acquisition in Latino children with specific language impairment. *American Journal of Speech-Language Pathology, 21*(1), 64-77.

Gutiérrez-Clellen, V. F., & Simon-Cereijido, G. (2010). Using nonword repetition tasks for the identification of language impairment in Spanish-English-speaking children: Does the language of assessment matter? *Learning Disabilities Research and Practice, 25*, 48-58.

Hakuta, K., Butler, Y. G., & Witt, D. (2000). *How long does it take English learners to attain proficiency?* Santa Barbara, CA: University of California Linguistic Minority Research Institute.

Hale, J. (2004). How schools shortchange African American children. *Educational Leadership, 62*(3), 34-38.

Hale, J. (2017). *HELP, I'm being pushed into classrooms! What's an SLP to do?* Paper presented at the annual convention of the California Speech and Hearing Association, Pasadena, CA.

Hammer, C. S., Morgan, P., Farkas, G., Hillemeier, M., Bitetti, D., & Maczuga, S. (2017). Late talkers: A population-based study of risk factors and school readiness consequences. *Journal of Speech, Language, and Hearing Research, 60,* 607-626.

Hampton, S., Rabagliati, H., Sorace, A., & Fletcher-Watson, S. (2017). Autism and bilingualism: A qualitative interview study of parents; perspectives and experiences. *Journal of Speech, Language, and Hearing Research, 60,* 435-446.

Hanson, M. J. (2011). Families with Anglo-European roots. In E. W. Lynch & M. J. Hanson (Eds.), *Developing cross-cultural competence: A guide for working with young children and their families* (4th ed.) (pp. 80-109). Baltimore: Paul H. Brookes Publishing Co.

Harrington, B. G., & Pavel, M. (2013). Using indigenous educational research to transform mainstream education: A guide for P-12 school leaders. *American Journal of Education, 119*(4), 487-511.

Harris, G. (1998). American Indian cultures: A lesson in diversity. In D. E. Battle (Ed.), *Communication disorders in multicultural populations* (2nd ed.) (pp. 117-156). Stoneham, MA: Butterworth-Heinemann.

Harris, K. L., & Moran, M. J. (2006). Phonological features exhibited by children speaking African American English at three grade levels. *Communication Disorders Quarterly, 27*, 195-205.

Heart of America Foundation (2017). *Transform learning, transform lives.* Retrieved from http://www.heartofamerica.org/

Hishinuma, E. G., Chang, J. Y., McArcle, J. J., & Hamagami, F. (2012). Potential causal relationship between depressive symptoms and academic achievement in the Hawaiian high schools health survey using contemporary longitudinal latent variable change models. *Developmental Psychology, 48*(5), 1327-1342.

Holmstrom, K., Salameh, E-K, Nettelbladt, U., & Dalhgren-Sandberg, A. (2016). Conceptual scoring of lexical organization in bilingual children with language impairment. *Communication Disorders Quarterly, 38*(1), 24-34.

Huer, M. B., Parette, H. P., & Saenz, T. I. (2001). Conversations with Mexican Americans regarding children with disabilities and augmentative and alternative communication devices. *Communication Disorders Quarterly, 22*, 197-206.

Huer, M. B., & Soto, G. (2006, November). *Cultural issues in the practice of augmentative and alternative communication.* Paper presented at the annual meeting of the American Speech-Language-Hearing Association, Miami, FL.

Hunter, D., & Sawyer, C. (2006). Blending Native American spirituality with individual psychology in work with children. *The Journal of Individual Psychology, 62*, 234-250.

Hutchins, S. D. (2017). Aid for people with hearing loss. *The ASHA Leader, 22*(6), 30-31.

Hwa-Froelich, D. A. (2012). *Supporting development in internationally adopted children.* Baltimore: Paul H. Brookes Publishing Co.

Hwa-Froelich, D. A., & Matsuo, H. (2005). Vietnamese children and language-based processing tasks. *Language, Speech, and Hearing Services in Schools, 36*, 230-243.

Hwa-Froelich, D. A., & Matsuo, H. (2010). Communication development and differences in children adopted from China and Eastern Europe. *Language, Speech, and Hearing Services in Schools, 41*, 349-366.

Hwa-Froelich, D., Matsuo, H., & Jacobs, K. (2017). False belief performance of children adopted internationally. *American Journal of Speech-Language Pathology, 26*, 29-43.

Hwa-Froelich, D. A., Pettinelli, J. D., & Jones, S. (2006). Interdisciplinary collaboration with internationally adopted children. *Perspectives on Communication Disorders and Sciences in Culturally and Linguistically Diverse Populations, ASHA SID 14 Newsletter, 13*, 8-16.

Hwa-Froelich, D. A., & Westby, C. E. (2003). Frameworks of education: Perspectives of Southeast Asian parents and Head Start staff. *Language, Speech, and Hearing Services in Schools, 34*, 299-319.

Ibrahim, F. A., & Dykeman, C. (2011). Counseling Muslim Americans: Cultural and spiritual assessments. *Journal of Counseling and Development, 89*, 387-396.

Iglesias, A., & Rojas, R. (2012). Bilingual language development of English language learners: Modeling the growth of two languages. In B. A. Goldstein (Ed.), *Bilingual language development and disorders in Spanish-English speakers* (2nd ed.) (pp. 3-30). Baltimore: Paul H. Brookes Publishing Co.

Ijalba, E. (2016). Hispanic immigrant mothers of young children with autism spectrum disorders: How do they understand and cope with autism? *American Journal of Speech-Language Pathology, 25*, 200-213.

Indian Affairs (2013). *Frequently asked questions.* Retrieved from http://www.bia.gov/FAQs/index.htm

Individuals with Disabilities Education Act (IDEA; 1997). *Federal Register, Volume 62, No. 204.* Part V, Department of Education, 34 CFR parts 300, 303.

Individuals with Disabilities Education Improvement Act of 2004 (IDEA, 2004). Public Law 108-446, 108th Congress.

Inglebret, E., Bear Eagle, D., & Pavel, D. M. (2007, January 23). American Indian stories enrich intervention. *The ASHA Leader.*

Inglebret, E., Banks-Joseph, S. R., CHiXapkaid, & Pavel, K. (2016, August). *Differentiated instruction: A culturally-congruent practice.* Perspectives of the ASHA Special Interest Groups, Vol. 1 (SIG 14), 43-55.

IOR Global Services (2017). *Arabs and Arab Americans: A quick guide.* Retrieved from http://www.iorworld.com/arabs-and-arab-americans-pages-235.php

Isoaho, P., Kauppiloa, T., & Launonen, K. (2016). Specific language impairment (SLI) and reading development in early school years. *Child Language Teaching and Therapy, 32*(2), 147-157.

Ispa, J. M., Thornburg, K. R., & Fine, M. A. (2006). *Keepin' on: The everyday struggles of young families in poverty.* Baltimore: Paul H. Brookes Publishing Company.

Ivy, L. J., & Masterson, J. J. (2011). A comparison of oral and written English styles in African American students at different stages of writing development. *Language, Speech, and Hearing Services in Schools, 42*, 31-40.

Jackson, C. W., Schatschneider, C., & Leacox, L. (2014). Longitudinal analysis of receptive vocabulary growth in young Spanish English-speaking children from migrant families. *Language, Speech, and Hearing Services in Schools, 45*(1), 40-51.

Jackson-Maldonado, D., Bates, E., & Thal, D. (1992). *Fundación MacArthur: Inventario del desarrollo de habilidades comunicativas.* San Diego, CA: San Diego State University.

Jackson-Maldonado, D., Marchman, V. A., & Fernald, L. C. H. (2013). Short-form versions of the Spanish MacArthur-Bates Communicative Development Inventories. *Applied Psycholinguistics, 32*(4), 837-868.

Jacob, N. (2011). Families with south Asian roots. In E. W. Lynch & M. J. Hanson (Eds.), *Developing cross-cultural competence: A guide for working with children and their families* (4th ed.) (pp. 463-470). Baltimore: Paul H. Brookes Publishing Co.

Jacobs, E. L., & Coufal, K. L. (2001). A computerized screening instrument of language learnability. *Communication Disorders Quarterly, 22*, 67-76.

Jacobson, P. F., & Walden, P. R. (2013). Lexical diversity and omission errors as predictors of language ability in the narratives of sequential bilingual Spanish-English bilinguals: A cross-language comparison. *American Journal of Speech-Language Pathology, 22*, 554-565.

James, C. (2007). *Climbing off dead horses: Changing to a life of balance.* Retrieved from www.cheewa.com

Jiménez, B. (1987). Acquisition of Spanish consonants in children aged 3-5 years, 7 months. *Language, Speech, and Hearing Services in the Schools, 18*, 357-363.

Joe, J. R., & Malach, R. S. (2011). Families with American Indian roots. In E. W. Lynch & M. J. Hanson (Eds.), *Developing cross-cultural competence: A guide for working with children and their families* (4th ed.) (pp. 110-139). Baltimore: Paul H. Brookes Publishing Co.

Johnson, L. C., Thomas-Tate, S., Spence, M., & Connor, C. M. (2011). *Impact of dialect use on students' writing.* Paper presented at the annual convention of the American Speech-Language-Hearing Association, San Diego, CA.

Juffer, F., & Van Ijzendoorn, M. H. (2005). Behavior problems and mental health referrals of international adoptees: A meta-analysis. *Journal of the American Medical Association, 293*, 2501-2515.

Juffer, F., Bakermans-Kranenburg, M. J., & Van IJzendoorn, M. H. (2008). *Positive parenting: An attachment-based intervention.* London: Lawrence Erlbaum/Taylor & Francis.

Justice, L. M. (2012). *Enhancing vocabulary practices for children: Promoting academic language in clinical interventions.* Paper presented at the annual American Speech-Language-Hearing Association conference, Milwaukee, WI.

Justice, L. M. (2013, October 01). From my perspective: A+ speech-language goals. *The ASHA Leader.*

Justice, L. M., Pullen, P. C., & Pence, K. (2008). Influence of verbal and nonverbal references to print on preschoolers' visual attention to print during storybook reading. *Developmental Psychology, 44*(3), 855-866.

Kaland, M., Moller-Nielsen, A., Smith, L., Mortensen, E. L., Callesen, K., & Gottlieb, D. (2005). The Strange Stories Test: A replication study of children and adolescents with Asperger syndrome. *European Child and Adolescent Psychiatry, 14*, 73-82.

Kan, P. F., Sadagopan, N., Janich, L., & Andrade, M. (2014). Effects of speech practice on fast mapping in monolingual and bilingual speakers. *Journal of Speech, Language, and Hearing Research, 57*, 929-941.

Kan, P. F., & Windsor, J. (2010). Word learning in children with primary language impairment: A meta-analysis. *Journal of Speech, Language, and Hearing Research, 53*, 739-756.

Kantor, S., Combi, S., & McQueen, C. (2013). *The Black family: Five decades after the Moynihan report.* The Urban Institute, Retrieved from http://www.urban.org/publications/904591.html

Kapantzoglou, M., Restrepo, M. A., & Thompson, M. (2012). Dynamic assessment of word learning skills: Identifying language impairment in bilingual children. *Language, Speech, and Hearing Services in Schools, 43*, 81-96.

Kapantzoglou, M., Restrepo, M. A., Gray, S., & Thompson, H. (2015). Language ability groups in bilingual children: a latent profile analysis. *Journal of Speech, Language, and Hearing Research, 58*, 1549-1562.

Karanth, P., Roseberry-McKibbin, C., & James, P. (2017a). *Intervention for preschoolers with cognitive, social, and emotional delays: Practical strategies.* San Diego, CA: Plural Publishing, Inc.

Karanth, P., Roseberry-McKibbin, C., & James, P. (2017b). *Intervention for preschoolers with communication delays: Practical strategies.* San Diego, CA: Plural Publishing, Inc.

Karanth, P., Roseberry-McKibbin, C., & James, P. (2017c). *Intervention for preschoolers with gross and fine motor delays: Practical strategies.* San Diego, CA: Plural Publishing, Inc.

Karanth, P., Roseberry-McKibbin, C., & James, P. (2017d). *Intervention for preschoolers using augmentative and alternative communication: Practical strategies.* San Diego, CA: Plural Publishing, Inc.

Karanth, P., Roseberry-McKibbin, C., & James, P. (2017e). *Intervention for toddlers using augmentative and alternative communication: Practical strategies.* San Diego, CA: Plural Publishing, Inc.

Karanth, P., Roseberry-McKibbin, C., & James, P. (2017f). *Intervention for toddlers with cognitive, social, and emotional delays: Practical strategies.* San Diego, CA: Plural Publishing, Inc.

Karanth, P., Roseberry-McKibbin, C., & James, P. (2017g). *Intervention for toddlers with communication delays: Practical strategies.* San Diego, CA: Plural Publishing, Inc.

Karanth, P., Roseberry-McKibbin, C., & James, P. (2017h). *Intervention for toddlers with gross and fine motor delays: Practical strategies.* San Diego, CA: Plural Publishing, Inc.

Karanth, P., Roseberry-McKibbin, C., & James, P. (2017i). *Intervention manual for prerequisite learning skills: Practical strategies.* San Diego, CA: Plural Publishing, Inc.

Kawach, N. (2010). *Arab world needs to rise to the literacy challenge.* Retrieved from http://www.emirates247.com/news/region/arab-world-needs-to-rise-to-the-literacy-challenge-2010-07-28-1/272076

Kay-Raining Bird, E. (2011). Health, education, language, dialect, and culture in First Nations, Inuit, and Metis communities in Canada: An overview. *Canadian Journal of Speech-Language Pathology and Audiology, 35*(2), 110-124.

Kay-Raining Bird, E., Cleave, P., Trudeau, N., Thordardottir, E., Sutton, A., & Thorpe, A. (2005). The language abilities of bilingual children with Down Syndrome. *American Journal of Speech-Language Pathology, 4,* 187-199.

Kay-Raining Bird, E., Genesee, F., & Verhoeven, L. (2016). Bilingualism in children with developmental disorders: A narrative review. *Journal of Communication Disorders, 63,* 1-92.

Kay-Raining Bird, E., Lamond, E., & Holden, J. J. (2012). A survey of bilingualism in Autism Spectrum Disorders. *International Journal of Language and Communication Disorders, 47*(1), 52-64.

Kayser, H. R. (2012). Hispanic and Latino cultures in the United States and Latin America. In D. E. Battle (Ed.), *Communication disorders in multicultural and international populations* (4th ed.) (pp. 102-147). St. Louis, MO: Elsevier Mosby.

Kelly, J. F., & Greene, B. (2010). Diversity within African American, female therapists: Variability in clients' expectations and assumptions about the therapist. *Psychotherapy: Theory, Research, Practice, Training, 47,* 186-197.

Kent-Walsh, J., & Rosa-Lugo, L. (2006). Communication partner interventions for children who use AAC: Storybook reading across culture and language. *The ASHA Leader, 11,* 28-29.

Kenyon, D. B., & Hanson, J. D. (2012). Incorporating traditional culture into positive youth development programs with American Indian/Alaska Native Youth. *Child Development, 6*(3), 272-279.

Kieffer, M. J., Biancarosa, G., & Mancilla-Martinez, J. (2013). Roles of morphological awareness in the reading comprehension of Spanish-speaking minority learners: Exploring partial mediation by vocabulary and reading fluency. *Applied Psycholinguistics, 34*(4), 697-725.

Kim, Y. S., Chen, Q., Wang, Y., Shen, Y., & Orozco-Lapray, D. (2013). Longitudinal linkages among parent-child acculturation discrepancy, parenting, parent-child sense of alienation, and adolescent adjustment in Chinese immigrant families. *Developmental Psychology, 49*(5), 900-912.

Kimble, C. (2013). Speech-language pathologists' comfort levels in English Language Learner service delivery. *Communication Disorders Quarterly, 35*(1), 21-27.

Kirk, S., Gallagher, J., Coleman, M. R., & Anastasiow, N. (2012). *Educating exceptional children* (13th ed.). Belmont, CA: Wadsworth.

Kohnert, K. (2013). *Language disorders in bilingual children and adults* (2nd ed). San Diego: Plural Publishing.

Kohnert, K., & Derr, A. (2012). Language intervention with bilingual children. In B. A. Goldstein (Ed.), *Bilingual language development and disorders in Spanish-English speakers* (2nd ed.) (pp. 337-356). Baltimore: Paul H. Brookes Publishing Co.

Kraemer, R. A., Coltisor, A., Kalra, M., Martinez, M., Savage, B., Summers, S., Varadhawajan, S., & Roseberry-McKibbin, C. (2013, July). *Speech-language assessment of English Language Learning students: A psychometric analysis.* Paper presented at the annual Schools Conference of the American Speech-Language-Hearing Association, Long Beach, CA.

Kraemer, R., & Bryla, J. (2017). *Clinical workbook for speech-language pathology assistants.* San Diego, CA: Plural Publishing, Inc.

Kraemer, R., & Fabiano-Smith, L. (2017, February). Language assessment of Latino English learning children: A records abstraction study. *Journal of Latinos and Education,* 1-10.

Krakow, R., Mastriano, B., & Reese, L. (2005). *Early intervention and international adoption.* Paper presented at the annual convention of the American Speech-Language-Hearing Association, San Diego, CA.

Kritikos, E. P. (2003). Speech-language pathologists' beliefs about language assessment of bilingual/bicultural individuals. *American Journal of Speech-Language Pathology, 12,* 73-91.

Krok, W. C., & Leonard, L. B. (2015). Past tense production in children with and without specific language impairment across Germanic languages: A meta-analysis. *Journal of Speech, Language, and Hearing Research, 58,* 1326-1340.

Kuder, S. J. (2013). *Teaching students with language and communication disabilities* (4th ed.). Upper Saddle River, NJ: Pearson.

Kulis, S., Dustman, P. A., Brown, E. F., & Martinez, M. (2013). Expanding urban American Indian youths' repertoire of drug resistance skills: Pilot results from a culturally adapted prevention program. *American Indian and Alaska Native Mental Health Research, 20*(1), 35-54.

Kummer, S. E. (2012). Promising strategies for collaborating with Hispanic parents during family-centered speech-language intervention. *Communication Disorders Quarterly, 33*(2), 84-95.

Ladage, J. S., & Harris, S. E. (2012). Physical growth, health, and motor development. In D. Hwa-Froelich, *Supporting development in internationally adopted children* (pp. 21-58). Baltimore: Paul H. Brookes Publishing Co.

Ladson-Billings, G. (1994). *The dreamkeepers: Successful teachers of African American children.* San Francisco, CA: Jossey-Bass/John Wiley & Sons, Inc.

Laing, S. P., & Kamhi, A. (2003). Alternative assessment of language and literacy in culturally and linguistically diverse populations. *Language, Speech, and Hearing Services in Schools, 34,* 44-55.

Lam, B. P. & Sheng, L. (2016). The development of morphological awareness in young bilinguals: Effects of age and L1 background. *Journal of Speech, Language, and Hearing Research, 59,* 732-744.

Landry, D. A. (2007). Alcoholism—from Russia to you and here in the USA. *Adoption Week,* Retrieved from http://e-magazine.adoption.com/articles (Adoption Media, LLC 1995-2007).

Langdon, H. W., & Saenz, T. I. (2016). *Working with interpreters and translators: A guide for speech-language pathologists and audiologists.* San Diego: Plural Publishing.

Lederberg, A. R., Schick, B., & Spencer, P. E. (2013). Language and literacy development of deaf and hard-of-hearing children: Successes and challenges. *Developmental Psychology, 49*(1), 15-30.

Leedom Shaul, D. (2014). *Linguistic ideologies of Native American language revitalization: Doing the lost language ghost dance.* New York: Springer Publishing.

Lerner, C., & Ciervo, L. (2010). Parenting young children today: What the research tells us. *Journal of Zero to Three, 30,* 4-9.

Leston, J. D., Jessen, C. M., & Simons, B. C. (2013). Alaska Native and rural youth views of sexual health: A focus group project on sexually transmitted diseases, HIV/AIDS, and unplanned pregnancy. *American Indian and Alaska Native Mental Health Research, 19*(1), 1-14.

Lewis, N. (2017). Our role in early identification. *The ASHA Leader, 22*(1), 6-7.

Listug-Lunde, L., Vogeltanz-Holm, N., & Collins, J. (2013). A cognitive-behavioral treatment for depression in rural American Indian middle school students. *American Indian and Alaska Native Mental Health Research, 20*(1), 16-34.

Literacy Project Foundation (2017). *Community statistics.* Retrieved from http://literacyprojectfoundation.org/community/statistics

Liu, L. X., et al. (2017). Research to establish the validity, reliability, and clinical utility of a comprehensive language assessment of Mandarin. *Journal of Speech, Language, and Hearing Research, 60,* 592-606.

Loakes, D., Moses, K., Wigglesworth, G., Simpson, J. and Billington, R. (2013) Children's language input: A study of a remote multilingual Indigenous Australian community. *Multilingua 32*(5), pp. 683-711.

Locke, D. C. (1998). *Increasing multicultural understanding: A comprehensive model.* Thousand Oaks, CA: Sage.

Lopez, F. A., Heilig, J. V., & Schram, J. (2013). A story within a story: Culturally responsive schooling and American Indian and Alaska Native achievement in the national Indian education study. *American Journal of Education, 119*(4), 513-538.

Lugo-Neris, M. J., Jackson, C., & Goldstein, H. (2010). Facilitating vocabulary acquisition of young English language learners. *Language, Speech, and Hearing Services in Schools, 41,* 314-327.

Lynch, E. W., & Hanson, M. J. (2011). *Developing cross-cultural competence: A guide for working with children and their families* (4th ed.). Baltimore: Paul H. Brookes Publishing Co.

Lytle, R. R., Johnson, K. E., & Jun Hui, Y. (2005). Deaf education in China: History, current issues, and emerging Deaf voices. *American Annals of the Deaf, 150,* 457-469.

Ma, J., van den Heuvel, M., Maguire, J., Parkin, P., & Birken, C. (2017, May). *Is handheld screen time use associated with language delay in children?* Paper presented at the annual Pediatric Academic Societies Meeting, San Francisco, CA.

Madding, C. C. (2000). Maintaining focus on cultural competence in early intervention services to linguistically and culturally diverse families. *Infant-Toddler Intervention: The Transdisciplinary Journal, 10*(1), 9-18.

Mahecha, N. (2003). Typical and disordered child narration in Spanish-speaking children. In A. McCabe & L. S. Bliss, *Patterns of narrative discourse: A multicultural, lifespan approach* (pp. 73-90). Boston: Allyn & Bacon.

Mahendra, N. (2012). South Asian stories: Firsthand client perspectives on barriers to accessing speech-language pathology services. *Perspectives on Communication Disorders and Sciences in Culturally and Linguistically Diverse Populations, 19*(1), 29-36.

Mancilla-Martinez, J., Gamez, P. G., Vagh, S. B., & Lesaux, N. K. (2016). Parent reports of young Spanish-English bilingual children's productive vocabulary: A development and validation study. *Language, Speech, and Hearing Services in Schools, 47*(1), 1-15.

Marian, V., & Kaushanskaya, M. (2011). Language-dependent memory: Insights from bilingualism. In C. Zelinsky-Wibbelt (Ed.), *Relations between language and memory.* Sabest Saarbrucker, Frankfurt: Peter Lang.

Marian, V., & Shook, A. (2012). The cognitive benefits of being bilingual. *Cerebrum Online Magazine.* Retrieved from http://dana.org/news/cerebrum

Marklund, U., Marklund, E., Lacerda, F., & Schwarz, I. C. (2015). Pause and utterance duration in child-directed speech in relation to child vocabulary size. *Journal of Child Language, 42*(5), 1158-1171.

Mattes, L. J. (2008). *Guidebook of objectives and activities for language skills (GOALS).* Oceanside, CA: Academic Communication Associates.

Mattes, L. J., & García-Easterly, I. (2007). *Bilingual speech and language intervention resource.* Oceanside, CA: Academic Communication Associates.

Mattes, L. J., & Saldaña-Illingworth, C. (2008). *Bilingual communication assessment resource. Tools for assessing speech, language, and learning.* Oceanside, CA: Academic Communication Associates.

May, S. (2017). Bilingual education: What the research tells us. In O. Garcia, A. M. Y. Lin, & S. May (Eds.), *Bilingual and Multilingual Education* (pp. 81-100). New York: Springer International Publishing.

McCabe, A., & Champion, T. B. (2010). A matter of vocabulary II: Low-income African American children's performance on the Expressive Vocabulary Test. *Communication Disorders Quarterly, 31*(3), 162-169.

McDaniel, B. T., & Radesky, J. S. (2017). Technoconference: Parent distraction with technology and associations with child behavior problems. *Child Development,* doi:10.1111/cdev.12.822

Mdlalo, T. (2017, May). *Are South African speech-language therapists adequately equipped to assess English additional language (EAL) speakers who are from an indigenous linguistic and cultural background? A profile and exploration of the current situation.* Presentation given at the International Conference on Speech Language Pathology, Las Vegas, NV.

Medical News Today (2017). *Top 10 leading causes of death in the U.S.* Retrieved from http://www.medicalnewstoday.com/articles/282929.php

Mehra, S., Eavey, R., & Keamy, D. Jr. (2009). The epidemiology of hearing impairment in the United States. *Otolaryngology, Head and Neck Surgery, 140*(4), 461-472.

Mendez, L. I., Crais, E. R., Castro, D. C., & Kainz, K. (2015). A culturally and linguistically responsive vocabulary approach for young Latino dual language learners. *Journal of Speech, Language, and Hearing Research, 58*, 93-106.

Mental Health America (2017). *Black & African American communities and mental health.* Retrieved from http://www.mentalhealthamerica.net/african-american-mental-health.

Merino, B. (1992). Acquisition of syntactic and phonological features in Spanish. In H. W. Langdon and L. Cheng, *Hispanic children and adults with communication disorders: Assessment and intervention.* Gaithersburg, MD: Aspen Publishers, Inc.

Migration Policy Institute (2017). Immigration trends. Retrieved from http://www.migrationpolicy.org

Miller, J. F., & Iglesias, A. (2008). *Systematic analysis of language transcripts (SALT), English and Spanish* (Version 9) [Computer software]. Madison: University of Wisconsin—Madison, Waisman Center, Language Analysis Laboratory.

Mills, M. T. (2015a). Narrative performance of gifted African American school-aged children from low-income backgrounds. *American Journal of Speech-Language Pathology, 24*, 36-46.

Mills, M. T. (2015b). The effects of visual stimuli on the spoken narrative performance of school-age African American children. *Language, Speech, and Hearing Services in Schools, 46*, 337-351.

Mills, M., Watkins, R. V., & Washington, J. (2013). Structural and dialectal characteristics of the fictional and personal narratives of school-age African American children. *Language, Speech, and Hearing Services in Schools, 44*, 211-223.

Misatauveve, M. A. (2012). *Samoans—culture and identity.* Te Ara, New Zealand. Retrieved from http://www.TeAra.govt.nz/en/samoans/page-3

Moeller, M. P., & McCreery, R. (2017). Children who are hard of hearing still forgotten? *The ASHA Leader, 22*(6), 16-17.

Mokuau, N., & Tauili'ili, P. (2011). Families with Native Hawaiian and Samoan roots. In E. W. Lynch & M. J. Hanson (Eds.), *Developing cross-cultural competence: A guide for working with children and their families* (4th ed.) (pp. 365-391). Baltimore: Paul H. Brookes Publishing Co.

Monreal, S., & Hernández, R. (2005). Reading levels of Spanish Deaf students. *American Annals of the Deaf, 150*, 379-381.

Monroe, C. R. (2005). Why are "Bad Boys" always Black? Causes of disproportionality in school discipline and recommendations for change. *Clearing House, 79*, 45-50.

Montgomery, J. K. (2013). *Vocabulary strategies to reach the Common Core State Standards.* Paper presented at the annual American Speech-Language-Hearing-Association Schools Conference, Long Beach, CA.

Montgomery, J. W., Magimairaj, B. M., & Finney, M. C. (2010). Working memory and specific language impairment: An update on the relation and perspectives on assessment and treatment. *American Journal of Speech-Language Pathology, 19*, 78-94.

Moore, B. & Montgomery, J. K. (2018). *Making a difference for America's children: Speech-language pathologists in public schools* (3rd ed.). Austin, TX: Pro-Ed.

Morgan, P. L., Hammer, C. S., Farkas, G., Hillemeier, M. M., Maczuga, S., Cook, M., & Morano, S. (2016). Who receives speech/language services by 5 years of age in the United States? *American Journal of Speech-Language Pathology, 25*, 183-199.

Morris, V. G., & Morris, C. (2013). Improving the academic achievement of African American children: The roles of principals in teacher induction and mentoring. *National Forum of Applied Educational Research Journal, 26*(1-2), 17-32.

Muñoz, M. L. (2017). Introduction to SIG 14's 2017 theme: Health disparities. *Perspectives of the ASHA Special Interest Groups, Volume 2, part 1,* 3-4.

Murza, K. (2013). *Common core state standards: Practical strategies for relevant, evidence-based instruction and intervention for grades K-12.* Summit Professional Education seminar presented in Sacramento, CA, 9/20/13.

Nakamura, K., Iwabuchi, M., & Alm, N. (2006). A cross-cultural study on the interpretation of picture-based sentences. *International Journal of Computer Processing of Oriental Languages, 19*, 239-248.

National Assessment of Educational Progress. (2011). *Grade 4 national results.* Retrieved from http://nationsreportcard.gov/reading_2011/nat_g4.asp?tab_id=tab2&subtab_id=Tab_3#chart

National Center for Education Statistics (2017). *Fast Facts: English Language Learners*. Retrieved from https://nces.ed.gov/fast-facts/display.asp?id=96

National Conference of State Legislatures (2016). *Federal and state recognized tribes*. Available frm http://ncsl.org/research/state-tribal-institute/list-of-federal-and-state-recognized-tribes.aspx

National Congress of American Indians (2017). *Native youth programs*. Retrieved from http://www.ncal.org.

National Farm Worker Ministry (2017). *Low wages*. Retrieved from http://nfwm.org/education-center/farm-worker-issues/low-wages

National Governors Association Center for Best Practices (2010). *Common Core State Standards*. Washington, D.C.: National Governors Association Center for Best Practices, Council of Chief State School Officers.

National Hispanic Heritage Month (2017). Hispanic Heritage Month. Retrieved from http://www.hispanicheritagemonth.org/

National Institutes of Health (2017). Cochlear implants. Retrieved from https://report.nih.gov/NIHfactsheets/ViewFactSheet.aspx?csid=83

Nelissen, S., & Van den Bulck, J. (2017). When digital natives instruct digital immigrants: active guidance of parental media use by children and conflict in the family. *Information, Communication, and Society, January 2017*, 1-13.

Nelson, N. W. (2010). *Language and literacy disorders: Infancy through adolescence*. Boston: Allyn & Bacon.

Nelson, P., Kohnert, K., Sabur, S., & Shaw, D. (2005). Classroom noise and children learning through a second language: Double jeopardy? *Language, Speech, and Hearing Services in Schools, 36*, 219-229.

Nippold, M. A. (2017). Reading comprehension deficits in adolescents: Addressing underlying language abilities. *Language, Speech, and Hearing Services in Schools, 48*, 125-131.

No Child Left Behind Act (NCLB), 20 U.S.C. (2001 & Supp. 2002). Retrieved from http://www.ed.gov/policy/elsec/leg/esea02/107-110.pdf

Norbury, C. F., & Sparks, A. (2013). Difference or disorder? Cultural issues in understanding neurodevelopmental disorders. *Developmental Psychology, 49*(1), 45-58.

Nydell, M. K. (2012). *Understanding Arabs: A contemporary guide to Arab society* (5th ed.). Boston: Nicholas Brealey Publishing.

Obama, B. (2006). *The audacity of hope: Thoughts on reclaiming the American dream*. New York: Crown Publishers.

Oetting, J. B., McDonald, J. L., Seibel, C. M., & Hegarty, M. (2016). Sentence recall by children with SLI across two nonmainstream dialects of English. *Journal of Speech, Language, and Hearing Research, 59*, 183-194.

Ogbu, J. (1992). Understanding cultural diversity and learning. *Educational Researcher, 21*(8), 5-14.

Ogbu, J. (1995). Literacy and Black Americans: Comparative perspectives. In V. L. Gladsen & D. A. Wagner (Eds.), *Literacy among African-American youth: Issues in learning, teaching, and schooling* (pp. 83-100). Creskill, NJ: Hampton Press.

One World Literacy Foundation (2017). Illiteracy statistics. Retrieved from https://www.oneworldliteracyfoundation.org/index.php/why-support-owl/illiteracy-statistics.html

Owens, R. E. (2016). *Language development: An introduction* (9th ed.). Upper Saddle River, NJ: Pearson.

Palafox, P. L. (2017). The unique speech needs of children in poverty. *The ASHA Leader, 22*(3), 30-31.

Paradis, J. (2007). Second language acquisition in childhood. In E. Hoff & M. Shatz (Eds.), *Handbook of language development* (pp. 387-406). Oxford: Blackwell.

Paradis, J. (2016). The development of English as a second language with and without specific language impairment: Clinical implications. *Journal of Speech, Language, and Hearing Research, 59*, 171-182.

Paradis, J., Emmerzael, K., & Sorenson Duncan, T. (2010). Assessment of English language learners: Using parent reports on first language development. *Journal of Communication Disorders, 43*, 474-497. Retrieved from http://www.chesl.ualberta.ca

Paradis, J., Genesee, F., & Crago, M. (2011). *Dual language development and disorders: A handbook on bilingualism and language learning* (2nd ed.). Baltimore: Paul H. Brookes Publishing.

Paradis, J., Rusk, B., Sorenson Duncan, T., & Govindarajan, K. (2017). English second language children's acquisition of complex sentences: The role of age, input and cognitive factors. *Annual Review of Applied Linguistics, 37*, 1-20.

Paradis, J., Schneider, P., & Duncan, T. S. (2013). Discriminating children with language impairment among English-language learners from diverse first-language backgrounds. *Journal of Speech, Language, and Hearing Research, 56*, 971-981.

Paradis, J., & Sorenson Duncan, T. (2009). *Differentiating between English L2 children with typical and impaired language development*. Paper presented at the Boston University Conference on Language Development, Boston University, Boston.

Parasnis, I., & Fischer, S.D. (2005). Perceptions of diverse educators regarding ethnic-minority Deaf college students, role models, and diversity. *American Annals of the Deaf, 150*, 343-348.

Parette, P., Chuang, S. L., & Huer, M. B. (2004). First-generation Chinese American families' attitudes regarding disabilities and educational interventions. *Focus on Autism and Other Developmental Disabilities, 19*, 114-123.

Parette, H. P., Huer, M. B., & Peterson-Karlan, G. R. (2008). Meeting the needs of persons with developmental disabilities across cultures. In. H. P. Parette & G. R. Peterson-Karlan (Eds.). *Research-based practices in developmental disabilities*. (2nd Ed.) (pp. 143-167). Austin, TX: Pro-Ed.

Parette, H. P., Huer, M. B., & Wyatt, T. A. (2003/4). Young African American children with disabilities and augmentative and alternative communication issues. In K. L. Freiburg (Ed.), *Annual editions: Educating exceptional children* (15th ed.) (pp. 76-81). Guilford, CT: Dushkin Publishing Group.

Patterson, J. L., Rodriguez, B. L., & Dale, P. S. (2013). Response to dynamic language tasks among typically developing Latino preschool children with bilingual experience. *American Journal of Speech-Language Pathology, 22,* 103-112.

Paul, R., Norbury, C., & Gosse, C. (2018). *Language disorders from infancy through adolescence: Listening, speaking, writing, and communicating* (5th ed.). St. Louis, MO: Mosby, Inc.

Pearson, B. Z., Conner, T., & Jackson, J. E. (2013). Removing obstacles for African American English-speaking children through greater understanding of language difference. *Developmental Psychology, 49*(1), 31-44.

Pelczarski, Y., & Kemp, S. P. (2006). Patterns of child maltreatment referrals among Asian and Pacific Islander families. *Child Welfare, 85,* 5-32.

Peña, E. D., Gutiérrez-Clellen, V., Iglesias, A., Goldstein, B. A., & Bedore, L. M. (2014). *Bilingual English Spanish Assessment.* San Diego, CA: AR-Clinical Publications.

Pence, K. A., Justice, L. M., & Gosse, C. (2007). *Narrative Assessment Protocol.* Charlottesville, VA: University of Virginia.

Petersen, D. B., & Gillam, R. B. (2013). Predicting reading ability for bilingual Latino children using dynamic assessment. *Journal of Learning Disabilities,* September 2013, 1-19.

Petersen, D. B., Chanthongthip, H., Ukrainetz, T. A., Spencer, T. D., & Steeve, R. W. (2017). Dynamic assessment of narratives: Efficient, accurate identification of language impairment in bilingual students. *Journal of Speech, Language, and Hearing Research, 60,* 983-998.

Pew Hispanic Research Center (2017). Hispanic trends. Retrieved from http://www.pewhispanic.org/

Pew Research Center (2016). 10 demographic trends that are shaping the U.S. and the world. Retrieved from http://www.pewresearch.org/fact-tank/2016/03/31/10-demographic-trends-that-are-shaping-the-u-s-and-the-world/

Pew Research Center (2017a). *How America changed during Barack Obama's presidency.* Retrieved from http://www.pewresearch.org/2017/01/10/how-america-changed-during-barack-obamas-presidency/

Pew Research Center (2017b). Meet the new immigrants: Asians overtake Hispanics. Retrieved from http://www.pewsocialtrends.org/asianamericans-graphics/

Pew Research Center Fact Tank (2017). Muslims and Islam: Key findings in the U.S. and around the world. Retrieved from http://www.pewresearch.rog/fact-tank/2017/02/27/muslims-and-islam-key-findings-in-the-u.s.-and-around-the-world/

Pew Research Center: Religion and Public Life (2017). Religious landscape study: Buddhists. Retrieved from http://www.pewforum.org/religious-landscape-study/religious-tradition-buddhist/

Pew Social Trends (2015). *The American family today.* Retrieved from http://www.pewsocialtrends.org/2015/12/17/1-the-american-family-today/

Pfeffer, R. (2011). *Growing incarceration of young African-American women a cause for concern.* Retrieved from http://oaklandlocal.com/posts/2011/05/growing-incarceration-young-african-american-women-cause-concern

Pham, G., Ebert, K., & Kohnert, K. (2015). Bilingual children with primary language impairment: Three months after treatment. *Journal of Language and Communication Disorders, 50,* 94-105.

Pham, G., & Kohnert, K. (2014). A longitudinal study of lexical development in children learning Vietnamese and English. *Child Development, 85*(2), 767-782.

Pham, G., Kohnert, K., & Mann, D. (2011). Addressing clinician-client mismatch: A preliminary intervention study with a bilingual Vietnamese-English preschooler. *Language, Speech, and Hearing Services in Schools, 42,* 408-422.

Phend, C. (2013). *Survey: Autism dx harder in Latinos.* Retrieved from http://medpagetoday.com/Pediatrics/autism/41046

Pieretti, R. A. (2011). *Response to intervention and literacy: A bright spot for Hmong-speaking English language learners?* (Order No. 3474448, University of California, Davis). ProQuest Dissertations and Theses, 158. Retrieved from http://search.proquest.com/docview/898363985?accountid=10358.(89863985)

Pieretti, R., & Roseberry-McKibbin, C. (2016). Assessment and intervention for English Language Learners with primary language impairment: Research-based best practices. *Communication Disorders Quarterly, 37*(2), 117-128.

Pindzola, R., Plexico, L., & Haynes, W. O. (2016) *Diagnosis and evaluation in speech pathology* (9th ed.). New York: Pearson Education.

Prath, S., & Palafox, P. (2017). *Literacy-based speech and language therapy activities: Successfully use storybooks to reduce planning time, easily work in groups, and target multiple communication and academic goals.* USA: Bilinguistics, Inc.

Pratt, A. S., Justice, L. M., Perez, A., & Duran, L. K. (2015). Impact of parent-implemented early-literacy intervention. *International Journal of Language and Communication Disorders, 50*(5), 569-579.

Preis, J. (2013). The effects of teaching about White privilege in speech-language pathology. *Perspectives on Communication Disorders and Sciences in Culturally and Linguistically Diverse Populations,* August 2013, *20*(2), 72-83.

Pronchenko-Jain, Y., & Fernando, D. M. (2013). Helping families with Russian adoptees: Understanding unique needs and challenges. *The Family Journal, 21*(4), 402-407.

Pua, E. P. K., Lee, M. L. C., & Liow, S. J. R. (2017). Screening bilingual preschoolers for language difficulties: Utility of teacher and parent reports. *Journal of Speech, Language, and Hearing Research, 60,* 950-968.

Rapoza, K. (2013). *Russian "baby ban" goes into full effect.* Retrieved from http://www.forbes.com/sites/kenrapoza/2013/01/02/russian-baby-ban-goes-into-full-effect

Ratner, N. B. (2017). Atypical language development. In J. Berko Gleason and N. B. Ratner, *The development of language* (9th ed.) (pp. 216-256). Boston: Pearson Education.

Reetzke, R., Zou, X., Sheng, L., & Katsos, N. (2015). Communicative development in bilingually exposed Chinese children with Autism Spectrum Disorder. *Journal of Speech, Language, and Hearing Research, 58*(3), 813-825.

Rescorla, L., Lee, Y. M. C., Oh, K. J., & Kim, Y. A. (2013). Lexical development in Korean: Vocabulary size, lexical composition, and late talking. *Journal of Speech, Language, and Hearing Research, 56*(2), 735-747.

Rescue.org (2017). *Refugee crisis briefing.* Retrieved from https://www.rescue.org/topic/refugee-crisis-europe-middle-east

Restrepo, M. A., & Gutiérrez-Clellen, V. F. (2012). Grammatical impairments in Spanish-English bilingual children. In B. A. Goldstein (Ed.), *Bilingual language development and disorders in Spanish-English speakers* (2nd ed.) (pp. 213-232). Baltimore, MD: Paul H. Brookes Publishing Co.

Restrepo, M. A., Morgan, G. P., & Thompson, M. S. (2013). The efficacy of a vocabulary intervention for dual-language learners with language impairment. *Journal of Speech, Language, and Hearing Research, 56,* 748-765.

Rezzonico, S., et al. (2016). Narratives in two languages: Storytelling of bilingual Cantonese-English preschoolers. *Journal of Speech, Language, and Hearing Research, 59,* 521-532.

Rice, M., & Wexler, K. (2001). *Test of Early Grammatical Impairment.* New York, NY: Psychological Corporation.

Riley, K. G., & McGregor, K. K. (2012). Noise hampers children's expressive word learning. *Language, Speech, and Hearing Services in Schools, 43,* 325-337.

Riquelme, L. F., & Rosas, J. (2014). Multicultural perspectives: The road to cultural competence. In N. C. Singleton & B. B. Shulman, *Language development: Foundations, processes, and clinical applications* (2nd ed.) (pp. 231-249). Burlington, MA: Jones & Bartlett.

Roberts, J. A., & Scott, K. A. (2011). Rose: A preschool child who was internationally adopted. In S. S. Chabon and E. R. Cohn, *The communication disorders casebook: Learning by example* (pp. 102-110). Upper Saddle River, NJ: Pearson Education.

Roberts, T. A. (2013). Opportunities and oversights within the Common Core State Standards for English Language Learners' language and literacy achievement. In S. B. Neuman and L. B. Gambrell (Eds.), *Quality reading instruction in the age of common core standards* (pp. 90-106). Newark, DE: International Reading Association.

Robinson-Zañartu, C. (1996). Serving Native American children and families: *Considering cultural variables. Language, Speech, and Hearing Services in Schools, 27*(4), 373-384.

Rosa-Lugo, L. I., Mihai, F. M., & Nutta, J. W. (2012). *Language and literacy development: An interdisciplinary focus on English learners with communication disorders.* San Diego, CA: Plural Publishing.

Roseberry-McKibbin, C. (2013a). *A survey of U.S. immigrants: Service delivery issues for SLPs.* Unpublished study conducted in Sacramento, CA.

Roseberry-McKibbin, C. (2013b*). Increasing the language and academic achievement of children in poverty* (2nd ed.). San Diego: Plural Publishing, Inc.

Roseberry-McKibbin, C. (2014). *Increasing oral and literate language skills of children in poverty.* Rockville, MD: American Speech-Language-Hearing Association.

Roseberry-McKibbin, C. (2015). Playing the classroom game: Supporting students who are environmentally at risk. In T. A. Ukrainetz (Ed.), *School-age language intervention: Evidence-based practices.* Austin, TX: ProEd.

Roseberry-McKibbin, C. (2018). *Love talk read to help your child succeed.* Carlsbad, CA: Crescendo Publishing.

Roseberry-McKibbin, C., Brice, A. E., & O'Hanlon, L. (2005). Serving English language learners in public school settings: A national survey. *Language, Speech, and Hearing Services in Schools, 36*(1):48-61.

Roseberry-McKibbin, C., & Hegde, M. N. (2016). *An advanced review of speech-language pathology: Preparation for PRAXIS and comprehensive examination* (4th ed.). Austin, TX: Pro-Ed.

Roseberry-McKibbin, C., Ibarra, C., & Kahrobaei, N. (2017, November). *Love, Talk, Read: Sharing Books to Increase Literacy Skills of At-Risk Children in Poverty.* Paper presented at the annual national convention of the American Speech-Language-Hearing Association, Los Angeles, CA.

Roth, F. P. (2004). Word recognition assessment frameworks. In C. A. Stone, E. R. Silliman, B. J. Ehren, & K. Apel (Eds.), *Handbook of language and literacy: Development and disorders* (pp. 461-480). New York: The Guilford Press.

Roth, F. P., Dixon, D. A., Paul, D. R., & Bellini, P. I. (2013). *RtI in action grades 3-5: Oral and written language activities for the Common Core State Standards.* Rockville, MD: American Speech-Language-Hearing Association.

Roy, J., Oetting, J. B., & Moland, C. W. (2013). Linguistic constraints on children's overt marking of *BE* by dialect and age. *Journal of Speech, Language, and Hearing Research, 56,* 933-944.

Roy, P., & Chiat, S. (2004). A prosodically controlled word and nonword repetition task for 2- to 4-year olds: Evidence from typically-developing children. *Journal of Speech-Language-Hearing Research, 47,* 223-234.

Rubin, E. (2017). Use developmental stages to guide treatment in ASD. *The ASHA Leader, 22*(6), 40-41.

Rueda, R., Monzo, L., Blacher, J., Shapiro, J., & González, J. (2005). Cultural models and practices regarding transition: A view from Latina mothers of young adults with developmental disabilities. *Exceptional Children, 71,* 401-414.

Rybak, C. J., Eastin, C. L., & Robbins, I. (2004). Native American healing practices and counseling. *Journal of Humanistic Counseling, Education and Development, 43,* 25-32.

Sanger, D., Mohling, S., & Stremlau, A. (2012). Speech-language pathologists' opinions on response to intervention. *Communication Disorders Quarterly, 34*(1), 3-16.

Santiago-Valles, W. F., Ward, E., Davis, T., & Morrison, A. (2016, November). *Making a world of difference: Delivering speech-language services to refugees and immigrants in the U.S.* Paper presented at the national annual convention of the American Speech-Language-Hearing Association, Philadelphia, PA.

Saunders, W., & O'Brien, G. (2006). Oral language. In F. Genesse, K. Lindholm-Leary, W. Saunders, & D. Christian (Eds.), *Educating English learners: A synthesis of empirical evidence* (pp. 24-97). New York: Cambridge University Press.

Schachter, R. E., & Craig, H. K. (2013). Students' production of narrative and AAE features during an emergent literacy task. *Language, Speech, and Hearing Services in Schools, 44,* 227-238.

Schroeder, S. R., & Marian, V. (2016). Cognitive consequences of trilingualism. *International Journal of Bilingualism,* 1-20.

Schwartz, M., Taha, H., Assad, H., Khamaisi, F., & Eviatar, Z. (2016). The role of emergent bilingualism in the development of morphological awareness in Arabic and Hebrew. *Journal of Speech, Language, and Hearing Research, 59,* 272-809.

Schwinge, D. (2017). Biliteracy and multiliteracy in bilingual education. In O. Garcia, A. M. Y. Lin, & S. May (Eds.), *Bilingual and Multilingual Education* (pp. 147-159). New York: Springer International Publishing.

Scott, K. A., Pollock, K., Roberts, J. A., & Krakow, R. (2013). Phonological processing skills of children adopted internationally. *American Journal of Speech-Language Pathology, 22,* 673-683.

Scott, K. A., & Roberts, J. (2011). Making evidence-based decisions for children who are internationally adopted. *Evidence-Based Practice Briefs, 6,* 1-16.

Scott, K. A., Roberts, J. A., & Glennen, S. (2011). How well do children who are internationally adopted acquire language? A meta-analysis. *Journal of Speech, Language, and Hearing Research, 54,* 1153-1169.

Sealofbiliteracy.org (2017). State laws regarding the Seal of Biliteracy. Retrieved from http://sealofbiliteracy.org/

Seymour, H. S., Roeper, T. W., & deVilliers, J. (2005). *Diagnostic Evaluation of Language Variation.* San Antonio, TX: Psychological Corporation.

Shakir, Z., & Roseberry-McKibbin, C. (2014). *A survey of families of children on the autism spectrum: Implications for speech-language pathologists.* Paper presented at the annual convention of the California Speech-Language-Hearing Association, San Francisco, CA.

Sharifzadeh, V. S. (2011). Families with Middle Eastern roots. In E. W. Lynch & M. J. Hanson (Eds.), *Developing cross-cultural competence: A guide for working with children and their families* (4th ed.) (pp. 392-436). Baltimore: Paul H. Brookes Publishing Co.

Sheng, L., Lam, B. P., Cruz, D., & Fulton, A. (2016, January). A robust demonstration of the cognate facilitation effect in first-language and second-language naming. *Journal of Experimental Child Psychology.* doi: 10.1016/j.ecp.2015.09.007

Sheng, L., Peña, L. D., Bedore, L., & Fiestas, C. E. (2012). Semantic deficits in Spanish-English bilingual children with language impairment. *Journal of Speech, Language, and Hearing Research, 55,* 1-15.

Shoebottom, P. (2013). *Second language acquisition—essential information.* Retrieved from http://esl. Fis.edu/teachers/support/cummin.htm

Shohamy, E. (1999, August). *Unity and diversity in language policy.* Paper presented at the AILA conference, Tokyo.

Shohamy, E., Levine, T., Spolsky, B., Kere-Levy, M., Inbar, O., & Shemesh, M. (2002). *The academic achievements of immigrant children from the former USSR and Ethiopia.* Report submitted to the Ministry of Education, Israel.

Silva, L. M. T., & Cignolini, A. (2005). A medical Qigong methodology for early intervention in autism spectrum disorder: A case series. *The American Journal of Chinese Medicine, 33,* 315-327.

Simon-Cereijido, G. (2013). *Intervention for English-language-learning preschoolers with language disorders.* Paper presented at the annual meeting of the American Speech-Language-Hearing Association Schools Conference, Long Beach, CA.

Simon-Cereijido, G. (2015). Preschool language interventions for Latino dual language learners with language disorders: What, in what language, and how. *Seminars in Speech and Language, 36*(2), 154-164.

Skinner, D. G., Correa, V., Skinner, M., & Bailey, D. (2001). Role of religion in the lives of Latino families of young children with developmental delays. *American Journal on Mental Retardation, 106,* 297-313.

Smiley, D. F., & Threats, T. (2006). Audiologists and speech-language pathologists working together to serve children in rural communities who are deaf and hard of hearing. *Perspectives on Communication disorders and Sciences in Culturally and Linguistically Diverse Populations (Special Interest Division 14 Newsletter), 13,* 22-28.

Smyk, E., Restrepo, M. A., Gorin, J. S., & Gray, S. (2013). Development and validation of the Spanish-English proficiency scale. *Language, Speech, and Hearing Services in Schools, 44,* 252-265.

Soodla, P., & Kikas, E. (2010). Macrostructure in the narratives of Estonian children with typical development and language impairment. *Journal of Speech, Language, and Hearing Research, 53,* 1321-1333.

Southern Poverty Law Center (2017). Hate groups rise, fueled by Trump campaign. Southern Poverty Law Center, spring 2017, volume 47, 1, p. 1.

Southwood, F., & van Hout, R. (2010). Production of tense morphology by Afrikaans-speaking children with and without specific language impairment. *Journal of Speech, Language, and Hearing Research, 53,* 394-413.

Sparks, S. (2016, May 11). Teaching English-Language learners: What does the research tell us? *Education Week..* Retrieved from http://www.edweek/org/ew/articles/2016/05/11/teaching-english-language-learners-what-does-the-research-tell-us

Squires, J., & Bricker, D. (2009). *Ages & Stages Questionnaires® in Spanish, Third Edition (ASQ-3 Spanish).* Baltimore: Paul H. Brookes Publishing Company.

Srinivasan, S., Mathew, S. N., & Lloyd, L. L. (2011). Insights into communication intervention and AAC in South India: A mixed-methods study. *Communication Disorders Quarterly, 32*(4), 232-247.

Stillman, D., & Stillman, J. (2017). *Gen Z @ work: How the next generation is transforming the marketplace.* HarperCollins Publishers, New York.

Stockman, I. J. (2010). A review of developmental and applied language research on African American children: From a deficit to difference perspective on dialect differences. *Language, Speech, and Hearing Services in Schools, 41,* 23-38.

Stoel-Gammon, C., & Menn, L. (2017). Phonological development: Learning sounds and sound patterns. In J. B. Gleason & N. Berstein Ratner, *The development of language* (9th ed.) (pp. 45-76). Upper Saddle River, NJ: Pearson.

Stokes, S. F., Wong, A. M. Y., Fletcher, & Leonard, L. B. (2006). Nonword repetition and sentence repetition as clinical markers of specific language impairment: The case of Cantonese. *Journal of Speech, Language, and Hearing Research, 49,* 219-236.

Storkel, H. L., Komesidou, R., Fleming, K. K., & Romine, R. S. (2017). Interactive book reading to accelerate word learning by kindergarten children with specific language impairment: Identifyng adequate progress and successful learning patterns. *Language, Speech, and Hearing Services in Schools, 48,* 108-124.

Sue, D. W., & Sue, D. (2016). *Counseling the culturally diverse: Theory and practice* (7th ed.). New York: John Wiley & Sons.

Swanson, H. L., Saez, L., & Gerber, M. (2006). Growth in literacy and cognition in bilingual children at risk or not at risk for reading disabilities. *Journal of Educational Psychology, 98,* 247-264.

Szlemko, W. J., Wood, J. W., & Thurman, P. J. (2006). Native Americans and alcohol: Past, present, and future. *The Journal of General Psychology, 13,* 435-451.

Tabors, P. O. (2008). *One child, two languages* (2nd ed.). Baltimore, MD: Paul H. Brookes Publishing Co.

Taddonio, R. (2003). *International adoption and language development.* Retrieved from http://www.adopting.org/adoptions/adoptive-parenting-international-adoption-and-language-development.html

Talbert-Johnson, C. (2004). Structural inequities and the achievement gap in urban schools. *Education and Urban Society, 37,* 22-36.

Taimanglo, P. L. G. (2010). *The Chamorro people of Guam.* Communique, American Psychological Association. Retrieved from http://www.apa.org/oi/oema/resources/communique/2010/08/chamorro-people.aspx

Tan, G. T. (2006). Diverse issues: Providing services to internationally adopted children. *CSHA Magazine, 36*(2), 11-12.

Tattersall, P. J., Nelson, N. W., & Tyler, A. A. (2015). Associations among nonword repetition and phonemic and vocabulary awareness: Implications for intervention. *Child Language Teaching and Therapy, 31*(2), 159-171.

Tatum, A. W. (2013). Common Core State Standards: Structuring and protecting equitable pathways for African American boys. In S. B. Neuman and L. B. Gambrell (Eds.), *Quality reading instruction in the age of common core standards* (pp. 75-89) Newark, DE: International Reading Association.

Tauili'ili, P. (2009). *The rat and the bat: And other short stories.* Bloomington, IN: Authorhouse.

Teaching Tolerance (2017). *On racism and White privilege.* Retrieved from http://www.tolerance.org/article/racism-and-white-privilege

Terry, N. P., & Connor, C. M. (2013). Changing nonmainstream American English use and early reading achievement from kindergarten to first grade. *American Journal of Speech-Language Pathology, 21,* 78-86.

Terry, N. P., Connor, C. M., Petscher, Y., & Conlin, C. R. (2012). Dialect variation and reading: Is change in Nonmainstream American English use related to reading achievement in first and second grade? *Journal of Speech, Language, and Hearing Research, 55,* 55-69.

Terry, N. P., Mills, M. T., Bingham, G. E., Mansour, S., & Marencin, N. (2013). Oral narrative performance of African American pre-kindergartners who speak Nonmainstream American English. *Language, Speech, and Hearing Services in Schools, 44,* 291-305.

Thordardottir, E., & Brandeker, M. (2013). The effect of bilingual exposure versus language impairment on nonword repetition and sentence imitation scores. *Journal of Communication Disorders, 46*, 1-16.

Thordardottir, E., Kehayla, E., Mazer, B., Lessard, N., Majnemer, A., Sutton, A., Trudeau, N., & Chillingaryan, G. (2011). Sensitivity and specificity of French language and processing measures for the identification of primary language impairment. *Journal of Speech, Language, and Hearing Research, 54*, 580-597.

To, C. K.-S,. Stokes, S., Cheung, H.-T., & T'sou, B. (2010). Narrative assessment for Cantonese-speaking children. *Journal of Speech, Language, and Hearing Research, 53*, 648-669.

Tsethlikai, M., & Rogoff, B. (2013). Involvement in traditional cultural practices and American Indian children's incidental recall of a folktale. *Developmental Psychology, 49*(3), 568-578.

Turnbull, K. L. P., & Justice, L. M. (2012). *Language development from theory to practice* (2nd ed.). Upper Saddle River, NJ: Pearson.

Tunison, S. (2013). The Wicehtowak partnership: Improving student learning by formalizing the family-community school partnership. *Journal of American Education, 119*(4), 565-590.

Tur-Kaspa, H., & Dromi, E. (2001). Grammatical deviations in the spoken and written language of Hebrew-speaking children with hearing impairments. *Language, Speech, and Hearing Services in Schools, 32*, 79-89.

Ukrainetz, T. (2017). Commentary on "Reading comprehension is not a single ability": Implications for child language intervention. *Language, Speech, and Hearing Services in Schools, 48*, 92-97.

United Nations Refugee Agency (2017). *Projected global resettlement needs*. Retrieved from http://www.unhcr.org/en-us/protection/resettlement/575836267/unhcr-projected-global-resettlement-needs-2017.html

Urban Institute (2013). *Racial wealth divide is 3 times wider than income gap, threatening economic opportunity integrity*. Urban Institute, Retrieved from http://www.urban.org/publications/904582.htm

U.S. Census Bureau (2016). *Educational attainment in the United States: 2015: Current population reports*. Retrieved from https://www.census.gov

U.S. Census Bureau (2017a). *Asian-American and Pacific Islander Heritage Month: May 2017*. Retrieved from https://www.census.gov/newsroom/facts-for-features.2017/cb17-ff07.html

U.S. Census Bureau (2017b). National African-American History Month: February 2017. Retrieved from https://www.census.gov/newsroom/facts-for-featurs/2017/cb17-ff01.html

U.S. Department of Education (2017). Every Student Succeeds Act (ESSA). Retrieved from https://www2.ed.gov/policy/elsec/leg/essa/index.html

U.S. Department of the Interior Indian Affairs (2017). *Frequently asked questions*. Retrieved from https://www.bia.gov/FAQs.index,htm

U.S. Department of State (2017). *Intercountry adoption statistics*. Retrieved from https://travel.state.gov/content/adoptionsabroad/en/about-us/statistics.html.

Utah State Board of Education (2017). *Dual language immersion*. Retrieved from http://www.utahdli.org/index.html

Van Keulen, J. E., Weddington, G. T., & Debose, C. E. (1998). *Speech, language, learning, and the African American child*. New York: Pearson.

Vygotsky, L. S. (1962). *Thought and language*. Cambridge, MA.: MIT Press.

Wagner, R. K., Francis, D. J., & Morris, R. D. (2005). Identifying English language learners with learning disabilities: Key challenges and possible approaches. *Learning Disabilities Research & Practice, 20*, 6-15.

Wagner, R., Torgeson, J., Rashotte, C., & Pearson, N. A. (2013). Comprehensive Test of Phonological Processing (2nd ed.). Austin, TX: Pro-Ed.

Walker, E., Adams, A., Restrepo, M. A., Fialko, S., & Glenberg, A. M. (2017). When (and how) interacting with technology-enhanced storybooks helps dual language learners. *Translational Issues in Psychological Science, 3*(1), 66-79.

Wallach, G. P., & Ocampo, A. (2017). Comprehending comprehension: Selected possibilities for clinical practice within a multidimensional model. *Language, Speech, and Hearing Services in Schools, 48*, 98-103.

Washington, P. S., & Iglesias, A. (2015). Tense shifting in Spanish-speaking English Language Learners. *Communication Disorders Quarterly, 36*(3), 152-161.

Watkins, N. L., Labarrie, T. L., & Appio, L. M. (2010). Black undergraduates' experiences with perceived racial microaggressions in predominately White colleges and universities. In D. W. Sue (Ed.), *Microaggressions and marginality* (pp. 25-51). Hoboken, NJ: Wiley.

Watson, S. (2017). Ten strategies to support hearing impaired students in classrooms. Retrieved from https://www.thoughtco.com/strategies-to-support-hearing-impaired-3110331

Westby, C. & Inglebret, E. (2012). Native American and worldwide indigenous cultures. In D. E. Battle (Ed.), *Communication disorders in multicultural and international populations* (4th ed.) (pp. 76-101). St. Louis, MO: Elsevier Mosby.

Wetherby, A., & Prizant, B. (1993). Communication and Symbolic Behavior Scales. Chicago: Riverside Publishing.

White-Kaulaity, M. (2007). Reflections on Native American reading: A seed, a tool, and a weapon. *Journal of Adolescent & Adult Literacy, 50*, 560-566.

Wiig, E. H., Langdon, H. W., & Flores, N. (2001). Nominación rápida y automatica en niños hispano hablantes bilingües y monolingües. *Revista de Logopedia y Foniatria, 21*, 106-117.

Wiig, E. H., Zureich, P., & Chan, H. W. (2000). A clinical rationale for assessing rapid naming abilities in children with language disorders. *Journal of Learning Disabilities, 33*, 359-374.

Wilson, W. J., Marinac, J., Pitty, K., & Burrows, C. (2011). The use of sound-field amplification devices in different types of classrooms. *Language, Speech, and Hearing Services in Schools, 42*, 395-407.

Windsor, J., & Kohnert, K. (2004). The search for common ground: Part I. Lexical performance by linguistically diverse learners. *Journal of Speech, Language, and Hearing Research, 47*, 877-890.

Winsler, A., Hutchison, L. A., De Feyter, J. J., Manfra, L., Bleiker, C., Hartman, S. C., & Levitt, J. (2012). Child, family, and childcare predictors of delayed school entry and kindergarten retention among linguistically and culturally diverse children. *Developmental Psychology, 48*(5), 1299-1314.

Windsor, J., Kohnert, K., Lobitz, K. F., & Pham, G. T. (2010). Cross-language nonword repetition by bilingual and monolingual children. *American Journal of Speech-Language Pathology, 19*, 298-310.

Wolf, M., Bowers, P., & Biddle, K. (2000). Naming-speed processes, timing, and reading: A conceptual review. *Journal of Learning Disabilities, 33*, 387-407.

Wong, A. M.-Y., Au, C. W.-S. & Stokes, S. F. (2004). Three measures of language production for Cantonese-speaking school-age children in a story-retelling task. *Journal of Speech, Language, and Hearing Research, 43*, 1322-1336.

Wood, C., Diehm, E. A., & Callender, M. F. (2016). An investigation of language environment analysis measures for Spanish-English bilingual preschoolers from migrant low-socioeconomic status backgrounds. *Language, Speech, and Hearing Services in Schools, 47,* 123-134.

Word Press (2017). *The Crisis in Black Education: Executive Summary 2017.* Retrieved from https://asalh100.files.wordpress.com/2014/11/2017-black-history-theme.pdf

World Health Organization (2017). *Environmental health in emergencies: Displaced people.* Retrieved from http://www.who.int/environmental.health.emergencies/displaced.people/en/

Wright, J. (2017). *The real reason autism rates are up in the U.S.* Retrieved from https://www.scientificamerican.com/article/the-real-reasons-autism-rates-are-up-in-the-u-s/

Wright, W. E., & Baker, C. (2017). Key concepts in bilingual education. In O. Garcia, A. M. Y. Lin, & S. May (Eds.), *Bilingual and Multilingual Education* (pp. 65-79). New York: Springer International Publishing.

Wyatt, T. (2012). Assessment of multicultural and international clients with communication disorders. In D. E. Battle (Ed.), *Communication disorders in multicultural and international populations* (4th ed.) (pp. 243-278). St. Louis, MO: Elsevier Mosby.

Wyatt, T. A. (2015). Contemporary approaches and perspectives for assessing young and school-age AAE speakers. In S. Lanehart (Ed.), The Oxford Handbook of African American Language (pp. 526-43). New York, NY: Oxford University Press.

Yeh, C. J., Chen, J., Kwong, A., Chiang, L., Wang, Y., & Pu-Folkes, F. (2002). Educators of Asian bilingual students: Pedagogical techniques, strategies and challenges. *Journal of Multilingual and Multicultural Development, 23*, 296-315.

Yu, B. (2013). Issues in bilingualism and heritage language maintenance: Perspectives of minority-language mothers of children with autism spectrum disorders. *American Journal of Speech-Language Pathology, 22,* 10-24.

Zhang, Y., Xiaojuan, X. & Fan, J. (2015). Effects of quantitative linguistic feedback to caregivers of young children: A pilot study in China. *Communication Disorders Quarterly, 37*(1), 16-24.

Zimmerman, I. L., Steiner, V. G., & Pond, E. V. (2012). Preschool Language Scale, Fifth Edition (PLS-5) Spanish Edition. Upper Saddle River, NJ: Pearson Education, Inc.

Zoski, J. L., & Erickson, K. A. (2017). Multicomponent linguistic awareness intervention for at-risk kindergarteners. *Communication Disorders Quarterly, 38*(3), 161-171.

Zuckerman, K. E., Mattox, K., Donelan, K., Batbayar, O., Baghaee, A., & Bethell, C. (2013). Pediatrician identification of Latino children at risk for autism spectrum disorder. *Pediatrics, 132*, 445-453.

Zuniga, M. E. (2011). Families with Latino roots. In E. W. Lynch & M. J. Hanson (Eds.), *Developing cross-cultural competence: A guide for working with children and their families* (4th ed.) (pp. 190-233). Baltimore: Paul H. Brookes Publishing Co.

Index

Academic Communication Associates publishes a variety of resources for professionals who serve culturally and linguistically diverse students with special learning needs. Some products are available in both printed book and CD formats. You can also download selected products from our online store.

Assessing Asian Language Performance: Guidelines for Evaluating Limited-English-Proficient Students by Li-Rong Lilly Cheng - Product No. 4800-BK

Bilingual Classroom Communication Profile by Celeste Roseberry-McKibbin - Product No. 4304-BK

Bilingual Communication Assessment Resource: Tools for Assessing Speech, Language, and Learning by Larry J. Mattes and Cristina Saldaña-Illingworth - Product No. 43210-BK

Bilingual Language Activity Book for Auditory Processing Skills by Deanna Lengua - Product No. 48015-BK

Bilingual Language Picture Resource by Academic Communication Associates - Product No. 49949-BK

Bilingual Language, S//peech, and Hearing Dictionary by Larry J. Mattes - Product No. 4037-BK

Bilingual Picture Symbol Communication Resource by Academic Communication Associates - Product No. 44403-BK

Bilingual Speech and Language Intervention Resource by Larry J. Mattes & Irene García-Easterly - Product No. 45555-BK

Language Activities for Young Hispanic Children: English and Spanish by Cristina Saldaña-Illingworth - Product No. 48013-BK

Spanish Articulation Measures by Larry J. Mattes - Product No. 49131-BK

Spanish Articulation Picture Resource by Academic Communication Associates - Product No. 4941-BK

Spanish Language Assessment Procedures by Larry J. Mattes - Product No. 40701-BK

Spanish Test for Assessing Morphologic Production by Therese M. Nugent, Kenneth G. Shipley, and Dora O. Provencio - Product No 4034-BK

Teaching Second Language Learners with Learning Disabilities by J. Dixon Hearne - Product No. 40694-BK

Teaching Spanish Speech Sounds: Activities for Articulation Intervention (3rd Edition) by Larry J. Mattes and George Santiago - Product No. 46101-BK

Academic Communication Associates, Inc.

P. O. Box 4279
Oceanside, CA 92052-4279

Many more products are available!

Visit the ACA website.
www.ACAwebsite.com